THE DESCENT

THE
DESCENT

GONCA ALBAN

Matador
9 Priory Business Park
Kibworth Beauchamp
Leicestershire LE8 0RX, UK
Tel: (+44) 116 279 2299
Fax: (+44) 116 279 2277
Email: books@troubador.co.uk
Web: www.troubador.co.uk/matador

ISBN 978 1784621 780

British Library Cataloguing in Publication Data.
A catalogue record for this book is available from the British Library.

Typeset in Aldine401 BT Roman by Troubador Publishing Ltd

Matador is an imprint of Troubador Publishing Ltd

To Persephone, whose burning flame beckoned me
To Mum, a constant source of inspiration, love and support
To Cedrus, who patiently guided me down and back up again

Foreword

Our dreams are communications from the unconscious. They bring to light what needs to be seen and felt. They are gifts sent us to help us connect with what is often not noticeable on the outside. Our unconscious, through our dreams, can lead us to understanding our nature better. This understanding helps us connect to what is real and important for us, which ultimately leads to healing and happiness. Dreams can shine a light on hidden patterns, old traumas and also our intrinsic strengths.

In a similar way, any conscious bodywork will bring to surface what is buried in the body, in the unconscious. Every action, thought, feeling or experience makes a mark on our bodies. If unnoticed, old traumas can leave deep wounds not only in our psyche, but also in our bodies. By accessing the deeper layers of the body, listening to it, feeling it, paying attention to what is there, we can allow old traumas to release to the surface. We can work with the body to heal old wounds, just like we can work psychologically to heal the body.

Any work done with dreams, bodywork and the likes involve delving deep into the unconscious, destabilising deeply rooted ways and patterns, bringing them to surface, looking at them, feeling and living them, again and again, until we are able to at last let go and move on. This results in much repetition, a feeling of being stuck and going round in circles, but it is the only way. If we want a wound to heal, we need to dress it more than once, each time removing the bandage, letting it air, using antiseptics and creams, re-bandaging it and then once again repeating the cycle. Eventually the wound heals. It needs the creams and medications, but also airing and especially time.

Deep psychic wounds are similar in nature. When after having been buried deeply in the unconscious for a long time they poke their heads up for air, we need to first see them, notice them and then assimilate what we have understood and learned from them into our lives. However, these wounds are like old tracks, driven over many, many times. The deeper the tracks, the longer the healing process takes. Our old tendencies need to resurface many times before we are eventually able to kill their toxicity, let nature breathe and allow healing to happen. It all takes effort and time, constant awareness, paying attention, listening, nurturing and patience. It takes time for inherent ways to release their grip on us. It takes time and patience to find new ways of being, hearing, understanding. Again and again we face our demons, each time with a little more understanding and awareness, each time with more perspective and strength, each time delving a little deeper, until over time, with care, we are able to heal the old wounds, clear out the debris, shed light on the shadow and find our true selves, feel and live the light and as we move on we start to realise that we are living our everyday lives differently, with more joy and energy.

The skeleton came to me in my dream. It haunted me even in my waking hours for weeks afterwards. Was the skeleton me? It felt like me. I was petrified. No flesh on the bones. The skull had a masochistic smile, more like a grin, a grin that screamed "I hate you, I will hurt you, I will make your life hell and a total misery, purely and only because I want to and I can. I get satisfaction out of destroying you, your happiness, your life, watching you suffer. I laugh at your tormented soul". I think the teeth are rotting. Is that even possible in a dead skull? Rotting teeth? There's something nasty about it. It reeks of destruction.

I feel my skin pulling tight. I think I'm losing my flesh. I'm becoming the skeleton as I watch it. Minute by minute I'm losing touch with life, I'm falling into a deep, never-ending abyss. My teeth are falling out. The skull, it screams death and destruction. The skull's the devil. I know it's the devil. I know it in my heart. It's come to take me, take possession of me, own me, force me to run away with it. Or is the skeleton me anyway? Am I the devil?

I wake up gripping the covers. I check my teeth and my flesh. I'm practically surprised to feel they're still there. What was that? What does it symbolise? What is it telling me? Is it communicating to me that I'm the devil and I destroy myself?

I try to draw the skeleton skull, but as much as I try, I can't. None of the pages of scribbling resemble it even remotely. I am about to give up, but then I decide to draw it with my eyes closed. I bring the image back up in my mind, in my heart. That part's easy, the image is so alive and at the tip of my fingers. Focusing on the image, eyes closed, I start to draw. When I know I am done, I hesitate, I can't open my eyes. I'm sceptical. What am I going to see on the paper once I open my eyes? Meaningless scribbling, I'm sure. Nothing coherent could emerge from this exercise. I'm afraid, petrified and the fear is real. Where does it stem from? Why?

I open my eyes. Much to my utter amazement, I recognise the drawing straight away. It's my dad. It's also the devil, demon, pure evil, the sadist, the torturer. I can't believe I am staring at my dad and all these things at the same time. It looks like a caricature my parents have of him hanging in their lounge, one he had bought from a street artist in Rome. Then again, it looks like nothing, just an evil looking skull. But I know it's my dad, I know in my heart it's him in some way, at some level. I recognise him straight away. My nemesis is my dad...

I'm not prepared for this. I feel stunned, frozen. I don't understand. My dad's not evil. My dad's a loving, sensitive man, who spent his entire life providing for his family and doing his utmost best for them, for us. My dad is good, not evil.

I know I have a rocky relationship with my dad. He has hurt me more than anybody else in the world, but he's had that power over me, because I love him so much. He means well, he wants the best for me, he wants me to be a better person, living a decent, successful, comfortable life. That is why he has always been so hard on me.

I bury the image in the deep recesses of my mind. It makes no sense to me and I'm not ready to bring the evil lurking in shadows out into sunlight. The image and its mystery need to remain buried for many years yet until I am eventually ready to face the darkness it hides in.

The earth is moving, an earthquake, perhaps a volcano about to erupt. People are running in every direction away from the entrance to the caves, the dark downward spiralling tunnels and caves. Dust and earth are lifting, creating clouds, a mist of earth and dust, so hard to see or breathe through. There's panic all around. I feel the panic in my abdomen as sharp moving butterflies, pangs, excitement, mild cramps, fast heartbeat. I feel it in my chest as constriction, fear, I'm finding it difficult to breathe.

Persephone is down there, in the deep darkness of the caves. Why is she not coming up? Everyone else is rushing out of the caves, people helping each other, people also pushing each other, running over others, panic-stricken people and chaos everywhere. People running for their lives, they don't want to die, they want to live, they're running out of the darkness and imminent, certain death into light, sunshine, back out into the world, running as far away from the site as possible. A cacophony of sounds, people shouting out to each other, some screaming, some calling, some crying. Chaos and turmoil surrounds me and through it all my eyes are fixed on the opening to the caves, now only an exit, no one goes in, just people rushing out. And still no Persephone. She's still down there. Why is she not coming out?

Less and less people are running out, the flood of petrified people racing out for safety is thinning. Most have already made their way as far away from this site of death and destruction as possible. And still no sign of Persephone.

I walk up to the entrance. I call down to her. It's so dark down there, there's not even the slightest hint of light. It's so dark, so far, so deep. She calls back, letting me now she's decided to stay down there. My panic is growing and yet her voice is so calm, so knowing. It's as if she's made her peace with the world, and with death. I'm afraid, deeply afraid, afraid for her, afraid for myself, I know I can't leave her there to die, I love her too much, I love her with all my heart. I try to reason at the top of my voice "you'll die, you have to come out, everyone else has come out"

"I'm staying, Sophia". Calm, decisive.

I look around me, there are less people now. They have already run away, made their way to safety. Only a few slower ones are still gradually making their way into the distance, but even the slowest of them all is already far enough to be safe. It is much quieter now. The calm before the storm and the calm after the storm. The calm is even more terrifying, I can hear my own panic in the silence, it's screaming from my heart, from my abdomen. I'm no longer overwhelmed by others' panic. My own fear is screaming. It's overwhelming.

I have no choice. I have to go down. I can't leave her there. I simply cannot leave her there. I swallow. My throat is dry, it hurts to swallow, I can feel the dust and earth in my throat and chest. What a way to die, to suffocate with earth in your lungs, earth caving in on you, burying you, no light, just dark, damp suffocation. I look around me once more. A barren landscape, the earth has cracked all around from the movement as the tunnels and caves are crumbling in. The earth wants to open up, swallow all those still remaining around, and then it will close down on those it has captured, suffocate them in earth and sand, slowly but surely and painfully to their death. I can feel the suffocation, I can feel myself getting buried in the earth, I can feel my horror and fear. I try to swallow again.

There's not much time left. I have to go down. I take my first step, the next steps follow more easily. I start descending down the spiralling staircase into deep, infinite darkness, damp dark earth all around. The smell of rot, of soil and earth, of roots and growth and of death, certain death.

Down and down and down I go. Pitch black all around. How much further can I go? I will not survive, I know it in my heart. I am descending to my death.

And then I come across a small opening. Persephone's kneeling there, looking down at the earth, a reddish, fiery glow reflecting on her face, on her beautiful, pure, glowing, young face. She's not afraid, she's calm and contained, oddly serene, at peace with herself and her surroundings, at peace with her imminent death and she is determined to stay.

"Persephone, you have to come up with me. You will die here. The earth is collapsing. Everyone else has fled. You must come up"

"No..... Why, Sophia?.... I'm staying"

"Please, you'll die. We need to leave now".

She shrugs her shoulders nonchalantly and gets off her knees. I grab her *hand and start pulling her up behind me. She doesn't struggle, she is a willing follower. We start the long ascent up. It's tough going, earth falling down all around us, we're trying to protect our heads and faces by attempting to cover them feebly with our arms and hands, masking our faces, blocking our mouths and noses. We manage to continue, slowly but surely, up, up, up, through the suffocating darkness. The tremors are increasingly stronger. Larger chunks of earth start falling around us, rocks too. We continue…*

Persephone, my beautiful, young, smart Persephone. Persephone who is lost to us, to what we call the 'real world', and to herself. Persephone who left us years ago. She lives still on this earth, but she is no longer here, her soul has left and I miss her desperately. I love her with all my heart. I empathise with her pain, her struggle. She is me, I am her. I know her, I know her pain, I understand her giving up, I know she's lost, I hope she can be found.

My childhood wasn't a happy one. I feared my father. My mother, although physically around, was not present, she was living in her own separate world. My sister and I fought a lot when we were kids. Our parents called us chalk and cheese. I was of course the chalk, the dry one, useless, ugly, unlikeable. My sister was the cheese, tasty, nourishing, good. Some of our fights were horrendous. I was so jealous of her. I knew both my parents preferred her to me, they made no secret of that, even when we were very young. She got away with everything. I got the blame for everything. She would steal, I would get punished for it. She would cry, I would get punished for it. She'd make up stories, I would get punished for whatever she did or accused me of doing. She wanted something, she got it. I wanted something, though I rarely did, I learned not to, I was told off for "always wanting things". She was the one believed, and I the one who got punished.

Ironically my parents caught her lying and stealing so many times, yet they still always chose to think I was the guilty party and they continued to punish me. I was unwanted and unliked by them, resented, the bad girl, a disappointment. I could not do right.

When I was about eight, both my sister and I were asked where a bottle opener was. We were both too young to use one, but it had gone missing. We both said we had no idea. I was punished for stealing it and hiding it. I was beaten and sent to bed without dinner. I was told that I was always lying and that I was a thief and my parents were embarrassed of me, no good could ever come of me. I lay in the dark, curled up under my covers and cried and cried and cried. I didn't understand, I couldn't understand. Why was I being punished for something I had not done? On top of that my dad's words were ringing in my head, playing table tennis in that hollow, pained head of mine "You're a thief, we know that, you have a rotten soul, you're bad through and through. I wish you weren't my daughter, I wish I never had to see you again". A few days later my mother found the bottle opener in my sister's bag. She went to my dad with it. I followed. Surely now they would realise they had made a mistake, that I wasn't bad, that I hadn't done anything wrong. Surely they would give me a hug and a kiss to make up.

My dad looked at me, shrugged his shoulders and said "that's weird. So that's where it went". I was ignored completely. They did not apologise to me for punishing me wrongly. They did not give me a hug and tell me I was okay after all and that they'd made a mistake. They did not punish my sister, or even ask her why she took it.

I went back to my bed, hid under the covers and cried again. Life was so unfair. I must be so utterly totally bad and horrible to be hated so much by my own parents. I hated myself. I wished I could vanish, stop existing. I imagined my death, in all its detail. I imagined my parents realising after I was gone and it was too late how much they really loved me. They cried over my coffin. It eased my breaking, aching heart somewhat to imagine that they did love me somewhere deep down inside, but simply didn't know they did.

Between me and my sister, I got the worse from my parents, maybe because I was the first born. They treated me badly, they hated and resented me for existing. They hated me for who I was, every cell of me incurred their hatred, every aspect of me, every breath of my character. They weren't good to my sister either, yet better than they were towards me. At least until I left home. After that their hatred turned on her and she got the beatings and the abuse.

There is a dark shadow in our family, lying far beneath the

ground. The shadow needs light, what lurks there needs to be brought to life, otherwise the shadow will drown us, overwhelm our souls, it will slowly kill us. It's time to go down and bring that shadow out into light. It's time to find my own shadow, forgive myself, leave the hatred where it belongs, outside of me, it is not mine to own, it's time to put it down and stop carrying it. It's time to become whole. It's time for Inanna to go down for Erashkigal.

At the time of this dream, I was confused. What is it in my deep unconscious that is symbolised by Persephone, the part that doesn't want to become conscious, to come up and out into the open? What is it that wants to remain underground. Remaining underground means death. What is it that is killing me, preventing me from truly being alive, keeping me cut in half, disconnected? Is it lack of self-worth? My parents' voices are so loud and clear within me: "you're worthless, unloveable, bad, disgusting". Is it those voices?

In spite of my fear and panic, I go down to get her though. I start out on the long, dark spiralling downward path. I need to bring her up into daylight and I begin my journey, the one that seems to lead to death.

What was it in me that my parents couldn't stand? Was it that I didn't live up to their expectations of being bad, evil? Did I become the martyr to carry all their blame and shadow? Was it that I did have friends and was loved? Did they feel guilty for not being able to love their own daughter, for resenting her and they couldn't own their guilt, so they turned it into hatred towards me? Did they resent me so much purely because I existed, or because they can't love me and they pile the guilt of my existence as well as that of them not being able to love me on me? They had children because that was the done thing at the time. You got married and had children, then you sent your kids to good schools and so your duty was done and you could stand proudly in society as the wonderful parents, ideal family. Everything done for the outside world to see, outwardly perfect, yet in the safety of home, hidden behind our four walls, unhappiness, abuse and hatred reigned.

My mother should never have had children, there's no space in her life for children, they are a burden for her, a threat to her single rule at home and being the centre of my dad's universe.

As far as my mother's concerned, the world revolves around her, it has to, by force if necessary, mostly through manipulation. She is not aware of anybody else as separate human beings, with feelings, needs, thoughts, they exist for her only through their impact on her. The only person she sees is my dad. The need to be the only person in my dad's life is paramount. Once she had a daughter, that singular priority was threatened. My dad's attention, his absolute love might now be divided. He might even love his daughter more than his wife. That, for my mother, was an impossibility. I was a threat. This fresh, young baby, this new life, formed in her very own womb, was seen only as a threat to herself. She resented me from the start and made it clear that my dad had to as well.

Was there more than a protective instinct in my dad that resulted in him treating me the way he did? He could not love me, that would have been too threatening for my mother. But also, as I grew older, he saw himself in me and he dislikes himself, but could not own that. His self-hatred turned to hatred towards me.

By descending into the darkness, the caves and tunnels, descending underground to get Persephone out, to rescue her, Persephone who is lost, the one that symbolises the hidden, the one who stands for those who are alive, but not living, the one who rebels and acts out unconsciously, by finding her, I will find myself and reclaim my lost part, my unnoticed, suppressed shadow also.

Inanna going down for Ereshkigal. The conscious suddenly aware of the depths of her being, the buried unconscious. She has decided to go and bring her shadow out into the sunlight, into consciousness. She has decided she needs to investigate the depths, conquer her fear and become whole. She is afraid of what she might find.

I'm at a dark stage of my life. Everything's falling apart all around me. Confusion, darkness and crumbling earth all around. Everything I have always believed in and held dear seems to be falling down, breaking up, turning to dust and suffocating me. My long relationship, my marriage is breaking down. I'm breaking it down, yet not willingly, I seem to have no control over what is happening. I'm questioning everything, my dreams, my hopes, my love, my ideals, my morals, my life. Nothing makes sense anymore. All I see is darkness. The weight of the earth around me is too much and I can't breathe. I can't see.

12 September 11

I'm at a yoga retreat. My parents are trying to get hold of me, but I have started to walk downhill towards the only cafe in the area. I need a coffee. The need for a coffee is foremost in my mind. Persephone and my mother catch up with me. I say "I'll be right back, I'm just getting a coffee".

Persephone says with a nasty smile "Why should you have the right to go and not us?" They start walking with me. I feel them as a burden, as if someone had just placed a heavy backpack on my shoulders. I no longer feel like having a coffee. I don't feel like having or doing anything. My steps become heavier. I no longer want to go, but I'm already on my way and it doesn't occur to me to turn back. I continue slowly, mindlessly. I think, 'this is the path I'm on now, I take it for granted that's where I must go, although I no longer want the coffee'.

I stop at a house on the way to use the toilet. I need to desperately. The woman who used to live in that house is in hospital for obesity. They had to carve her skin off the sofa to be able to take her away. She had sat in the same place for so long without moving, just eating and eating, nothing else except eating, her skin had become glued to the fabric of the sofa. She was so heavy, her skin had moulded into the sofa and she could not be removed without cutting her skin away from it. Her skin and the sofa had moulded into one. The living one with the dead.

I leave the house after using the toilet. I feel physically relieved. I notice on my way out that Persephone is urinating in the sink. I say "that's rude, this is someone's house". She smiles that evil smile again and shrugs.

Persephone, defying all social norms, rights and wrongs, defying all accepted morals. Persephone and my mother defying me, my right for individuality and space. They're invading me.

I want a coffee, I love coffee, it's my greatest weakness and pleasure, something that gives me comfort and happiness. I want to go and get that for myself, nurture myself in this simple way. I want to do something for myself that gives me pleasure and comfort. But I am not allowed this, my space and privacy get invaded. I end up carrying Persephone and my mother like a heavy burden.

I am at a yoga retreat, yoga is union, bringing together mind, body and soul. It is a place I normally find inner peace, wholeness and comfort. But they are there to poison this experience for me.

Persephone asks me why I should have a right to nurture myself and not them, but by joining me, they take the pleasure out of the act for me too and they themselves get no pleasure out of what they're doing. Their resentment that I might get what I want, do something good and nurturing for myself turns it into a burden for me. It is no longer a joyful act, something to look forward to. It becomes a toil.

I need to relieve myself, express myself in some way and I do. So does Persephone, but in a way that does not take other people's rights and boundaries into account. She does not respect someone else's home. She relieves herself in a way that is harmful to others. She does it in an inappropriate place.

The woman who's house we entered, her addiction to food, her inability to do anything about it, her lack of will, desire or energy to move from the sofa, incapacitating her, making her a case for the hospital to such an extent that they even had to cut off her skin. She went all the way to her destruction and was not able to do anything to save herself.

Persephone smiles her evil smile at me both times I express myself. She belittles me in a way, ignores me, insults me, undermines me.

Persephone is also my shadow. The shadow that opens up its feelings inappropriately, with the wrong person, in the wrong place, in the wrong way. The shadow that will go all the way to its own destruction, and to the destruction of its conscious side as well. I have that drive, that ability within me, the unrecognised side of me that will react inappropriately, at the wrong time, in the wrong place, against the wrong person.

I've carried the shadow of my parents throughout my life, the shadow that says "you are evil, bad, useless, worthless, unloveable" and the shadow has always acted out. It has ruined my relationships, attracted abuse and on occasion led me down destructive paths.

Enough now. I claim my shadow and we will urinate in toilets as we ought to from now on. We will stop killing ourselves. We will say no to the evil shadow and the mother. We will draw our boundaries and keep those boundaries, not allowing invasion to occur. We will grow in our yoga retreat, uniting soul and body and we will enjoy our coffee, without having to carry the burden and the resentment of the mother.

My body, mind and soul
Taken over by an uncontrollable force
No logic, impossible to understand
My being is getting tossed
From land to land
I can't let go
Clutching on, knuckles white
I cannot steer
This is madness
For my sanity I fear
To die, to live fully
To fade uncontrollably
My life is meaningless
Without him next to me

We're in Amsterdam. I hate this city. It's so dark, small dingy streets, all grey, rammed with obnoxious people. The one saving grace the city has to offer are my friends Ann and Jen. I went to Ann's yoga class. It was brilliant. I felt so alive afterwards. It awakened my body back to life and joy. I came out feeling like a new person.

We all went for dinner and I felt so loved and supported by them, I could see they care, I also felt they felt my pain and they were worried for me. I felt so grateful for that love and compassion, that selfless care I found in them. My heart warmed.

I'm finding it so hard to be with Arthur at the moment. I love him, but can no longer be with him. I desperately want to get away. My inner turmoil poisons everything for both of us. My guilt, my self-hatred run like poison through the veins of our relationship. I don't want to be around him. I want to be left alone, yet when alone I feel so lonely and desolate. If I left, I would miss him so much, I know that, but I can't see a way out of our predicament and suffering at the moment, I can't see a way of making things better. I feel hopeless, lost, tormented. I know this is not the case, but I feel that if I ran away, I could escape from these horrible feelings, this pain, this loneliness and torment.

Everything's so unclear. Murky mud, dark caves, no light, no air.

I can no longer meditate either. The inner darkness is so overwhelming and suffocating, I can't sit with myself. I need to run and hide and distract myself. I know meditation would do me good, but I simply can't. All that anger and disgust turn inwards, all those dark feelings are too much to sit with.

15 September 11

I'm lying in bed and my skin starts pulling towards my bones. There's a pins and needles feeling throughout my entire body, all my skin is completely taken over by it. I feel absolute panic and fear. I'm shrinking, my skin is shrinking into my bones, then my bones start to shrink as well. I'm dying. I'm turning into a skeleton and the fear is more overwhelming than any pain involved. Pins and needles everywhere. I want to scream, in pain, through fear, but no sound comes out. I think my lips have shrunk too far to be of any use any longer. I feel crawlies along my arms, they're eating my flesh. My fingers are in pain, flesh going, fading, shrinking gradually, forever being eaten away.

I wake up startled, anxious. I used to have this sensation when I was a child, always just before I got ill. It has been so many years since I last had it, more than twenty.

I embody the feeling of shrinking, of pins and needles. It involves intense muscular contraction, becoming all cramped up, drawing into a ball, entangled, eventually to the point of not being able to move, muscles in spasm. It feels like mini convulsions, like electric shocks travelling along my fingers. My whole body is cramping up in active spasms.

Then I embody the opposite. There's expansion, skin expanding, lightness and space, but too much space, I don't fit in it any longer. I'm going to explode, I've expanded too much, so I contract again, draw myself back in to survive.

The motion is like living, going from one state to the other, life moving in spirals, the intense contraction, closing up, spasms and then the letting go, the expansion, feeling lost within all that space. It's like sex, contracting to feel the pressure, tension in the concentration, and then the release.

My life, the endless cycle of being pulled in and out and back into the centre. I am fighting both, resisting both. All that struggle and resistance taking up so much energy, so tiring, resulting in pain and suffering, fear and an endless struggle, a battle against myself. I'm fighting against life. My life has been a battleground of constant resistance against myself and against living.

All that pain I go through, wanting to contract into a painful ball, being pulled out in all directions, the electrocutions, spasms, the endless struggle, the resulting fatigue. No wonder I feel so fatigued.

I had this dream so often when I was a child, always before I got ill. I took it as a message from my body telling me it's about to break down, but perhaps it was also a message from my soul, depicting the inner struggle, letting me know it's tired.

I wasn't heard or seen as a child. I had to curl up into a ball to protect myself, I had to make my body rigid for safety and survival. It's time to hear that little child and show her it's safe to uncurl and live. She no longer needs to close up, cramp up and freeze. She can live her life and let the tension release. Flow with life rather than fight it. Allow the expansion to take place, without freezing with fear and contracting back again.

What is it in me that needs to be heard and seen? Why am I fighting the natural ebb and flow of life? What is the need in me that has not yet been met? What is the inner battle I'm fighting, against who or what? Who is the fighter?

I struggle against everything. I try to contain and control everything and life becomes a battle ground, a constant struggle. So much of my energy is wasted in trying to control, trying to hold everything together, trying to protect. It's time to let go and flow with life, to welcome it and enjoy it.

I was in tears by the end of the session. The realisation of the tormenting battle I had been fighting all my life, resisting life itself, always struggling, always suffering.

Life moves in spirals, circles. It is not rigid, nothing in nature grows in straight lines, nothing. Yet I'm constantly fighting for that straight line. A line can't flow. Keeping things straight takes constant effort and always results in failure, because nothing can be straight.

Why make every moment a struggle, a painful, hard, life killing struggle? Enjoy life, every moment of it, the good and bad, happy and sad, hard and easy, roses and thorns, death and life, spring and autumn, every moment is life, enjoy it for what it is, as life, without expectations or demands, just as it is. Nothing can be perfect, perfection doesn't exist, but constantly fighting for a perfection that can never be takes up a lot of energy, it's draining and it results in feeling like a failure, being disappointed, fatigue.

This is also an attitude towards sex, stressing so much about getting that orgasm, contracting muscles intensely to get there, focusing so much, to the exclusion of the other, focusing on the act and localised sensations, never really enjoying it. It is also a burden, something that needs to done, something to get through, not something to enjoy. How wonderful it would be to just flow with the feeling, enjoy the love making, the process, the journey, the touch, and let go of the end result expectation.

You get pins and needles in your limbs, when the natural flow in your body has been stopped, hindered in some way. That's what I have been doing for so long. A stoppage, a blockage of my life force, caused by my resistance to life. Contraction means death. Expand and live. Let life flow through you and you will flow with it. Don't question it or resist it, don't blame yourself for everything or hate what's happening, and most importantly, stop hating yourself. Accept life, accept yourself, flow and enjoy.

Resistance increases pain. Accept the flow, learn from it, grow through it and flow with it. You can't resist your nature and what the universe throws at you, but you can accept it and flow with it.

Life can be so beautiful, living so full, if only you'd relax and flow with it, rather than curling up into a ball, fighting, resisting, contracting, afraid, protecting.

As a child I had to protect, I had to cramp up to survive. As a child all I had were my parents, I depended on them for survival. I took their words for granted, what they said was right without question. I was bad, I tried to be good. I was resented, unloved, I did my best to be accepted and loved. I learned to shut down and protect. I learned to disengage and close up. I am no longer a helpless child though and my parents are no longer governing my life. I can at last live. They no longer threaten my survival. I can let my life force flow, it will no longer distribute pain and hurt throughout my body. I can live, if only I learn how to get out of my own way. If I can let go and accept, if I can let myself be, relax the tension, I know I can live, I can engage with life and enjoy it. But first I must loosen my grip on myself, ease the tension out of my muscles, unblock the current, let myself be.

Stop the internal war, the battle of you against you! It's so tiring. You no longer have to protect yourself from your parents. Their words and beliefs are killing you, but they no longer ought to. It is no longer they who are killing you, but you yourself by holding on tightly to all they instilled in you, keeping the poison they pumped into you. Let it go. It's time to disentangle yourself from them. Otherwise the spasms will be deadly, they will eventually result in your tension crushing your heart, and your body.

This old dream, a regular childhood dream of mine, it has come back to me today, because it wants to be seen and heard. It is asking me to let go of all that contraction. It is suggesting I look at why the contraction's there, so that I can see it is no longer necessary. That child and her anguish want to be seen and heard. The injustice she suffered, the pain and suffering she went through and also the messages planted deep in her soul and body, they need to be seen and heard and released. It's time they left. It's time I let them go.

Arthur was so good to me after the session. I got home and broke down. I had nothing left in me. I cried and cried. Arthur came over and gave me a massage, he said it seemed like I needed one. And then I slept, a deep, long sleep. Bliss, sleep that brings numbness, no awareness, no thoughts, no feelings.

I feel like my soul has left me. Or maybe it's dried and shrivelled up. Would Arthur come out into the rain with me, or is he the one who's drying my soul out? Is there any hope for us? Can we make things better? Will I ever feel happy again?

19 September 11

Deep deep depression
My heart is a dark cave
Heavy with the weight of steel
My body's pinned down
Unable to move or breathe
My conscience is heavy
My limbs are tired
My eyes are swollen from crying
My head is in pain from thinking
My heart is breaking

I brought it upon myself
And now I realise
There is no deep love
To excuse me
It's all a questioning
Running and hiding
In an imaginary world

The stars are against me
They're plotting my demise
I am so lonely
I've got so much to hide
My heart is heavy
It's painful, carrying my lies
The fear of loss is huge
So big, I can't stand it
And yet I am continuing
And forever sinning

No big love theme
Just a temporary madness
Uprooting, questioning
And day dream world wandering

The pain in me is so deep and complete, like something scraping a dark hole within me. The hole getting larger, increasingly more painful and darker. I have created my own hell, my own darkness, my own loneliness. I am dying a slow, painful death.

Seeing life as if every decision is final and a matter of life and death is freezing me into inaction. I must go with what feels right at the moment, I need to trust life, my intuitions and instincts, the guidance of the universe, so often referred to by others as fate, luck, coincidence. If I don't grab this time of questioning, pain and turmoil and grab it by the horns, really live it, feel it, look at what it's bringing up, what it's trying to teach me and show me, it will slip away, it will pass by me, over me, it will move on, leaving my immobilised body behind. My body contracted into a spasm, frozen into inaction. And I will become a distant spectator rather than an active participant of life. All life and joy within me will fade and die.

Yet it's so much easier to make decisions rather than put them into practise. Pain is painful, suffering hurts. My brain is screaming, my heart is breaking, my soul is withering and dying. Life is floating away from me, and even when I manage to reach out, somehow it's still beyond my fingers, I cannot connect to it. I am so lost, so buried in darkness, in hopelessness, in confusion. I no longer know what I want, I can't feel my dreams and hopes any longer, as if they always belonged to another and I have no feel for what they were.

I want to live, I want to let go. I understand I'm too contracted, too tense, too closed, but how do I open up, how do I let go, how do I release and trust? I cannot seem to do it and my parents' voice shouts at me in my head, louder than ever, "you failure. You have failed in your marriage. You can't even relax and let go. You can't accept. You don't understand. You're stupid. You're worthless. You deserve all the suffering you can get." And I listen. I tell the voices to go away, but they are too strong. They take over. And I end up on the floor in a heap, crying "why God? Why am I so bad? Why can I not live? Why do I have to suffer so much? This is what I deserve. I am so bad, so evil. I'm living the life I deserve". All hope, all life, all light is stamped out. I close my eyes. I pray to die. I beg to die. But I live, breathing, in this world, but not of this world, not alive. My soul is dead. I am dead. And I cannot stand it any longer. I want to give up. I want to close my eyes and never wake up. But the hours pass. I get up and go to bed. And the next morning, I get up and do what I need to do. God isn't forgiving. He won't let me out the easy way. I have to suffer, death would be too easy, it would be a release. God isn't done with me yet.

24 September 11

I have my period. I can see the womb release its lining and the blood starts to poor out.

The egg has not been impregnated and so no longer requires the nest. The nest is unnecessary and it is released. The period of virility of my relationship with Arthur is over. I have to face that. That relationship is no longer fertile. It can no longer create new life and growth, at least not in the form it is now. The nest we have created together, the nest I've created for him and the one he has for me, it is no longer healthy. It's time to let go and allow a new cycle to begin. This does not mean that I or he are not fertile, it just means that our relationship together can create no new life in the form that it currently takes.

My relationship with Arthur as it is right now is killing me. I need to let it go. And yet I love him, to the extent that I am not sure if I will ever love so deeply and fully again. But I'm depressed, I'm lonely within a marriage, I feel like I'm dying, my soul is shrivelling up. I feel hopeless, desperate. I need to leave.

I can't protect him from pain. This suffering, this turmoil, this chaos and ending are along his path as well as mine and I cannot live them for him, I can no longer carry all the emotions, all the shadow in our relationship. He will need to deal with this ending in his own way. He can learn and grow from this too, if he chooses to.

A woman's period is also a symbol of her femininity. Femininity, me as a female, me as an attractive, beautiful young woman has been allowed no space in my relationship with Arthur. Neither from me, nor from him.

The nest is no longer necessary and needs to be shed. It scares me, it hurts me to think about the ending, let alone ask for it, state it and make it a reality. It does make it easier for me to let go if I believe the relationship as a positive force in my life is over. Then I can blame my current unhappiness and depression on him. Then I can hope that if I leave, go away, go back to London, everything will be okay again, I'll be fine and happy. All that he gave me, the feeling of security, feeling good about myself, feeling good about who I am in society, amongst my friends, the stability he offered me, that he was my rock, that we built our dreams, our home, our sanctuary together, we made plans together, we shared family and friends... I am finding the qualities I received from him within myself for myself now and I no longer need the nest he provided me. Fine to hear and to say, but so painful to accept. And what happens to the rest?

That same nest, it is also a trap, preventing me from taking flight. Or is it? I feel he is trapping me, he is confining me into a tight, closed space that allows for no freedom, no expression, no growth. But maybe that's just my projection onto him. Maybe it's me that has stagnated and it's easier for me to place the blame on him.

So far I have always projected perfection onto Arthur and I have carried the shadow, all the messy emotions, all the faults. There must be some of those elements of good within me. There must be some of the mess, some of the shadow within him, although unrecognised, suppressed, crushed down. He didn't own all the good, all the beauty, although I readily placed these qualities on him. Similarly, I didn't own all the faults, I took them upon myself. I made positive projections onto him and it's now time to own some of the positives myself. I took on all the shadow elements, the 'inappropriate, weak, messy' emotions, some of them although being expressed by me, were his.

The dream feels so definite. It sounds like a confirmation the relationship is over... And what that brings up in me is fear, fear, fear, so much fear and immense pain, too much for me to sit with, too harrowing for me to accept.... Yet, I knew it. I tell myself I already knew it.

Arthur, my soul mate, my partner, my love, my rock, my sun. Arthur, Mr Perfect. Arthur, the detached one, mature, so mature he never showed emotion, never any anger, or passion, never any love or devotion. Arthur, the one I chose to spend the rest of my life with. Arthur, who was always too good for me. I was unworthy of him, I was never good enough. I willingly took on all the blame for any fight, for anything that ever went wrong in our relationship. I carried the shadow and let him take all the light. I was grateful for him in my life, he gave me everything worthwhile. I loved him so much, I love him so much. I felt good in his presence; I was able to be the person I wanted to be. I had strength, compassion and love to share and I was grateful to him for providing me with the secure and strong base from which I could take flight and to which I could then return to when I needed my sanctuary, my safety, my home.

We had a wonderful relationship in many ways. He was my best friend, my support and sense of reason, the person who put things into perspective for me, who brought me back down to earth, who reminded me of what was important in life.

He was also the person I loved, deeply, with all my heart. Yet I was unable to love without fear. Love triggered in me the protection impulse. Love meant curl up and be prepared to defend, freeze or fight. Love meant fear. Love meant pain and hurt, abandonment and betrayal. So I was also incapable of receiving love. I loved with all my heart, yet at the same time I could not be comfortable with the relationship. I lived in fear of him walking away, having enough, realising I was shit, bad, evil, worthless, any day now. So I lived in defence. I fought when there was no need. I hurt with spiteful remarks, sometimes just to get an emotional response out of him. Surely even anger or hurt would show he cared. Yet he was and remained so emotionless, cold, he didn't even get angry, that would have been some show of emotion, a sign he cared. His indifference eventually killed me, killed my soul.

It is now time to let go. Whether of my own doing or not, the relationship is cold. I get no love or warmth from him. I'm left out in the winter ice. It hurts me so much to even imagine a world without him, a life without his presence. But every day I stay with him, my soul dies a little more. I am so isolated and alone in my marriage. He can't hear me cry or scream, he doesn't see me reach out. I'm whimpering in the dark. My uterus remains unused, unnecessary. He does not desire me. He does not love me. I can no longer love for both of us. I can no longer carry the shadow for our relationship. I deserve to be happy. I deserve to feel loved and wanted. I wish to be cherished.

He is unreachable for me, up there on his pedestal and I have no strength left any longer to serve my ideal, the ideal of him. I wish for an equal. Someone whose soul I can touch with mine.

Over a decade together, mostly happy, mostly fulfilled. But even relationships, even good ones can have an expiry date. If an egg is not impregnated, there is no longer any need for the womb. Another womb will be created in time for the next egg, but the current one needs to be shed. In spite of all the beauty in our relationship, in spite of all the love I feel for him, in spite of desperation and grief the idea of leaving him fills me with, I now need to let go and move on, otherwise the womb that is of no use will slowly rot and become poison. It will eventually kill me. It's time...

A friend of mine said that in a relationship the man should bring out the baby in the woman. She should be able to become vulnerable with him. Yet I can only survive if I feel strong. If I let go of control and strength, I fear I will melt into weakness and nothingness. Arthur forced me to be strong and that was good, for a while. Now I want him to also accept my vulnerability, fragility, but he can't. And where does that leave me? Put on a mask of strength? Forever?

26 September 11

I'm taking some sort of university entrance exam somewhere. A handful of us are having breakfast, discussing some things at the table. One of them has brought toilet paper with her for the exam. I'm not ready for the exam yet, I still need to get my stuff together. I feel totally unprepared. I'm afraid.

The exam's at 7:00. I need to have my photo taken at 6:50. I go to the toilet and throw up.

As I'm coming out of the toilet a girl with very heavy make-up, loads and loads of bright green eye shadow, is coming in. She's Chinese, but with dark skin, a petite girl, not pretty, made even less attractive by the extensive make-up she's used. But she's a girl full of confidence. She has used her make-up thinking it makes her more attractive and she glows with an inner knowledge that she can conquer. I hate her with all my heart.

I'm running late and my stomach's empty and I'm not prepared for the exam.

I fall asleep at breakfast. I'm told I've been a good girl, and so I can have a smartie.

Intense green eye shadow, that's my mother. The Chinese girl looks nothing like my mother, but my mother has used the same make-up for as long as I can remember, it's a unique style, it doesn't look good. I've always wondered what she sees in the mirror, it's witch-like somehow, a bright green shade of eye shadow smeared over her eyelids. It looks odd actually. Or maybe it looks that way only to me. She doesn't use much else in the way of make-up, but always the same green eye shadow. My mother, the green of envy, the symbol of my denial of womanhood and femininity, denial of my being, denial of me, denial of being a young, vibrant, attractive woman, denial of life, love, acceptance, the mother who denied her daughter life and love, the withholder, the dark shadow in our home.

It's ironic really. My mother calls herself a feminist, it's a badge she wears and shows off like a badge of honour, she thinks herself a feminist and defines herself as such, she shouts it out at the top of her voice to all around her. She reads feminist books, writes feminist papers, goes on and on about women's rights, but she is one of the most sexist people I have ever met, she is male-ist. She wants women to have the same rights as men, fine, I agree with that, but she doesn't want women as women to have those rights, she wants women to be men, act as men, have the same values and priorities as men, lead men's lives and hence be equal to men on men's terms. To her feminism means being a man and denying everything feminine. Everything feminine is bad and must be suppressed, squashed denied, women must be male.

She is the enemy of anything that's female, anything that's nurturing, yin, earthy, motherly, nourishing, feminine, womanly. Women should have careers, fine, but she looks down on any woman who prioritises her children and family and decides she wants to nurture her children and bring them up. She criticises a woman if she can cook, if she cleans, if she nurtures, loves and takes care of those she loves. She sees earthy pursuits as a waste of time. Emotions, feelings, following your heart, listening to your intuitions, these deserve no respect as far as she's concerned. A woman should act like a man, otherwise she despises her. She is the carrier of the male banner, the torch of 'the only way is the male way, the better way is the male way'.

Anything nurturing, loving, accepting is squashed. She looks down on my aunt, because my aunt is like mother earth, all that is feminine. My aunt loves, nurtures, takes care of others, cooks and cleans for those she loves. My mother cannot see the value in that. She looks down on these things.

When my breasts started to grow, she bought me a sports bra, so I could hide the fact that I was becoming a woman. The bra squashed my breasts. It worked for a while, but it didn't exterminate my breasts, eventually they showed. I remained embarrassed of my breasts for decades, always trying to hide them. I wore t-shirts at least two sizes too big for me.

When I had my first period, instead of cherishing my first step into womanhood, instead of sharing the joys of femininity with me, rejoicing the power of women, our ability to grow a child, a human being in our own bodies, she treated it like a curse. It was the beginning of pain and decades of inconvenience. I hated the fact I had a period. I didn't tell any of my friends for years, even when they asked. I lied when we talked about the age our periods started. I was so ashamed of becoming a woman. Other girls would talk about their periods, I'd say mine hadn't started yet.

I knew nothing of sex, orgasm, desire. These were all things that were taboo, evil, not to be mentioned.

My mother never showed me how to use a tampon. It was Mum who did, years later when I was living with her. I was meant to be taking part in a swimming contest and I had to explain to her that I had to back out, because I had my period. She was shocked. She asked me why I didn't use a tampon. I told her I couldn't. She took me to the bathroom and patiently taught me how to insert a tampon. To her amazement, I didn't even know where my vagina was. That area was so taboo, I had shunned it, never explored it. I was embarrassed. My beloved Mum was not. I call her Mum and she has been the loving, accepting, supportive Mum to me that my real, blood mother was never able to be. She taught me what it was to be a mother, how it was possible to love, infinitely, all your daughters, without withholding, cherishing them, proud of each of them for their own sake. She saw the beauty in all of her own daughters, and she still had enough space in her heart to love me fully. She brought out what was individually special in us. She did not compare or criticise, she loved and rejoiced in us. She was proud of us.

She showed me how big a heart can be. Her potential to love is infinite and I have been tremendously lucky in being welcomed into her heart. I lived with her and her three daughters as a teenager for over a year. I was treated as one of her daughters, and shown as much love as she showed them. She gave me her time, her heart. I started calling her Mum about half way through the year and still call her Mum.

I was a member of the tennis team that year and towards the end of the year we had the inter-school tennis competition. The competition ran after school hours, so the first day of the competition I was late home. Mum asked me where I had been and I told her. She said "why didn't you tell me? I would have come to watch". I'm not a very good tennis player and these are insignificant competitions. Furthermore Mum had to work three jobs to make ends meet, she was after all providing for four daughters. I couldn't imagine she would want to, or would have the time, but I told her when our next date was anyway. And there she was, sitting on a bench, clapping and supporting me, shouting words of encouragement. I lost and after the game she came up and hugged me and said "I'm so proud of you. Those two girls you were playing against (it was a doubles match) were really good and you held your side very well. You did great" I was already stunned by the fact that Mum had taken time out of her busy schedule, probably asked to leave work early and come out to watch me play badly at some silly school thing, but for her to then be proud of me, still show me love although I had lost? This was beyond my comprehension, it couldn't even be true. Not possible.

Mum told me years later that each of her daughters were special and unique in their own way. They were gifted and beautiful. She cherished what was valuable and beautiful in them. My parents on the other hand had only ever thrown our weaknesses in our faces, in fact I have come to realise, sometimes what they called out as weaknesses didn't even exist. They threw their poison at us. They constantly compared and criticised us, me and my sister. She didn't work hard enough. I was evil, I had no friends, no one could like me, I was ugly. I was a disgrace. Conversely, my sister is exceptionally intelligent, and I always had friends. I was and am a pretty decent person. I have my faults, but I love people, I'm loyal to my friends, I'm there for them. I'm certainly not evil, nor ugly.

At home nothing we ever did was good enough. We could never do right. We were always criticised and abused. How different it was with Mum. She appreciated and cherished everything her daughters did. She thought they were amazing and she let them know it. Then

I came along and for the first time in my life I experienced unconditional love. I received no insults from her, no criticism, she loved me as I was and told me I was an amazing young lady. She still does. Her positive energy, her immense capacity for love, her joy of life are a constant source of inspiration for me. Her support is so valuable and is never withheld.

Going to the toilet can symbolise expressing yourself, relieving yourself, it can also symbolise relationship issues or problems around sex. We throw up when we take in something our body can't accept or digest and assimilate, either because it's bad for us or because our body simply can't take it. Our body feels the need to get rid of it. There is a need for me to express myself and an inability to digest something, a feeling I need to purge myself of it.

University entrance exam could be the exam of life. What is it that's really important to me? Whatever it is, I feel completely unprepared for it. I can't take whatever it is I've eaten, I can't digest it. I'm unprepared for the exam. I can't deal with the photo, a snap shot of who I am, what I look like right now. All of these happenings cause me stress and create fear within me.

I hate the female, the attractive one, but she is a part of me, the part I have I denied for so long. I hate her, because I learned to hate her from a very early age. The young girl, the girl growing into a woman was somehow a threat to my parents and they denied her. I had to deny her as well, accepting her would have meant standing up to my parents, attracting their wrath, and that would have been life threatening. It was too dangerous, so I denied her myself, I hated her.

I always felt uncomfortable with my femininity, I was never able to let it out, live it, I hid it as best I could, I've been a tomboy, hung out with boys, lived like a boy. As a teenager my femininity was hidden under baggy, large t-shirts. I was the tomboy, never a girl, or a woman. I could never wear make-up, never have my hair done. In fact for most of my life I had very short hair, cut like a boy's. My femininity was denied me by my parents. It was something to be hidden, to be ashamed of. My mother instilled in me that having my period was a curse. I had horrendous period pains until I eventually went on the pill. My body had to fight that most basic of female cycles and that fight resulted in excruciating pains.

Were my parents threatened by a blooming teenage girl, opening up to womanhood so much that they needed to crush it? Why?

I have to sit a test to enter the higher realm, or enter the world of acceptance of myself and peace with myself. My feminine side wants to come out, it has been suppressed for so long, it's screaming to come out.

I need to take a picture of myself as I am now, of the real me. I need to see me as I am. But I'm afraid of doing this.

This growth, realisation is painful, I try to ignore it, but it's so painful I can't deal with it, I fall asleep, I become numb. I can't face what's coming. I switch off because I'm overwhelmed.

But my guardian angel, a higher self is telling me that I have been good and can have a smartie. My parents potty trained me with smarties. If I successfully went to the toilet, they would give me one. Even later, when I was at primary school, sometimes, if I had been good, I would be given a smartie. It was the only chocolate I ate, or in fact knew of, when I was a kid.

Maybe the dream's about trying to fill the emptiness inside, the hole created by lack of motherly love and acceptance, the hole dug deeper by emotional, psychological and sometimes physical abuse from both parents. The feelings of betrayal, abandonment. And now, after all these years, my body can't accept nurturing, but desperately needs it. It's like a poison for me. It can't stay in, it is wanted, desired, needed, but my body reacts to it and it has to come out.

I have learned to completely bury the physical, sensual side of life, of being a woman, acceptance, intuition, nurturing, beauty. My life has been about logic, analysis, sensible stuff, personality growth and betterment, achievement on worldly male terms.

The feminine in me is awakening, but I'm afraid of it, I'm not yet comfortable with it. I have not yet learned to accept it. A threat creates fear, fear causes hatred. I am still afraid of the female within me and so I still hate that most basic side of me, the buried side, the side that is sick of staying buried, the side that now is ready to be seen, to be lived.

27 September 11

I'm waitressing at a bar. The bar is long and oval shaped. There are stools surrounding the bar area in a half oval. A woman asks me for a lot of specific things when ordering her drink. She is ordering my favourite cocktail, a bloody mary. She asks for ingredients like vinegar chilli and gives me some other weird specifics. I give her salt and pepper and guess that she's asking for green Tabasco sauce, but we've run out, so I ask her if red Tabasco sauce would do instead. And I give her Lea Perrins Worcestershire sauce. As far as I'm concerned these are the basic ingredients essential in preparing a bloody mary and she will be content with the drink.

Arthur is having a conversation with Louise and someone else about hamburgers and sausages and he tells this other person that he and I would always stop for plastic cups on the way home when we were in Chicago.

My teachers won't let us leave before we allow them to take us to their favourite restaurant.

I have short hair, I can see the back of my head in the reflection in the mirror behind the bar. I am looking in from the outside, I am not seeing the setting through my own eyes, through the eyes of the person waitressing, but looking at it as if watching a play on a stage. I don't like my haircut.

I'm serving a demanding customer, who, like me, is specific about what she wants. I do the best I can with the ingredients I can find.

Arthur and my trip to Chicago was a magically happy time for me. We went there to do an anatomy and yin yoga teacher training course with my teacher. We ended up staying there an additional five days after the course, unplanned, because all flights in and out of Europe were cancelled due to adverse air conditions resulting from some volcanic activity in Scandinavia. It was a fantastic holiday and that year was a special time of my life. We had an exceptionally good time there. We were staying in a small flat-style hotel, which had a mini kitchen, so that we could cook at the hotel. We ate healthily. The hotel also had a gym which we used every morning and we walked to the course from the hotel, which was a 70 minute walk. It was spring, the cherry blossom was out, it was sunny, yet cool. The city was simply glorious, I fell in love with it. After the course was over we went to blues clubs and nice restaurants as well as a luxury gym a friend of mine got us day passes to.

That was also the year Arthur proposed to me and we got married the same year. The whole year was a magical time of happiness, joy, activity, planning, friends, learning and fun. It was the first year I assisted my teachers in their teacher training courses and I loved every moment of it.

Plastic means junk, hamburgers and sausages are junk food. They are unhealthy, plastic is unnatural. There is some unhealthy, unnatural element being brought in by Arthur.

I don't understand how such a happy period of my life, happy and healthy, gets mixed up with junk. I'm doing fine myself, but Arthur is bringing in these unhealthy elements. Yet he was the main source of my happiness. After ten years together, with me always insecure in the relationship, unsure whether he loved me, wondering if he was about to leave me, he at last proposed to me, in effect telling me that he wanted to spend the rest of his life with me. It was an incredible feeling, this wonderful, perfect man, the man I adored and loved, had chosen me as the person to spend the rest of his life with. I spent the year in a happy daze.

But now I'm in the grips of a dark depression, overwhelming in its intensity. So much light, joy, life and love I had only a year ago and now it's all gone, evaporated. Now there is only darkness, not even the glimmer of a light, I see no way out. The darkness is suffocating, I can't breathe, I can't feel anything but anguish, torment and pain. Hatred all turned inwards, absolute pure hatred of myself and there's nowhere to run. I can't get away from myself. I follow me wherever I go and I bring the darkness upon myself.

My throat's muffled, my chest constricted, I can't even scream,

I can't even cry. There's no release, just a dark, heavy load on my shoulders, on my chest, it has overtaken my heart. My heart no longer beats vibrantly, it is no longer pumping blood out to my cells, it trickles poison instead.

I have no will to live left in me. I'm dying, suffocating in my own fog, drowning in my own dark, deep shit.

God help me, send me a sign, a light, no matter how weak, anything. I can't bear this any longer. I feel so alone and small. Everything is so dark. I can't breathe. Dear God, please give me some air.

God, please forgive me. Arthur, please forgive me. I'm tormenting myself. I feel broken, utterly broken.

Can you not accept me in some way, accept me as I am, the broken, damaged goods at your doorstep, the miserable half-being, the worthless sack of rubbish. Accept me if you can and hold me, just hold me. Let me feel your warmth. Can you love me? Can anybody love me? I fear not, because I do not love myself. This pile of rags, soiled, dirty, useless, lying on the floor, it deserves only to be abandoned, thrown out. But maybe you could clean your floors with these rags, or would they soil your clean floors?

Utter desperation throughout me, painful, excruciatingly painful despair. No hope. No way out. I'm drowning in bog. I'm sinking. I'm sinking. God help me.

28 September 11

There's a competition going on in a school-like setting. We're sitting at large tables, filling in some kind of exam papers. Darcy cheats several times, or at least that's my belief. I tell the teacher. But the teacher takes his side. Darcy and I start to fight. I start hitting him.

After class finishes I go up to the teacher and say "You know he was cheating, don't you?"

She says "yes".

"But you took his side every time"

"There's nothing we can do, so we just show it up"

I'm furious, absolutely fuming with rage because of the injustice of it all.

I have the knowledge. I have the answers. Darcy's copying them. Darcy is a close friend of mine. He is a wonderful person, overly sensitive, sometimes judgemental and can be stuck in his views, but good fun, loyal and completely trustworthy. Darcy symbolises my over-sensitive, but critical side. I stand up to him and fight him. I'm strong, I have the answers, they are mine and I will fight for them. But at the same time, I want to deny myself the answers, I lack confidence in my inner knowledge, my intuition, but they're there nonetheless. I should trust them more.

I'm angry with this critical, judgemental side of me that is trying to rob me of the knowledge I have, and have every right to have. I'm furious with it. The critical, sensitive side to me that denies me my knowledge, always telling me I'm not good enough, I'm bad, I'm worthless. I fight this side, but the teacher, the person in charge of the situation takes his side although she knows he was cheating me of my rights, stealing from me what was rightly mine. This side of me is also a side I have always trusted and had complete faith in.

I should have more confidence in my instincts, my inner knowledge. I have the answers within me, if only I would stand by my knowledge and not allow my critical side to steal them from me, denying me my rights.

I have no confidence in myself, in the knowledge and understanding I have, in my ability to succeed. I judge myself, criticise myself and rob myself of these attributes. But at last I'm standing up for myself, I am fighting the thief within me.

The teacher takes his side, but tells me that there is nothing she can do about the theft, she can only show it up for what it is, for me to see. And I see it. In my mind I know it, yet I continue, the impulse is too strong.

The first step for any healing to take place is to see the wound. The theft has been shown up, I have seen it and fought it, I have stood my ground, but not won. I am angry at the injustice of the situation. I feel powerless to change it and my powerlessness rages me, the theft rages me.

12 October 11

I'm desperate to go to the toilet. My bladder's full and has my complete attention. I'm bent over to hold it in. But there's a queue for the toilet and I'm last in a long line. One of the toilets is blocked. I beg a girl next in line to go before her. I can't possibly hold it in any longer. The girl is non-committal, she doesn't respond, she's numb, feeling-less, expressionless.

We have all of us, everyone in the queue, been brought there by higher powers and we are being controlled.

The greater super-consciousness is controlling me. It is controlling release, preventing it. I might not survive the wait, the long queue, I'm in pain. Is my super-conscious feelings of guilt and duty, my critical, perfectionist, harsh side that always finds fault with me, preventing me from release somehow? Nothing I ever do is good enough. I'm always on the back foot. The side of me instilled in me by my parents from birth onwards. Their voice that tells me nothing I do is ever good enough, I am always to blame, I am always in the wrong, I am worthless and can never do anything of value, I am bad and can never do good, I don't deserve to be happy and can't allow happiness in my life.

I need to let go of these values, so strong within me, but not my own, although I have adopted them, grown up to believe they are the only truth. I need to throw them away to be able to see clearly, to sort things out, to clarify and understand.

Life is on hold for me at the moment, I've hit the pause button, or it's been hit for me. Life is stagnating, I am stagnating, nothing's moving. Life, at the moment, won't let me accomplish, succeed, create, because I need to pause my life in the outer world and turn inwards. I need to sort out what's inside first before I can move on. Life has gone on hold for me to do this, so that nothing can distract.

I can't find work, I can't fill my time, I have to focus on the release, the act of cleansing and emptying the body symbolised by urinating.

I need to stay within that holding frame. I need to listen to what comes up and follow the guides inwards. It is now time for me to release, to let go and stop holding on. To urinate is to release, to let out. Something in me desperately wants to come out, but I'm not letting it, I can't. Parts of me won't allow me to express myself and let go of what is making me so uncomfortable, taking over my life and mind, incapacitating me to do anything else or think of anything else.

Like the girl in the queue, I feel numb, there's no emotion, no expression, no release. Maybe that's what's stopping me, maybe I need to let all emotions release, be active, live.

All this loneliness I feel, this guilt and pain, the fear, the confusion.

I feel so dead inside. There are times I feel nothing, no emotion. I go through life as if I'm a spectator, watching this ridiculous character who wades her way through with no emotion at all. I watch from above, from outside. I'm not involved. I don't feel. I don't live. And I'm alone. And this poor being is doubled over in pain from holding everything in, from being controlled by the super-conscious, prevented from getting it over and done with by the emotionless, numb side of me that keeps me back, keeps me on hold.

And guilt, my God, the guilt. I have shut down, because I can't bear the guilt. I can't stay with it. It's too much, too painful. I kill off emotions so that I don't feel it. I can't stand the guilt.

The guilt of what I have done to my relationship with Arthur. The overwhelming guilt and the excruciating feeling of loss. I have lost the person I love, the one person I treasure and trust, my partner, my husband, my rock, my best friend, the person I love beyond anyone or anything, the only person I would want to spend the rest of my life with. I have thrown away a good relationship through thoughtless actions, guided by who knows what, some unconscious drive for expression? A drive to feel, to be loved, to have my emotional needs met, to stop feeling so alone?

And the self hatred that follows. I despise myself for what I have done, so much so that I can no longer carry the burden. But then I was always inclined to blame myself, carry the guilt and hate myself for who I am. How can a person love themselves, value themselves if their own parents despised them and resented them for being, blamed them for being alive, hated them for existing?

It's time to let go of my parents' burden. They were not able to love. They brought their own baggage and dumped it on me, their self hatred, their guilt, their resentment, they could not see it, face it, own it, so they dumped it all on me to carry. I have carried it so far, now it's time to relieve myself of this burden that doesn't even belong to me, that isn't mine to carry, otherwise it will kill me. I need to let go and move on, freely. It's time to live a fulfilling life that is my own, unburdened by my parents' voices, so loud and overwhelming within me. It's time to separate what is theirs from what is mine and leave their burden behind.

It's time to stop those screaming voices, those deep rooted beliefs within me, constantly there, telling me over and over how bad I am, how despicable, how hateful, how unworthy. Those voices are not mine, although I have adopted them as my own. It's time to leave them now.

We did some bodywork around the feeling I get at my navel. That horrible feeling of knives scraping away from the inside, spades scraping the skin off, the flesh being torn off, so painful, immense pain. The feeling of craving, knowing that the pain will continue forever, no matter how much is scraped away, there is always more that can go, more to provide me with that indescribable pain. The gnawing away at my innards. My navel screams. The knives and spades, some serrated, some sharp, some nearly blunt, causing the most pain and damage possible. They dig and scrape continuously. The serrated knife goes in and then twists around and around and then pulls out partially, only to dig back in again with even more force. The spades are scraping my insides out, my insides that are already hollow, they scrape around the sides, it's excruciating. Everything in me is getting hollowed out, my organs, my flesh. It's like scraping nails along a blackboard, along the surface of a stone floor, cold, unfeeling stone and the screeching sound and the pain, God, the pain.

They want to scrape my whole body out, leave nothing behind, the pain is so tremendous, I want them to succeed, scrape everything out so that I no longer feel, so that there's nothing left to hurt. Every cell, every disgusting cell of my body, to be rid of it all. Get rid of the toxicity, the pain, the dirt, the damage. It's poisonous, something in me is poison, it needs to come out. Get it out, get rid of it.

The mother, the poison of the mother, the ultimate betrayal, the inability of the mother to love and accept her own child. Scrape out the mother, matter, earth. There can be no nurturing in my abdomen, no food can replenish and heal the hole, everything turns to poison in there, no silky cushion to comfort and soothe. My body cannot digest anything good, anything nurturing, it simply cannot take it in. The feeling kills me, the poison, the acid, the knives. Even any good that comes in, everything, turns to poison and pain in there. The hole is painful, mother nature is poison, the mother is poison. Her love, her existence and acceptance so necessary, so unavailable, so toxic and dangerous, it needs out, it's killing me. The indifference of the mother, the toxic, poisonous indifference. Even when she gave, it was done with so much resentment, so much withholding, her giving brought pain and death. She stole as she gave, her gifts were poison.

I feel hopeless, I want to close down on myself, curl up into the foetal position, become a baby, cry and sleep, sleep and never wake up. I can't face the world. I'm in agony and I feel hopeless. Crumpled up in a baby's position, scrunched up as small as I can become, trying to protect, to become invisible, curl up and sleep, sleep and not feel, not live, sleep and die.

I want to vanish, moving in spirals anti-clockwise, against life, against nature. I'm fighting the natural movement of life. I don't want to live, I don't want to flow with life, enjoy it, love it, I go against it, fight it and my battle kills me slowly, I have no energy left. I hate myself for doing this to myself and my hatred feeds the poison, it feeds into more hatred and all that nasty stuff spirals out of control, grows and grows.

I'm alone. I want to turn into a stick, a lone standing pole, taking up as little space as possible, unnoticeable. Still turning anti-clockwise, sometimes so fast I lose perception, I lose awareness of myself and the world on the outside.

And then I curl up like a baby and start rocking, rocking, rocking, like a baby being rocked with a lullaby, but there's no lullaby. I want to be a baby receiving attention and love and care, receiving nurturing, nourishment, acceptance. There is nobody there to give it to me, I am rocking alone and yet I start to feel accepted, I feel held, I'm moving with nature now, not against it. My pain is easing. Why was I never rocked as a child? It's such a gift. My mother never did, but I can learn how to, I can nurture myself, as a mother should, as my mother was never able to, I can feed myself, I can heal.

As a baby and then as a child we learn how to balance ourselves through our parents, especially the mother. We learn to accept love and nourishment, we learn to have our needs met, but only if the mother provides these. If we're hungry and we cry and we get fed, we learn that our needs will be met. If we're afraid and we cry and we get held and soothed, we learn how to hold and sooth our inner child. But if the mother withholds, if we are ignored when we cry, if we are punished, shouted at, degraded, then we learn that our needs will never be met, we learn not to ask for our needs to be met, we learn to squash them, because if we ask, we get punished or ignored. We never learn to hold and soothe ourselves, because these needs were never recognised, we were told off for needing, wanting, we had no right to, so as grown ups we give ourselves no right to need or to ask, we withhold our own love from ourselves, we refuse to accept or hear ourselves. We squash ourselves, bury our feelings, our instincts, our needs.

As a child I was left to cry or scream myself to sleep. My mother thought that was the best way to discipline a child. They cry and cry, no one comes, so eventually they give up and fall asleep. They learn their needs will not be met, there's no point asking anymore. The only way to survive is to shut down, to ignore, to freeze. I was not held or rocked when I cried, I was left alone to cry myself out.

I don't blame her for that, she thought that was the right way to bring up a child, but as a result, I learned as a baby that I would not be heard, my needs would not be met, the only solution was complete shut-down, falling asleep, denying myself even the sadness around not receiving what I could not get.

My parents believed I was bad, the only way to make me a better person was to discipline me, to always point out my weaknesses, my failures, to never notice the good, which might make me conceited or spoilt. I learned to hate myself, to believe I was bad and worthless. I could never do well, never be good enough, something was always wrong, always missing. I got punished for everything, but never rewarded, no matter what I did, I could and should have done better.

I learned I was not wanted, I had to shut up, I could not express needs, expression resulted in punishment or abandonment, it led to heartbreak.

As a vulnerable, dependent child, I could not hate my parents, they could not be wrong, I was dependent on them, I desired and needed their love and acceptance, and did all I could and more to try to get it. I didn't understand that they simply couldn't give me what I needed, that they didn't hate me because of what I was, but

42

because of who they were. I learned to hate myself, so that I need not hate them. They must be right, they the grownups, the parents, they were always right, so I must be bad, worthless, ugly, a failure, just as they told me I was.

I tried so hard to make myself better. I did as I was told, I studied and was good at school, I behaved well and yet it was never good enough. I could do better at school and I was horrible to be around, so they told me.

I got punished for crying, my dad could not stand crying, he hated it and my mother ignored it. I got punished for laughing, what was there to laugh about, what was wrong with me? I got punished if I was happy, I was acting out. I got punished if I was sad, I was an ugly, moody bitch. They had a degrading name to give me whatever my mood. It was always my fault.

I was really happy one day, I was only about seven years old and I was dancing in the living room. My dad came in and saw me dancing. He hit me right across the face "you're going to break something, what the hell are you doing?" I was punished for expressing joy and life. I learned to fear my joy, I learned to not be happy.

I'd get punished if I was unhappy or sad. "wipe that disgusting look off your face, you're so ugly". Any show of emotion brought up hatred and anger in my parents.

I came home one day from school and I was very ill. I had a high temperature and sore throat. I went straight to bed. When my mother came in, I asked her if she could get me something from the chemist. She just looked at me and sternly said "you get it yourself, why should I get for you?" I was too ill to get out of bed, so I remained there, feeling hurt, betrayed, alone and in pain. I felt too weak to live.

I was sitting in the kitchen once, I was much older then, around fifteen. My dad walked in. I was in his way, he wanted to put an empty bottle out on the balcony and I was sitting in front of the opening that led to the balcony. He shouted at me "Get out of my way". I started to get up, but was not fast enough. He started yelling at me. I was up by this time, but had frozen. I couldn't move. My dad took the few paces over to me with vigour and hit me with the glass bottle he was holding. I lifted my arm just in time to protect my face. The bottle broke. I was bleeding and still frozen, in shock. My dad then yelled "Get out of here, you're making a mess. Clean the blood off the floor before you go and make sure you're out of my sight"

I used to close myself up in my little room, snuggle up under the covers, turn my face to the wall and cry. I'd cry and cry and cry. I was not heard, I was not loved. I was hated and resented. I was miserable. I'd lie there in the darkness of my room feeling sorry for myself, feeling alone. I was sure I deserved all the hatred I was receiving, I must be such an abomination of a child. It never occurred to me that maybe it wasn't my fault, that maybe I wasn't all that bad. I was so sure I must be terrible enough to deserve all the punishment, abuse and hatred I received.

One day my dad walked in when I was crying in my room. He sat on the chair by the bed and in a calm voice lectured me for over an hour. It was dark in the room, dark as my soul and heart. He told me what a horrible person I was. How he was ashamed I was his daughter and if I were not his daughter, he would have nothing to do with someone like me. He said I was rotten through and through. I was bad and disgusting. He went on and on. He said I would never have any friends, because no one could possibly like someone like me. He told me my nature was evil. He had tried his best to make me better, but it was no use, I was too rotten to be saved. I disgusted him.

I lay there listening. Darkness took over my soul. I cried when he left. I felt so tired, so depleted, I had nothing left within me. I told myself "that's enough. I will never cry again. I will not cry. I will live. I will not be sad or unhappy. I will force happiness on myself. I will never listen to sad music again. I will not think of sad things. I refuse to ever cry again"

I succeeded for a long time, but I didn't realise that sadness is a natural feeling and there is a time and place for it and that crying is a natural way of release. I did not cry again, no matter what happened, until fifteen years later. By that time I had been practising yoga and meditation regularly, my body, crammed with so much trauma and baggage was starting to open. I was getting in touch with my body and feelings started to flow. I allowed myself to cry again and that was a relief. So much had been locked down for so long in that poor, pained body.

The journey has been long and not easy. Sometimes I feel there is too much locked down there, it's overwhelming, but gradually, step by step release is happening, my body is becoming freer and lighter. I have greater awareness and can feel and even bear my feelings.

So much hatred placed in me, on me. It was not my fault. I was not bad, in fact I was pretty good. I always had friends, good friends, loving, close friends. I was not despised by anyone except my parents and myself.

That pain in the navel. I still re-live it whenever there's a sense of betrayal, of abandonment. I now know that it is not the events happening at the time that create that pain, they simply trigger in me the old trauma, they re-activate the pain of years ago, they open an old wound. The pain is always overwhelming when it comes. It takes me into darkness and despair. It takes me to a place where I wish to die. But it is an old wound. It is time to heal it. It is time to separate what is happening in my life now from what happened when I was a child.

I felt that pain again months after this bodywork. I couldn't stand it. It took over. I wanted to die. But I stayed with it. I lay on my bed and felt into it. Felt where it was in my body and watched it. I stayed with it for over three hours. Eventually I couldn't any longer. It was too much. So I let my mind wander. I thought of other things. I held my two toy animals I've had since I was a child and felt their warmth. And suddenly I started to tremble all over. My whole body was trembling uncontrollably. I knew the release was happening. I felt my body was adjusting itself. It had gone deep into that pain and allowed it to express itself, given it space to have a voice. Now it was releasing, letting go.

In Somatic Experiencing we learn that as animals we are naturally conditioned to go into fight or flight mode when we face danger. Our bodies don't differentiate between real, life-threatening, physical danger and emotional danger. Our bodily responses to both are the same. My body was so traumatised, it went into flight or fight mode and never came out, never re-adjusted. When we re-adjust we tremble all over and then usually fall asleep, if the trauma is that great. In the past I had been overwhelmed and eventually I froze.

But the release came, it's what happened with me when I stayed with the pain and then trembled and fell asleep. I knew the navel pain I experienced again and again for decades had been resolved. I had given it awareness, time and space and my body had let it go, it had released it, it had re-adjusted.

I have not felt that pain since, although certain circumstances have taken place that in the old days would have triggered that pain in me. My body has healed the wound. It is now closed. I am free of one trauma inflicted damage in my body, one that was so strong and determining of my actions. I would have done anything to prevent that pain and what I did was to protect myself, by not being able to give or receive love, by being on guard, doing my best to not let anyone in. But they do get in, and I do get hurt. No longer. Now I will let them come in, without my knee-jerk, unconscious, defensive reactions and they will not be able to open my old wound, because it is now healed.

I have since felt hurt and pain, but I have felt them where they belong, in my heart, not in my navel, and they have been bearable. I have cried, shouted and then let go, a healthy response, rather than wanting to die, fighting the pain in my navel, being overwhelmed by it, losing life, freezing.

Mick and I part. He goes to his room after a TV show. I crumple up against a door crying as if I've gone mad. My mother sees me.

When Mick goes to speak to Persephone, she ignores him, she doesn't even remember his name. She calls him by the wrong name. She says "I know you're John". When he tries to tell her he's not John, he's Mick, she doesn't believe him. She takes no notice of him.

My mother is sitting at a square table. She is watching me from there, crying in a little desolate bundle, leaning against the door, crying my heart and soul out. There is no expression on her face. No care, no compassion, no love, no concern. She sits there and watches. She's indifferent to my pain.

Mother, society, the wider consciousness, and of course my own mother herself, who for me should be the source of non-judgemental, unconditional, infinite love and acceptance, of compassion, caring and nurturing. But she gives me none of that, she is just watching. Her expression is judgemental, but lacking any emotion. She doesn't care about me, she has no sympathy or care for my grief and pain, no compassion. She's not giving me anything, not a warm word, not a smile, not a single facial expression. She's watching and judging and she's withholding what should come naturally, what is every child's right: care and love from the mother. She is withholding anything and everything from me. She will not give from herself, even a smile, or a small sign of recognition.

The table, the square table left to me by my grandfather. I love him and I love that table. For me my grandfather symbolises unconditional love, absolute acceptance, non-judgemental free flowing love. He loved me as I was. He always had time for me, time to chat, to go for walks, to play tennis, to play ball, throw a Frisbee, to discuss books or politics. If I recommended a book, he always read it and talked to me about it afterwards. He didn't necessarily like everything I suggested, but he always took the time to read it. He shared his love of reading and music with me, starting from a very young age. He would always send me books to Turkey. He would read into tapes and send me those. He would record interesting programmes from the radio and send them. He would send me music.

He shared his time and love with me without restraint. It didn't matter what I did, what path I chose, what career I ended up in, as long as I was happy, he was happy. He thought I was amazing no matter what. He knew I would be okay in life. He had faith in me. Whatever I chose to do would be fine by him, he loved me anyway. He thought the world of me.

He was strict, but in a loving way. He never shouted at me for no reason at all. In fact he never shouted at me. He would tell me off in a stern, calm voice if necessary. He never character assassinated me, criticised who I was, made things personal.

He was a calm, loving, sharing presence in my life and I carry his memory and his love with me fondly.

However, my mother sits at his table, the table of unconditional love and giving, things which she should have provided, but she withholds. She has nothing to give me, nothing to share. Only judgement. Cold, harsh, emotionless judgement.

Persephone calls a spade a spade, she won't let anyone else tell her what's right or wrong. She won't be moved. She stands by what she believes. Even when sometimes what she calls a spade is a fork, she will still stand by it, although it's wrong.

Mick is honest. He tells Persephone who he is. But Persephone won't listen. She is convinced she knows who he is in her mind, except that her knowledge is incorrect. Who she believes Mick to be is not the true Mick, it is someone else, someone she has made up. She's dismissive of him. She doesn't see the real Mick, she sees who she thinks she's looking at.

A part of me dismisses Mick and who he is. I don't appreciate his positive attributes, I see him through a veil of judgement placed there by society: someone with no career potential, someone who is awkward in social circumstances and society in general, someone with no interests, no joy of life, no interest in life and no passion for it. I dismiss him. But there is more to him than these general norms we judge people by. We brand them, stamp them directed by these limited attributes and constrained ways of seeing things. That is not the real Mick. He is also highly sensitive, sensual and intuitive. He is someone who is in touch with his emotional side, with the feminine side of his being. He can love and share and give fully and unconditionally.

The dream is showing me the contradictions I am facing in every part of my life. Logic on one side, society and judgements; and on the other side, at war with them, emotions, instincts, gut feel. The dream is asking me to look at the whole picture and not stamp judgements and labels on things, they could be the wrong labels. Logic can come to conclusions that are very convincing, that fit into the laws society has created a wall out of. But there is also the feeling side, the side that can love unconditionally and give of itself. A mother who cannot love, a table that symbolises love. A mother who is judgemental and uncaring, a square table that accepts and nurtures. A side of me that calls a spade a fork and believes that is right, a side that will not hear or see otherwise, it will not be convinced, although it is wrong.

And there I am, crying my eyes out in the corner, alone, desolate, abandoned. My mother has taken over the table and she will not share. I lie there in pain and suffering. I look to her for sympathy, comfort, nurturing, love and I receive nothing but cold, harsh judgement. She is unavailable to me. She always has been.

Society is uncaring, judgemental, moralistic but in a very narrow, limited way. Are those the rules I want to live my life by? Do I want to be governed by the laws set down by a society that has lost touch with its feminine, emotional side, a society that lacks awareness?

Mick is in touch with his shadow, his sentimentality, his emotions. Yet these attributes are dismissed by society. They are dismissed by me. These attributes have always been dismissed as weaknesses by my parents. Be a man, be strong, don't cry, don't laugh. Stand up, get things done yourself, don't ask, don't need. You will not receive what you need from us. We do this for your own good, so that you learn to provide for yourself, to stand on your own two feet.

Yes, I have learned to survive and take care of myself. I expect no need of mine to be met, I do not know how to ask for even the simplest things. I get everything done myself, or I live without it. But where is acceptance in that of us as human beings who do have needs and who can help and support each other? Where is the love and nurturing I could give myself? Nowhere, only judgements, cold, analytical decisions, only never good enoughs. It's time to connect to my emotions, give them the value they deserve, hear them, feel them, not be embarrassed by them, squash them and hide them. Let myself live, whole, without constrictions. I am who I am, a feeling, living being. It's time to give myself that space and respect, to provide myself with the nurturing, accepting, loving environment that was never shown me. It's time to see a spade as a spade and a fork as a fork and cherish both as they are for what they are and use them appropriately. No more mislabelling. It's time to free myself from under my mother's cold, unfeeling, judging stare.

Love is lost to many
Cause they can't accept
Too defensive, afraid
To let it into their depths

Need persistence banging on your door
Those who do may not be right
You lose your love, loyalty no more
Looking for a spark, a love that's bright

But that also fades and dies
Cause it's hard, so hard
To get through the innocent lies
And from love's gate not be barred

My anger and guilt as they eat away
Also kill love of life, of what's new and gay

I am the hand of destruction
Nobody survives my heart-felt corruption

To lie here, to close my eyes
And stay asleep for a while
And when I awake to start anew
Not forgetting the experience that was my due

5 November 11

I'm in a large, rectangular room. It looks like a hotel lobby. There are heavy, red, drape curtains everywhere. There is a casino in the centre of the room, slightly to the left. There is a newspaper recycling area against the back wall, behind the casino. There are slot machines along the left wall and half way up the front and back walls on the left side. The right side centre is open space. There are double doors, the doors my parents force their way through, opposite. The doors are linked in a weird way. They are hard to close. There are some couches to the right. There is a toilet in the right front corner and it has no separating walls. If I want privacy while using the toilet, I need to keep people out of the whole area.

I want to throw up, my abdomen is in turmoil, my insides rising. I need to get to the toilet fast. My mother, father and someone else walk in through the double doors. I try to, but can't get them out. I shout at them "get out, get out" several times. I try to push them out, but they keep coming back in. They won't leave and even when I manage to push them to the other side of the doors, I can't close the doors on them while they continue to struggle against me.

Eventually I manage to get them out. A worker at the hotel turns to me with a grin and says "life is too short".

Another hotel worker appears on the casino side, collecting thrown away recyclable rubbish, mainly newspapers. He asks me "why did you touch the thing? Ah, it's here after all". He has a weird, irritating voice and my father's face.

My dad says, as way of an excuse for their behaviour, something along the lines of "we can't get in touch with you any other way", meaning they have to force their way into the room where I want to use the toilet. They have to force themselves on me during what should be a personal time, they invade my private space.

But the space is anything but private, filled with hotel workers, couches, a casino, slot machines. Such a private act as using the toilet will have to be done in full view of everyone, in a common, public area. I can't do that though.

Casinos are public spaces, they are where people act out their addictions, they are quite often immoral.

I'm trying desperately to keep my parents out of what should be my private space. Their voices are forever in my head, in my private thoughts and views, the beliefs they instilled me, their morals, their ideas, their rights and wrongs, their views of the world and of me, their way of life, these are what overwhelm me on the inside, they take over my own thoughts and views, my thoughts are not my own, invaded by theirs.

I'm trying so hard to refuse them and what they stand for. I'm trying to kick them out, keep out what they have instilled in me, what is preventing me from performing even the most simple, natural functions, like going to the toilet, relieving myself, expressing myself. There is forever the belief that I am worthless, evil, ugly, bad, unloveable by anyone and everyone. I have the strength in me to keep them out, but they persist and the doors that should work as a barrier between myself and them are not functional, they are flimsy, they don't shut properly. My boundaries aren't working, they aren't strong and functional enough to keep my parents out. The room is working against me. I fight and struggle, but it's easier for them. They win.

Arthur also plays on those feelings in me. He ignores me, makes me feel guilty, leaves me with all the shadow to carry, his, mine, our relationships'. He undermines me, acts indifferently, making me feel insignificant, valueless, worthless, telling me that he doesn't love me or care for me through words as well as his indifference. He looks down on me, always takes the side of the other, never ever ever sides with me. My emotional outbursts, my passion need to be buried, controlled, he finds them uncomfortable, embarrassing. My natural way of being is too much for him, too raw, so he undermines me, makes me small, makes me feel ashamed of myself, ashamed to be me. I am never good enough for him, I can never do well enough. It is always my fault, every fight or argument we've had has been my fault, every disagreement I've ever had with anyone else has been my fault, every time something goes wrong the question he asks me is "what have you done?"

In 2008, for the first and only time in my life I spoke back to my dad. I raised my voice and cried as I spoke. I told him of my pain, of how wrongly I felt they had treated me, of how his treatment of me had hurt me and harmed me. I said all this in gentle terms, nowhere near as strongly as I felt inside. Although it was an emotional outburst, it was relatively controlled. I talked more of my feelings, hurt and pain and left out accusations or blame. Yet my dad couldn't hear me. He shouted at me, he was furious, he disowned me. I ran to my room and cried as though my heart would break. All this happened in Turkish, Arthur was there, but he doesn't understand Turkish. He saw what happened and did not follow the conversation. He came in after me, he was angry with me. He asked me "What the hell did you say to him?", his voice full of accusation. It never occurred to him that I might have not said anything wrong, that maybe my dad was not in the right and I was not bad and wrong, that maybe I hadn't misbehaved, but rather voiced my pent up feelings, feelings and hurts pent up inside me for years. This did not even occur to him. It was a given that I had misbehaved somehow. I must have said terrible things. I must have deserved my father's anger.

In fairness to him, once I stopped crying and translated the conversation, he did hold me, but he didn't apologise for accusing me wrongly, for automatically blaming me. That was the natural way of things between us. I was always to blame, always the questionable one.

Arthur allowed me for years to carry the responsibility and the blame, he still does. He also leaves me with the hurt and pain. I get to carry all the emotions. I'm a willing participant. I carried the shadow and the blame in my family. It was forced on me from when I was a baby and I have accepted it as my load, all that is bad, all that is at fault. I'm the wrong doer, the sinner, the one who acts up. There's something wrong with me. I'm damaged goods. I'm evil. I'm unworthy and deserve nothing good. It's all my fault, everything bad is my fault. Every fight we've ever had, every break-up, it's always been my fault. Arthur untouched, on a pedestal, perfection, and I, the one who carries the burden of all that's wrong and evil.

I can now learn to let go of all that blame and guilt. It's not all mine to carry. I carry my parents' unconscious resentments, complexes, anger, I carry their resentment of me as though it were my doing, I carry their shadow. I was always bad, nothing I ever did was right or good, never and nothing I have ever done, ever achieved has changed that belief in their eyes.

So deep in me is the belief that I cannot be loved, that I am unworthy, it determines every day of my life, it directs all my actions, controls my thoughts and feelings. Unconsciously I set myself up, inviting blame, indifference, anger. I reject love and acceptance, I can't digest them. I'm starting to notice this pattern now. I see it in every part of my life. Becoming aware is the first step in the process of letting go and healing. I notice I blame myself even when it is not my fault. I blame myself fully for my break-up with Arthur, yet it takes two to tango. He has remained unblemished through our separation, but that is not possible. It took two to build the relationship and two to break it up.

I'm afraid to be vulnerable, because as a child I was vulnerable, and that brought nothing but betrayal, abandonment and abuse. Crying, feeling sad was a weakness. I was punished for crying. I was taught never to show weakness. But without allowing for vulnerability in an intimate relationship, something always remains missing. The guards are up, the walls strong, each person isolated somewhere deep inside. Without that deep intimacy, how can love blossom and grow and stay alive?

I was strong with Arthur. I had to be. He could not, would not deal with emotions. Crying was inviting the comment "pull yourself together". "Get a hold of yourself". Anger invited "get a grip, control yourself". Sadness demanded "come on, this is ridiculous, why do you have to make such a big deal out of things?". I carried the emotions within me, controlling them as much as I could outwardly. All that repression meant that I sometimes ignited, my emotions erupted like an uncontrollable force of nature, like a volcano. They took even me by surprise. Usually what sparked the fire was so minor and insignificant, I myself could not understand where all that anger came from. Emotions don't vanish just because we suppress them or ignore them, they get stored in our bodies, in our souls. They will eventually find a way to release. Unless done with awareness, consciously, naturally, they will always come out inappropriately, at the wrong time, for the wrong reasons, towards the wrong person.

Casino, such a public space, immoral in many ways, and that's where I end up needing to relieve myself, express myself, where I need to create my own space, I can hold it in no longer. Also in a casino, if there's no risk taking, there is no potential for gain either. If you're too afraid to be vulnerable, you're too afraid for love.

And even then my parents won't let me be. They have to invade. And they still blame me for their invasion. It is my fault because they "can't get hold of me any other way". I am to blame for their act of disrespect.

I know I need to keep them out somehow, put in effective boundaries, protect myself from them and their invasions, but my doors are flimsy, they won't close, they don't work properly. I need new doors. I need a new space. A space my parents cannot enter. Boundaries they cannot simply walk through. They have no place in my unconscious, reminding me all the time of my worthlessness, they belong outside of my space, their shadow is no longer mine to carry.

10 November 11

I dreamt I was using someone else's toothbrush. It was a hard and large toothbrush, way too hard and way too large for me.

Night after night, still the same theme, begging to be heard. I am being warned, my dreams point out to me that I am using other people's internal ideas, judgements and their closest beliefs for myself, even though they are wrong for me, they hurt, they're the wrong size and they're too hard. They are not mine and they are not right for me. Even though the people themselves might be close to me, they should keep their own toothbrushes and I should use my own, one that is the right size and is soft, one that is right for me.

Arthur refuses to believe that I have done my best to get work, that I have been trying so hard. He is giving me more of the undermining, more of the blame placing act. "You're not trying hard enough. Why are you feeling so low? Pull yourself together. It's your fault".

And yet I have tried so hard. I have built my classes up to ten classes per week from nothing, from knowing nobody, with no contacts. I have designed and printed fliers and spread them all over town, I have advertised on websites and yoga venues, I have met managers and offered help in many ways to get a foot through the door in their studios.

I have also applied for finance jobs, contacted head hunters, been to interviews.

The doors are shut. I have tried very hard and have found no openings. My classes won't build, no one comes. I fail to meet people. People in Zurich are cold and closed. They are unfriendly and unwelcoming. They don't want foreigners and I am a foreigner. I stand no chance.

I have joined different classes to meet people, an Italian course, zumba classes, dance classes, the gym,... I meet people, but no one is friendly. They're polite, but they are closed to me and I am shut out. I feel like I'm slamming my head against brick walls.

Arthur is not here. He's always travelling. He is hardly ever in Zurich. He does not know, he doesn't understand. He blames me for my depression. I say I have no friends here, no fulfilling work, he blames me for these too. It's all my fault, it must be. But is it? What more can I do?

I'm isolated and alone, cut off from everyone I know and everything I'm used to. I have no aims or goals, nothing that makes me want to get out of bed in the mornings, nothing to look forward to, to live for. I stumble along. I force myself to live, it no longer comes naturally. Everything has become so hard, such an immense struggle and I am so alone. I sometimes spend weeks on end without having a single conversation with another human being. Arthur is away for weeks at a time, my friends are not here and there's no one to talk to. I exchange the odd sentence with someone in a shop or when buying coffee and that's it. I have no further human interaction.

I turn up to my classes, only to face an hour of teaching a non-plussed student or two, they are disinterested and unlikely to return. I get nothing out of it myself. Even my passion, my joy of teaching yoga no longer gives me satisfaction. It brings only disappointment. Will someone turn up? Will I again be teaching only one student? I don't enjoy teaching in German, but do they like being taught in English? Does it matter? I've tried both.

I've reached the end of the road. I see no way out. I can't go on like this. I'm going deeper and deeper into depression, into black, unfeeling darkness. One day I will no longer have the will or energy to get up at all. I will give up the fight and sink into nothingness. One day I will no longer have the will to breathe. The day is drawing closer. Should I not cut my losses and give up? I can go back to my friends and work in London. I was happy there. At least I would have them, even if not Arthur. But would I want a life without Arthur?

Deeper and deeper and darker, depression taking over. Some days

I can't get out of bed. I simply can't face the day. And this from a person who in the past always embraced the new day, leapt out of bed with energy and hope, rejoicing in what it might have to offer. Now I dread the new day. A whole day to somehow drag myself through.

The pain of depression. It's not just a feeling, it's a physical sensation, it's painful. Everything in my body is closed up, cramped, constricted. It hurts to breathe, my heart is aching, it no longer wants to beat. There's a void in my abdomen, a craving, cutting sensation that digs hollower, wider, scrapes away at my organs more and more each day.

I am dying, slowly, painfully, surely, I am dying.

Yet still I think with others' ideas and thoughts imposed on me. I can't free myself from judgements, assumptions of what's right for me and how I should be, how I should live. I know these outer thoughts, ideals, judgements are wrong for me, they harm me, but I can't shake them. I am still using someone else's toothbrush. Even my most personal space, my dreams, aims, wishes, my hopes and plans, even my views of myself, who I am, how I should lead my life, they're all poisoned from the outside. I am taking on others ideals, ones that don't belong to me, ones that hurt, that make my gums bleed.

Heartache and pain
Wanted to hear your voice so bad
Nothing came
Now I'm sitting here so sad

Nothing good comes of love
It never has a happy ending
Might as well bolt the door and hide
No more love in your direction am I sending

I'm shutting down, closing up
I refuse to be the only one trying hard
I thought I could manage myself
But effort by just me, it simply can't be

I'm walking off, goodbye my love
I'm done with all this suffering
Crying alone in the night
Too much heartbreak, I'm hurting

I'm sorry my love, I'm sorry
I killed me while killing us
But I have no more strength
Left here, alone, I will be dying.

I arranged to skype with Mick at 12:00, but my parents walk in suddenly at 11:45. I can't possibly skype with them there. I hurriedly try to email him to cancel our skype call. I'm slightly panicky. But my parents won't stop talking at me, they don't give me a chance to write an email. They ask me if I want to go to a film at the church. I ask them what film they have in mind.

My dad doesn't hear me I think, or maybe he just ignores me. It somehow feels to me like my voice is not within his hearing range, as if it's an octave too high or too low. He says "Fine then, don't come", although I've said nothing about not going, in fact I've asked what's on. And so the saga continues. I keep trying to tell them I'll go and asking what we will see, I try to answer them, but they're completely ignoring me, hearing nothing I say, not paying any attention at all. It's as if I don't exist.

They can't hear anything I say at all. There is loud music playing in the background. They simply assume I'm saying what they have already decided I would say, but it's all wrong. They've made up their mind and every time I open my mouth, they imagine the words they expect to hear flowing out of it, but those are not the words uttered.

I can't email Mick, no matter how hard I try. I have loads of different windows open on my computer. I'm rushing desperately to try to close them and get to my email before my parents see what I'm doing, but their oblivious anyway. They don't see me, they don't hear me, but they think they do and they know they're right in what they see and hear, but they're completely wrong.

I can't connect to my inner Mick, because my inner parents are not hearing what I'm saying. Instead they shout: "you're horrible, bad, unloveable." I can't connect to him, the one that isn't afraid of feeling, loving and being loved, because of these voices. I can't connect to anyone intimately because of these voices. They take over. They don't know me, they don't hear me, but they think they know me, they're so sure they know me all else is overwhelmed. But what they think is wrong.

I was not able to receive Arthur's love because of these voices. Always on the defensive, always expecting the worse. I spent the whole of our relationship until he proposed to me waiting for him to tell me he's leaving, that he's had enough. If he ever said "we need to talk", my heart sank, I was so sure he was about to break up with me, but he didn't. Yet I still waited for Armageddon. I kept my defences up, I continued with my knee-jerk reactions, unconsciously acting out because I was so sure he didn't love me, but he stayed. So eventually I pushed him away.

I could not love and I could not receive love, because deep down inside I'm so sure no one could possibly love me and that I am unworthy of anybody's love or loyalty.

There are so many windows open, too many distractions preventing me from accessing what's really important. There are too many thoughts, too many voices, too much chaos. I need space, calm, quiet. All these goings on are so loud, constantly there, sometimes right in front of me, preventing me from accessing what I need, sometimes in the background, preventing me from being heard. I can't hear, I can't feel anymore, I'm so confused about everything. Windows, loud music and I'm not heard, just the judgemental, misguided voices of my parents get through, no other connection is possible.

Arthur and I have agreed to separate. Some release came from reaching a decision at last, some release, because I won't have to face him with my heart and soul bared, the idea of which petrified me. But I also felt so much pain and hurt. It was so easy for him, he didn't even seem sad. That proves I need to leave. How can I be with someone who doesn't care, who's not even affected when a twelve year relationship and a marriage ends? I knew he didn't love me. He said he did, but I felt he didn't. I was right. Maybe it wasn't my complexes that kept telling me he didn't love me, maybe it was my instincts.

Maybe our relationship worked so well for so long, because

neither of us are capable of love, showing love or receiving love, so we reached a perfectly harmonious balance, until suddenly I decided I did want to feel loved, and the whole thing came toppling down, falling apart, crushing to the ground.

I'm broken, relieved but broken. I'm in pain, but I can't face my pain. I need to act, move, do, anything but sit still. If I sit still the pain will overwhelm me, it will bury me, drown me. I will not survive. So I must plan, move, pack, talk, run, anything but be still and feel.

18 November 11

I'm experiencing problems with the trains. I'm trying to get to City Airport, but I end up at Gatwick Airport instead. I got on the wrong train somehow. I'm now stuck at somewhere called Sutton. I look around for some help or guidance, but there is no railway staff around, no ticket offices, nowhere I can ask for help. I go into a Chinese gift shop and ask them how I can get to City Airport. They have copies of the train timetable behind the counter and look trains up for me. It turns out I need to go back to Gatwick and change there. The situation feels so desperate. Gatwick is not where I want to be, I ended up there by mistake, I managed to leave, I've just come from there and now I have to go back there. I'm worried and stressed and upset. The people at the shop keep telling me not to worry.

In my frantic need to move and get somewhere, I get on the wrong train and get stuck in the wrong place. It would have been wiser and more efficient and much less stressful for me if I had looked at my options at the start and taken my time to make the right choice and get on the right train. Instead I jumped on the first train I came across in my desperation to use any route to get out and it turned out to be a very wrong one.

Trains are a form of transport, a way of getting from A to B. I'm trying to get to A, but I'm panicking, I'm not choosing my route wisely. I end up in B, even further from A than I was at the start, all because I panicked and didn't pause to check, to enquire, to understand and make an informed choice.

The Chinese are completely foreign to me. I have never been to China, I know no Chinese and the language is completely different and alien to me. Something that's foreign within us is usually a very quiet voice within us. And yet, this usually quiet, foreign voice within me is telling me it will be okay, I'll get there, there is no need to panic. This foreign voice is trying to soothe and reassure me. He knows nothing of me, but he has more confidence in me than I do in myself.

It's true, I do feel like I'm moving frantically, desperately. I'm so confused and lost, I feel so depressed, I want to get out, run away, flee as fast as I can, wherever I can, as soon as possible. I'm flapping my arms around uselessly. I'm fighting a tide that cannot be fought, a current that is trying to guide me to where I want to go, and in my panic, I am fighting against it, rather than flowing with it. I need to calm down, sit, think and feel, if possible meditate. But how? The turmoil within is so chaotic, so loud, I can't stay still for a second. If I do, I get overwhelmed. I'm screaming inside and I can't stand the sound. If I stop to listen, my screams will deafen me, they will freeze me, they might even kill me. So I try to shut down, not hear. I run and run, but I'm getting nowhere. I'm in a state of panic. It's darkness all around, there's no air. I'm gulping for air, but nothing enters my lungs. I want to scream, no sound is released. I'm choking on my own screams. I can't breathe. And I run. I run and run. I already know I'm going in the wrong direction, but I can't stop now. If I stop, my screams, my pain, my anguish, my regret, my loss, my despair will catch up with me. Instant death I do not fear, I do not mind, but the excruciating pain that will catch up with me and kill me slowly, that I cannot stand, so I keep on running. Running. I'm breathless. And still I run. And now I'm in Sutton. I don't even know where I am. I don't know how I got here. I'm lost. I want to go home, but in my panic I destroyed my home. There is nowhere to go back to. Somehow I must go on. I must find a way, get on another train and reach City Airport. From there my journey will take a better course. But where is City Airport? Does it even exist?

God, help me! I can't breathe. It's so dark, I can't see. There's so much mud, bog, shit around me, I can't hear. God, please help me, because I can't stand this a second longer. I want to go home. Can't You erase the past year of my life and let me go back home? It's too dark here. I don't want to save Persephone any longer. I'm not strong enough, I was wrong. I overestimated myself. I'm lost in these caves. Let me go back out. I don't care about finding my shadow, bringing it to light. I'm not strong enough. I want to go back to oblivion. I don't care if it's a half life, led by a half recognised me. I can't follow this path any longer. I'm so sorry. I'm so afraid. I'm so full of regrets. I miss Arthur so much already. Won't you let me go back?

Ignorance is bliss they say. How wise they are. Why did I want to learn and understand? I could have remained happy, in oblivious light. Who cares about becoming whole? It's too painful. Let me out. Let me go. I don't want to any longer. It was a mistake. Let me die, I prefer that to all this pain, this darkness, this hopelessness. Let me die, why won't You? God please. Hear me! Either release me, or kill me. I'm begging You!!!

I take on the form of my parents one by one. I become them. I take on their persona, their feelings, their bodies and their souls.

As I take on the form of my mother, I feel my shoulders broaden, I feel a certain pride rise within myself, my head tilted to the left slightly, as if I want to show off to the world how compassionate and understanding I am, but it is only an act, it's not genuine. I notice my eyes become very, very, very sad and my arms want to open and receive, but are unable to open, my body is too closed to be able to receive. My chin takes on a proud tilt. The most overwhelming sensation is in my pelvis, it feels completely blocked, so utterly inaccessible, as if it is filled with dark, damp earth. It is in total darkness and I have no access to it at all, no feeling of it. I feel totally disconnected from my pelvis, I simply can't feel it no matter how hard I try. All I feel is darkness and that damp earth, I feel nothing down there, lost in so much darkness, it feels closed up, tight, locked.

My gate is off too. My pelvis being so locked up, it is an odd walk and it is my mother's walk, I recognise it.

I then become the pelvis. As the pelvis I feel resented by her, blocked off, shunned. I'm only nourished as part of the procedure gone through to keep the body healthy, but I'm not really nurtured. I'm cut off from the soul. I'm ignored, closed off, unwanted, not accepted, not seen or felt. I know she would rather not have me. I am a burden, an anomaly. I am hated by her.

I become my dad and feel a burden, a heavy, so heavy burden on my shoulders, an unnecessary burden built up of work, life, family, the past, feelings of responsibility and rights and wrongs. I feel that everything that entered his life, good or bad, was placed on those shoulders as a burden, even joy and happiness became a heavy weight for him to carry, all a burden, a heavy, heavy burden. But the burden doesn't belong there. Most of it should not have been taken on, it doesn't belong with him. Some of it shouldn't even be a burden at all. He has taken ownership of all this weight unnecessarily, he carries it unnecessarily. The burden is not accessed, not felt, not noticed, just placed there

*and ignored. It's as if he takes on the cloak of a martyr, a cloak that's heavy,
despised, but carried nonetheless, without any understanding of what it consists
of, without any connection to it, without dealing with it, without relieving
others through his sacrifice. It's a useless burden and he is no martyr, because
he wants that burden, it is who he is, who he thinks he should be. I'm sure
he's never opened up that heavy sack he's carrying and looked through it to
see what's in there, to understand, to leave out what doesn't belong, to sort it
out, maybe solve what problems he can. No, it's there as a huge heap, as heavy
rocks, stone.*

*I become his burden. As the burden I feel the need to move to the heart to
be accessed and then released.*

My dad's burden and rigidity was no surprise to me, it seemed
natural, I understood it, I knew it to be true, but the extent of my
mother's pelvis area's darkness, the extent of disconnect there was
between her and her pelvis was a huge surprise. Once I felt it, I knew
it was true though, I knew in my soul that was how it was. I
understood at last. It was no wonder she can't hear anyone, she can't
be receptive to anyone. All reception, earth, acceptance, connection
to the body, the feminine, feeling side of life, sensuality, nature, all
that is yin is cut off, shunned, possibly hated and despised.

The pitch black, dark pelvis. The extent of disconnect within
her own body, from her most female part! The resentment and
shunning of the body, of what is irrational, emotional, instinctual,
of what is truly female and part of femininity, the nurturing side of
the universe of life, all this is blocked off, resented, hated.

And then there's me, in spite of all of this. In spite of the
darkness my mother instilled in me against my own femininity, my
emotional, instinctual, accepting, nurturing side, I have survived,
I'm not too closed to it, I'm not completely blocked off from it, there
is an opening and I have started my exploration, I am finding my
way into that area, I am finding my shadow.

What I have learned is to not shut out emotions and instincts, not
to ignore them. It's natural for them to speak, we can only be whole
if we listen to them, hear them, otherwise part of our body and
awareness will get buried in darkness, inaccessible to us. We become

blocked, rigid. We are no longer our real selves. We can't be logic only driven. We can't live only analytically. There is a need for feelings, for instincts, for dreams, for awareness. It is part of nature, an equal part, it is a natural part of being human, of what we are. If we close that part of us down, we carry darkness in our body, rigidity, part of our body dies, we have no access to it and there is no life in it.

I know I'll be okay eventually. I have some awareness of my feelings, although I fight them, I shun them, undermine them, often reject them, tell myself to stop being so stupid, but I am starting to understand them more. Parts of my body that were disconnected, unfelt, are starting to open up to me. Energy is starting to flow more freely.

I need to stop focusing on the fear and guilt I carry. They freeze my body and my soul. I have options, I need to take my time to choose the right one. I need to learn to follow my instincts, my heart. My heart is closed, I need to connect to it. I want to be free of the darkness that is part of my mother. I want to be free of the burden my father carries. They have both instilled their own shadow in me. I have inherited my mother's dark pelvis and my father's heavy burden, but they do not belong to me. They could not face their darkness or burden, so they passed them on to me to carry. I have carried them so far, without even understanding what I was doing, but I want them no longer. I need them no longer. I want to live. I want to feel every part of my body and I want every part of my body to feel light, to be full of light. I will carry the burden no longer and I will spread light down into my pelvis. I am not afraid of my intuitions, my feelings, I do not shun my femininity. I do sometimes, but I will learn how not to.

It's final with Arthur. We've agreed everything. He doesn't seem sad or upset. He isn't questioning whether this is the right decision or not. He seems happy with the decision, at peace with it somehow, without even an hour's mourning. I feel betrayed. I'm in turmoil. How can he be so indifferent while I am in so much pain?

We were together a long time. We are married. Something shifted for me when we promised each other till death do us part. I thought it was only a piece of paper, something people did to make things official, to make it easier for the kids, that it didn't really matter. I was wrong. It turned out to make a big difference to me. I became a family with him, part of his family, we were bound, we became one, I was no longer part of the family my parents built. It felt good to be with him, to become one with him. I felt good becoming a family with him, and no longer being part of my old family, the poisonous one. I became a unit with him. We always acted as a unit before, but now I really felt we were joined, for life. Something did change. But obviously not for him. He always said it was only a piece of paper for him and it seems the actual experience didn't shift that. Our marriage for him was meaningless, it still is. Then why is it not so for me? Why do I feel so deeply, strongly bound to him?

I hope we stay friends. A life without him in it is unimaginable to me. I don't want that. I can't imagine it.

He was my rock, my support, my best friend, the person who brought me back to reality, put things in context, reminded me of what was important in life. He was my light, my warmth, my sun. I am finding some of these strengths within myself, the ability to provide myself with guidance and balance, to support myself, to have courage and trust. I can do it. But I can't see myself with anyone else. Do I want to live the rest of my life alone? Die alone? I know I can, but do I want to? He is the only one I love. Do I want to give up on my love? No. But the path is set, the ship has sailed and I will face the winds.

Recently I can't stand being with him. It feels like he's holding up a selective mirror to me. A mirror that reflects only the bad in me, so that when he's there I see only bad in myself. I want to bury myself, close my eyes, never have to wake up. I could just stay like that in blissful oblivion. Feeling is painful. Sleep brings numbness, no feeling. I wish for sleep.

I'm ruining my life, pulling it with all my strength into a dark, cramped, derelict alley. I'm crushing, burning, throwing away everything that ever mattered to me, everything I cared about and loved, all my dreams, all that has made me so happy. I know I'm doing this, but the force is so strong, I can't stop. Persephone has a huge self-destruct button she presses regularly, whenever there's any danger of her becoming happy, achieving something, getting out of the hole she has got herself into. I realise I have that very same button and I have just pressed it. Now I'm falling. The depth is dark, I'm still falling, I cannot see the end. Will I die from the force of the fall when I reach the bottom? Or will I survive so that I suffer in darkness and claustrophobia for all infinity, alone and abandoned.

I don't understand myself any more. I hate myself. What have I done? What am I doing?

I have no strength in me, no hope, no light. Who am I?

I have a Sunday morning class at Yogalives. Arthur and I go somewhere else first. Then we go home and eat chocolate, because he wants to. I want to leave to get to my class, but by then it's too late. When I realise I'm late, I start crying and ask Arthur through tears "Why did you do this? Why? Why? Why?"

The class was constantly on my mind, throughout the entire time we went other places and did things, but I left all the logistics to Arthur although intuitively I knew it was wrong. I trusted him and left the planning to him. He knew what time my class was and where. I felt ambivalent, I wasn't concerned. I didn't think I'd be late, I thought he had it all under control. But I didn't want to miss the class and when I realised that I had, I became overly distressed.

Why am I placing the whole responsibility on someone else? I call Arthur my rock and support, I trust him completely, but I have the ability to plan things myself, I can make correct decisions, I have reason. I should trust and listen to myself more. My instincts were right, the class was on my mind, but I ignored them, placing my trust in Arthur rather than myself. It is my class after all, I should take responsibility for it.

I left the decision of whether Arthur and I should stay together or separate ultimately with him, but it is a decision that has profound affects on my life, changes my life in every way. When I talked to him about what I saw as problems in our relationship and how I was feeling, I decided that if he said "we can solve these problems, let's work together", I would stay with him and put everything I have into making the relationship better, but if he walked away, I would let him go. He'd already broken up with me twice before and I had decided after the second time that if he did it again, I would not try to convince him to stay. He chose to walk away and the decision was made. That was not my decision, it was not my choice. I always said

I would not try to hold on to him a third time, because I can't spend the rest of my life expecting him to leave, him leaving, and me trying to convince him to come back. But this time I was the one who went to him with a list of issues that needed to be faced. I didn't say let's deal with these, I left the decision up to him.

I resent others too for what has happened, but they happened as a result of my actions, I should own them rather than placing the responsibility outside of me.

Arthur wants to feel good instantly and superficially, so he eats chocolates, although apart from the short term satisfaction they give a person, they are not good, healthy or nourishing. He'd rather walk away and ignore problems, decide the relationship is not worth saving rather than face the uncomfortable, the reality and what needs to be done.

I'm feeling confused, emotional and nervous. I'm afraid of myself, afraid of what's coming up from deep inside, from my unconscious, from my memories and past, I'm afraid of my emotions, my reactions, my ability to hate, to feel what I feel. I'm petrified of regretting what I've done and the choices I've made. I'm afraid of being hurt and hurting.

My therapist sees in me strength and determination. I can't see these qualities within myself. I haven't accessed them yet, at least not consciously. Others see them too, people have told me wonderful things about me over the years, but I can never take them in, believe them, own them. What they say always seems like a misunderstanding, I think "if they only knew me better, they'd see how bad I am, how far I am from what they see, what I'm really like". I need to open up to my positive aspects and qualities more, I need to own them.

I know now that the expression of feeling and emotion was always curbed in themselves and in us, their children, by my parents. I was taught to never show emotion, to never lose control and never embarrass myself by showing emotion. I am now learning that there's nothing wrong with my feelings, there is no need for me to be embarrassed by them. There is no need for me to try to avoid showing them. They are part of me, they are real. Why am I so embarrassed of who I am? Because I was always told I'm evil, bad, someone my parents are embarrassed to call their daughter, someone who's personality should be hidden from the world, because I am such a disgrace and an abomination.

Arthur chatted to me all the way home last night after dinner. We talked about spirituality, books, the Bhagavad Gita. I will miss our conversations so much. He is so interested in life, people, everything they have to offer. He engages and is stimulating. We talk about everything, from the cultural and intellectual to the banal and personal. I will miss sharing my life, every aspect of my life, my thoughts, my music, my books, my interests, my passions and joys with him.

I had complained that I was tired at the beginning of the journey and what a long way we were going to have to talk. As we reached home I expressed surprise at how fast the walk seemed to have finished and Arthur said to me "see baby, I may not carry you physically, but I do carry you". He is right. He allways has in his own way. His way that is so valuable to me, such an immense support, he is my rock, the person I trust infinitely. The only person in the world whom I trust.

But then maybe I need the independence. I've always been able to depend on him. He has provided me with so much. Now I will need to learn how to provide all that he gave me for myself. That can only make me stronger. Maybe this is really what I need. Safety can be stifling, maybe I need the challenge. But is it going to be worth the price I'm paying? Losing him might be the one greatest loss in my life, a loss I will never be able to replace, one I will always regret.

I'm noticing some changes in myself already. I no longer feel self-conscious in Turkey. I didn't while we were last there. I always used to feel extremely self-conscious there, somehow I would regress back to my teenage years every time I stepped off the plane into Istanbul. I'd become the uncomfortable, unloved, ugly teenager, at least I felt that way then and until recently, every time I was there. But this time I felt completely comfortable in my own skin. Maybe this is all part and parcel with finding myself, owning my shadow, good and bad, and becoming more whole. I'm starting to set my boundaries, be who I am and not be shy or embarrassed of myself. I sometimes even like myself.

7 December 11

*I want to work with emotions versus logic and try to resolve the conflict raging
between them within me. I embody emotions on one side and logic on the
other. I try to move from one to the other naturally, and then combine the two
in simultaneous action. I then allow myself to move in any way I want, in
any way that my body is naturally inclined to.*

*I embody emotions and warmth spreads all over me, into every cell of my
body. I get pulled from one place to the other, in various directions. My arms
are open and raised up heavenwards, I am rising, then hovering, closing,
flying, moving backwards, being pulled from the ground to the sky, from side
to side, up and down, and diagonally. I feel completely alive throughout. I
sometimes fall, but I am all the time alive and moving. My movements are
fluid, unconstrained, wave-like, graceful.*

*I then embody logic and I start marching with firm steps. I feel much colder
throughout my body. Yet I am full of determination. I march with strength in
one direction and then in another. My movements are rigid, strong, sharp,
without fluidity or grace, but with determination. When I turn, my movements
are abrupt. Sometimes I have to stop to think and decide which direction I will
next go in, then I move in the decided direction with determination. I feel so
much stronger and full of purpose. I know I can get to places, I can go anywhere.*

*When I try to move from one state to the other I feel pulled apart, I can't
move between the two seamlessly, I can't combine the two. I am attracted
towards emotion, but I need logic to be able to proceed, especially when I fall.
I have wings with emotion, but no control, no direction. And when I fall,
there is nothing to help me up, unless I bring in the strength and determination
of logic. There is no guidance in my emotions, no aim, no destination, no
specific direction. But then if I switch to logic, I can proceed, I can get up and
continue, but I lose the lightness, the fluidity, the warmth, the joy.*

*At first I cannot combine the two, I switch from one to the other, but they
will not work together. I think that might be the lesson to learn from this
exercise, the conclusion being that it has to be one or the other and they cannot*

both exist simultaneously. I need emotions to feel alive, I am naturally pulled in their direction, but I need logic to be able to keep moving. I simply cannot find a way to combine them.

And then suddenly a moment of clarity flashes through me, a moment of realisation. I don't search for it or think it. It happens organically. It comes to me from within me. Suddenly they combine of their own accord. My steps aren't as rhythmic as they had been when I was controlled by logic, but I am able to keep moving, there is enough of logic within me to keep me going, even with my arms up, down or being pulled from side to side under the influence of emotion. I suddenly know, in my body, how it needs to be, how it can work. The only way it can work. I need to open myself to my emotions, feel them, let them in, let them fill me. I need to allow myself to be with them, but I need the logical side of me to not get jerked around by emotions uncontrollably. I need to give them space as well, let them find direction and take me where I want to go. I need to take the emotions with my logic, they both live inside of me. I can allow my logic to understand, analyse and use my emotions, but I need to also allow my emotions to guide me and shed light. They are my intuitive side, the part of me that knows, feels, understands at a deeper level, at an organic, instinctual, being level. With my intuition as guide and my logic as rudder I can keep moving, maybe not with as much determination, rhythm or strength as comes from pure logic, but with more life, feeling, warmth, intuition, natural being, in a way that is more alive, more organic, warmer, a warmth that spreads throughout every cell of my body and feels good.

And I know! I understand at all levels. The emotions need in. No sense or health in blocking them or shunning them or ignoring them or suppressing them just so that I can keep walking. I need to allow them to penetrate into my logic and let my logic help me move on with the emotions alive within me, guiding me.

I need both elements to work together to live wholly, to be whole.

And with this realisation I feel happy, energised, full of life and energy, as if I've suddenly unlocked life's biggest, deepest, most significant secret.

Then I move as I feel like moving, instinctively, guided from within, as comes intuitively, naturally. I feel free and happy and light and I dance.

So much of my life has been spent either ignoring my feelings and intuitions, or suppressing them. I have marched on in life with determination, nothing could stop me once I'd chosen my route. I was strong, but only half of me had a voice. Only part of me was acknowledged, the thinking, logical, pragmatic part. I shunned my feelings for the sake of strength, in fear of showing vulnerability, because feelings equal weakness, that was what I was taught. You cry, you will be ignored or beaten. You're upset, you will be punished. You're happy, you will be punished also. You're intuition tells you something? It is stupid, misguided, it needs to be suppressed, changed. A life of rigid rules, ought's, should's and must be's. No space for needs, wants, likes. No space for passions and joys.

A life so limited and constrained, it's a miracle I survived at all. Now my body tells me otherwise. It is screaming to me to let the feelings flow, to unblock the blockage. It is inviting me to live, to live fully with every cell of my body, alive with each membrane and drop of fluid, vibrating, understanding, with awareness, accepting, caressing, listening, feeling.

14 December 11

It's Mick's birthday. We're at a Christmas market. He's physically all over me, grabbing me, kissing me, trying to get me to kiss him. Bob's watching. I feel very uneasy.

My dad appears and tells me what to do. He vanishes and I forget everything he said as soon as he leaves.

Mick's coming and going, appearing and disappearing. Every time he disappears I search for him with my eyes, looking around trying to see where he is, but he does it so many times, eventually I give up looking out for him.

Birthday, a beginning, the birth of new feelings in me, the birth of connection to my sensual, emotional side, connection to acceptance and nurturing, connection to the feminine within me. The ability to feel love, ability to have a sexual, sensual connection, ability to allow myself to be vulnerable and open.

But the old tapes, stuff from the past, symbolised by my dad intervene. I show complete disconnect with my dad. I forget about him and everything he has said as soon as he leaves. This is positive. Those old voices aren't affecting me as strongly as they used to. Or maybe I'm shutting down to them, which wouldn't be so good.

However I still can't stay connected to my internal Mick, the one that can love and be loved, the one who can feel vulnerability and show it, the emotional, sensual side. Connection is intermittent, coming and going. Eventually I give up trying.

15 December 11

I go to the bank. A short dark haired woman takes my Turkish ID, credit cards, money and even clothes. These are all necessary to complete the transaction, but something happens on her system and she can't complete the transaction. I have given her one million dollars. She gives me six hundred and seventy thousand dollars back. She still needs to give me another three hundred and thirty thousand dollars. She has my ID, clothes, credit cards and three hundred and thirty thousand dollars of my money.

I try to complete the transaction, but she moves on to the next customer. I plead with her, then shout at her, she doesn't respond, she ignores me and concentrates on the next customer. I go from person to person, pleading for help. I feel helpless, powerless, vulnerable, upset, angry and afraid. I need those things, but I can't see any way of getting them back if the woman won't give them to me. I don't know what to do. I start to feel a fearful despair. I spend hours trying to get what is rightfully mine back, speaking to everyone I can find, even people outside of the bank, just in case someone can help me or give me advice. I'm explaining what happened and when the person I'm speaking to won't or can't help, I continue, moving onto the next person.

Eventually a young man with black hair agrees to help me. Somehow he manages to recover my money and clothes from the woman.

Only my credit cards and ID are left at the bank, so I go back into the bank to retrieve those. The bank's a large building with a huge front courtyard and stone steps leading up to it from either side. It is very similar to an existing building at Tunel, a district in Istanbul, where we all used to catch our school buses.

The guy who helped me remains with me. We take my clothes to the car. By the time I go back to the bank the woman who took my things has left. I feel lost. What can I do now? I have no point of reference left.

I'm at the bank to get something done, a material, worldly affair most probably. The bank looks like a place from my childhood, an unhappy time of my life, a place we gathered after school before starting our journey home, a place of ending a phase of the day and starting the journey towards the new one. It's a grand, imposing building.

I didn't like the school bus journeys much. I lived in a bad part of town and all my friends were on other buses, some of them journeyed together, but I was on a bus that had no other students from my year. My friends used to have a lot of fun during the bus journeys, while I never did. I felt alone during those journeys and they were long.

I also hated going home. School was a sanctuary for me, in spite of some bad experiences, overall I enjoyed my school life. It was an escape from home above everything else. I had some friends, we had fun. I was always happy when the weekend or the holidays ended so that I could go back to school again. Home meant being shouted at, insulted, punished. Home meant a tiny, dingy little room, in which I closed myself up to avoid being around my parents as much as humanly possible. But we all had to have dinner together, so I couldn't avoid them completely. Home meant being alone and unhappy, being tormented and abused.

Credit cards symbolise the vehicle that provide us with an ability to transact with the outer world, with the collective, with society, with the collective consciousness. My ID is my identity, my sense of myself, who I am, my place in this world. Money symbolises libido, the energy to engage with life. And clothes symbolise the persona we take on when interacting with others and in society.

I am robbed of all of these and I cannot even complete the transaction I went into the bank for. In the end, with help, I get my money, my libido, life energy back, as well as my persona. However my ability to transact with society and the outer world and my identity are still kept from me.

The woman who steals from me and refuses to help me or complete the transaction is a character within me, she's a part of me. The transaction fails, there are problems with the system. She gives up and moves on to the next customer. I'm short changed and can do nothing about it.

But the guy who helps me is also within me. He is relaxed, helpful and patient. He gets my persona and my energy back.

The unhelpful woman's gone when I go back. My identity, who I am, remains left behind, left aside for now, not owned. And so with the credit cards, my ability to transact with the world, my place in life, work, friendships, these are also lost and left behind for now. I leave who I am and my place in life, jobs, interactions behind for the time being, in a place where they are inaccessible to me.

It is true. At the moment I no longer know who I am. Everything I believed in, dreamed of, thought I was, all my hopes, dreams, ambitions, morals, where I thought I was in life and where I thought I was going, they have all come crushing down on me and I'm standing naked in amongst the rubble. I feel lost. I don't know or understand myself anymore. I spent 35 years building my life up to this point, or the point that was a year ago and now none of it exists anymore and not only that, but I no longer know whether I want it anyway or what I want instead. I don't feel desire for anything, I see no logical path, I'm in darkness and I can't even connect to myself.

And my persona, who I was in society, who I thought I was, my interactions with my friends and family, all of these have also collapsed.

Arthur and I brought the best out in each other. Now he no longer is a part of my life or of who I am. He has been a constant in my life throughout my adult years. Without him who am I? Where am I? What are my dreams now? Where is my belief in 'till death do us part'? I can no longer see.

I'm lost and searching. Work is put on hold, I search, but cannot find. I don't even know what my work options are, what I could do, how I can survive. I certainly don't know what I want to do.

I had found my place in life, but that was before it all collapsed last year. I knew who I was, I loved what I did, I had plans for the future, I got married to the man I love, I was happy and content. I had friends and I cared for them deeply. I had morals, ideas, ideals and I felt good about them. I liked where my life seemed to be going. But then it all collapsed, including my understanding of who I am, my place in society and amongst my friends, my plans, hopes, dreams, everything collapsed.

There is a part of me that simply does not sympathise. She keeps telling me "you brought this destruction upon yourself. This is a result of your choices. You pay the price, it's a just price, so stop complaining. You asked for all of this destruction, you invited it in. That's what you do best anyway, destroy". That part of me feels the pain is deserved, she won't waste any time helping me, she thinks I deserve to rot in my own shit.

And then there is another part of me, which is desperately trying, searching, trying to understand and make sense of it all, trying to find a way. And something in me must be helping otherwise I would be dead by now, otherwise I would not have the strength to go to the gym, to meet with people and interact, to seek help through therapy, to try to communicate with Arthur. There is just enough there within me that keeps me alive and trying. Whoever this person is though, whatever he symbolises, he is not known to me, he is not familiar. I should try to connect to him more.

I embody the guy who helped me. He tells me that "Life's too short. Relax. Don't stress. Take pleasure in the small things in life. When things overwhelm you, listen to music, go into nature, find beauty and peace in the little things that surround you. Live in the moment, not in your worries, not in regrets, not in the past or the future, but in the moment. This moment is the only reality, the rest is our mind, our imagination, wasted energy".

I'm a natural worrier. I can get stressed very easily and these suggestions are bang on. I seem to take life and myself way too seriously. I find that the happiest people I know are ones who can take life as it comes and laugh at things, they are light hearted and have a humorous approach to life. Those of us who take things too seriously are carrying way too heavy a burden to be able to enjoy life. After all, life throws so much shit at all of us, if we fall every time we're hit, get angry and resentful, we won't have much fun or get very far. Each step becomes a struggle, every movement a burden. Instead, if we focus on the immediate beauty around us, the things in our lives we treasure, things we love to do, people we enjoy being with, if we laugh at what's happening and at ourselves, if we lightly brush the dirt off our clothes and move on, life will be so much easier, so much more enjoyable. Shaking off those unnecessary stresses and burdens, we will free up so much energy previously wasted on worries, we will be able to live much fuller, joyful lives.

I'm living in the upper floor of a large Victorian house. A trap door separates my space from the flat below. The people from downstairs walk into my flat while I'm on the toilet without asking for permission or knocking first. The owner of the lower flat is showing her friends around. I shout at them to get out and that I'm on the toilet and this is my flat and they have no right to walk in like that. They make fun of me and shout back. They're laughing and snickering.

Once I'm done, I go to them and apologise for shouting and try to explain that I freaked out when they walked in while I was on the toilet. I want to make amends and don't feel it was right of me to react so strongly, but I still believe they had absolutely no right to walk into my space without my permission.

Nearly all of them are female and they're pure nasty people. They continue to make fun of me, or they ignore me. They disregard the olive branch I'm offering them, they dismiss it, undermine me, disrespect me and make fun of me. They stare at me with disdain, dislike, sometimes hatred. There are only two men amongst them, who are both nice, but all the women are horrible towards me.

I go back to talk to one of the men about the ghosts in the house. I want to show him something in my flat. Both men come to see what I want to show him and also one of the men's girlfriend comes along, as well as one more woman. Eventually three of them leave. Only the one I wanted to talk to in the first place stays. His girlfriend is jealous of me and mocks me before she leaves. The three of them that leave are disinterested.

I tell him of the footsteps I hear when I'm near the trap door. We go there so I can show him and he hears them too. He says the sounds are probably coming from somewhere else and he expects there to be a perfectly reasonable explanation for the footsteps. I say I always hear them and when I check, there's never anybody there.

I tell him of a time when I felt a warm body leaning against me, but when I looked there was no body there.

I also tell him that I keep finding jars of frozen sand lying around, but although the sand is frozen, the jars are warm to touch. They appear from nowhere. When I bring them into my flat, they melt and turn into normal sand. They lose their extra-ordinariness.

The man is sympathetic towards me and listens to everything I say, although he has no opinion or suggestion to offer. He just listens. I cannot tell whether he believes me or not. I can't guess at all what he's thinking.

A trap door, it's a door to trap animals or people in. I'm trapping myself into believing that these ghosts, ghosts that are not made of the material world, that are not real, physical, are actually real. Perhaps these ghosts symbolise the mocking people, the people who undermine me, make fun of me, disrespect me, ignore me, laugh at me, ignore my boundaries.

The nasty women are voices within me. They are the degrading, harsh voices telling me I'm bad, hopeless, worthless, unloveable. I'm trapping myself into thinking these voices speak the truth. I believe them. I'm trapped into thinking they are real, but they are only ghosts, voices that speak lies and make nests in my being.

I'm on the toilet, disposing of unwanted, unnecessary stuff, perhaps my past, the luggage, the unnecessary baggage I have been carrying all my life. I have been trying to free myself from these opinions, these voices of the past, my parents' opinions of me, their disregard of me, but as I try to do that, these people walk in. The mocking people who show me no respect, they disregard the boundaries of my space and flat, they ignore my right to privacy while I am on the toilet, they disturb me and I trap myself into thinking they're real and right. They bring into my life my parents' voices, make them real, loud, present. I can't get rid of the voices, they invade me. I lose my own boundaries. I even go to apologise to them, I feel I have wronged them by reacting to their invasion, but my apology is belittled, not valued, ignored and also made fun of. There is no way of reaching them or coming to some understanding with them.

I'm the first to believe that I am always the one to blame, that I do wrong and cannot do right, that I'm bad and evil, I am unloveable and worthless.

If someone tells me I have done wrong, if someone dismisses

me, treats me badly, I automatically assume they are right and that I deserve to be dismissed and treated badly. I believe inside I have done wrong. It's all my fault, of course it is.

I have trouble drawing my boundaries. I let people invade me all the time. They invade my feelings and thoughts, they use my time, they have at times used me, my goodwill, even my body. I allow them to, because the belief within me that I am worthless is so strong, it's as though as far as I'm concerned they have a right to invade me and use me, while I have absolutely no right to have my own boundaries and protect myself, stand up for myself and for what's right for me. What I need and want is not important. I am not important. My inner negative beliefs are so strong, they collaborate with those who treat me in this way, they win.

The sand filled jars are full of contradictions. Glass is made from sand. The sand is frozen yet it is warm, a physical impossibility. Sand is hard to grasp, it's made up of so many grains, just like all the contradicting emotions within me. Millions of different thoughts, feelings and beliefs, all scattered, falling, pouring through my fingers. I can't grasp them, just like I can't grasp sand.

But the nice guy is there, he listens, maybe he is sympathetic, I don't know. He takes me seriously and possibly believes me, even though I myself don't believe myself. He gives me more time and space than I give myself. He is also a persona within me. A little persona who pays attention, who has brought me where I am now, making me take notice of what's going on within me, valuing my feelings, listening, hearing, trying to understand, not judging.

The others mock and shout. They are also within me. I'm my worst enemy. I judge myself more harshly than anyone else possibly could and I also punish myself more harshly than anyone else would. I deny myself my natural rights. I disregard myself. I don't value myself. I don't feel I deserve anything worthwhile or good, I don't deserve to be happy.

Ghosts are not real, they are not made of earth and cells. We have no proof they exist. But I am trapped into believing that they are real. The harsh judgements I am so ready to believe in, in fact they govern my life, they are what I believe in most, I make them real for myself. I can't trap myself with them anymore. I need to release myself from their grip and be free. The guy has listened and understood. I need to too. I have a right to set my boundaries, protect my flat, keep them out. I have a right to shout at them if they barge in or laugh at me. They have no right to enter my space without permission. If I don't want them in, I have every right to keep them out. If only I could really truly, from the heart believe this, then I will be able to protect my space, keep my boundaries, be safe, not be laughed at, mocked, disregarded.

Saying I love you to someone brings out my vulnerability, lays me bare, which leads to self defence because I am afraid of feeling vulnerable. Vulnerability to me has always meant weakness. Weakness has meant others will hurt me, use me, abuse me. I want to block out emotions in the hope I can then avoid getting hurt. I don't feel I deserve to be loved, or that I ever will. I don't believe my feelings have any worth or value. I believe I have no right to ask for what I want or need. So I shut down, push away. But I can be loved and I deserve to be loved and appreciated, cherished and respected, valued and have my needs and wants met.

I notice Martin is turning into my dad in terms of his actions, his priorities, the way he sees the world. This is not a good thing. He is prioritising work over family. He feels his role in the family is to provide for them financially and not emotionally or by spending time with them. He works in an environment he hates, he hates his job and he earns well, but it's highly stressful and he takes his stress out on his family. He becomes distant to them, gets angry with them, doesn't spend time with them, punishes them. He shouts at his son, eight years old, for playing games, just like my father used to always shout at me for no reason, because he was stressed and resentful of life, doing things he hated, living a life he was unhappy with. His son runs off, crying to his room. He's very upset and hurt. He feels betrayed, harshly and unfairly treated. Martin's wife follows their son, so Martin gets angry with her as well.

I feel so sad and sorry about the situation. It is such a loss. Martin is a truly wonderful person and that much bitterness and anger within him, being acted out towards the two people he loves most, his son and wife, is painful to see. His actions will only make him even more unhappy and angry, I know. He'll feel bad about himself, but he won't be able to apologise, because he won't be able to face what he's doing. He'll try to suppress it, which will only result in more bitterness, resentment and unconscious, harmful reactions. The whole thing upsets me badly.

I feel so much sympathy for Martin. It's painful for me to see him so unhappy and acting out in a way that will only increase his unhappiness. I don't want him to end up like my dad, bitter, unhappy, resentful, fearful. I try to speak to him. I want him to understand that his priorities are wrong, that a well earning job and providing money for his family are not the most important things he can do for them. His love and time are what they want and need. His angry outbursts are so incredibly damaging and harmful. The hurt he causes is detrimental for all concerned. His financial stability does not justify the cost, the bitterness and anger growing inside of him, his unhappiness and all of that resulting in him mistreating his son and wife.

He does not understand me. He can't hear what I'm saying. His mind and heart are closed. He believes so strongly that this is his path. He's a martyr, but not one that believes and gives, one that pays with bitterness and resentment.

Martin is a close friend of mine. I have known him for decades and he holds a special place in my heart. He has a solid character, trustworthy, dependable, strong. He is also quite sensitive for a guy, but with inner strength. He is handsome and very intelligent. He has built a good life for himself in terms of family, career, income. In fact he really is like my dad. However, I have been noticing a struggle going on within him. He hates his job, although he has embarked on a well recognised and socially appreciated career. It is stressful and he has to work extremely hard. His dream is to give it up and do something more enjoyable and less stressful, something that is true to his heart, that he enjoys doing, but he feels that because he needs to take care of his family he can't afford to really live. He talks about his dreams, but feels he needs to give them up for his family. He is afraid of failure, afraid of society's judgement, afraid he will not be able to provide a good life for his family, afraid to follow his dreams. It is important to him to provide them with a good life, high living standards. His priority is to give his son a good private education. He cannot see the importance for them of him being happy and content, sharing his time with them, giving them love. Those values aren't within his radar. They should simply know that he loves them, because he's sacrificing his happiness and life for them. But he shouts and ignores. He withdraws.

I didn't know my dad when he was young, but I wonder if my dad went down a similar route. I always imagine he did. He had dreams, he's highly sensitive, he has a good, loyal heart. But he opted for a high profile job and earned well, so that he could provide for his family. As a result he was forever stressed and tired. He provided me and my sister with a good education, but he never had time to spend with us. By the time he got home, he was tired and wanted to relax. His stress and resentment, his overwhelming discontent and unhappiness came out towards us. He'd get furious at even the smallest thing and shout, criticise, insult and sometimes hit us. We were afraid of him. I dreaded hearing his sound at the front door. As soon as he arrived, we withdrew to our rooms.

He reigned terror in our home and my mother fed his abuse. If she was annoyed with me or angry, she would tell my dad, who would then punish me severely. She always sided with him, even when he mistreated us. There was an atmosphere of them against us, and as the younger, weaker ones, we could never win.

My dad's a perfectionist. Nothing is ever good enough for him. A 'B' should have been an 'A', an 'A' should have had a star. He hated me because I wasn't perfect. I think he also grew to hate me because he treated me so badly. There is no greater hatred than the hatred of a person who has committed a crime against the recipient. He might have also had to hate me, because my mother could not stand us getting attention or love from him. To protect their relationship, to keep peace at home and protect her feelings, he had to turn against me. It could never be both my mother and I and he chose my mother, unconsciously I'm sure, but the damage he caused was no less.

I want to tell Martin not to make the same mistakes my father made. I want to tell him that feeling love and acceptance from a parent is so much more valuable than the parent being able to pay for the best education. My sister got the best education possible, but she has been so broken by my parents, she has hardly been able to make use of it. What use has her education been to her? None. How different her life would be now if she hadn't been so severely abused by her parents.

My dad was sure he was doing right. He needed to sacrifice his happiness for his family and then he resented us for it. What could possibly be right about that?

We can only provide a good life, a loving home for our children if we are content, loving and happy within ourselves. We can only help our friends and support them, if we can support ourselves. We are able to love others only if we can love ourselves. Otherwise not only do we end up bitter, unhappy, resentful and poisonous, but we also spread these negative feelings around, nothing positive can flow from us.

It is not selfish to take care of ourselves. If we don't take care of ourselves, we are no use to others either. People who are the most valuable to others, who help others the most, support and love them are people who love themselves, who are happy with their lives.

2 January 12

I get my period on my birthday. There's a CD of a boy band in the boot of the car.
  There are Germans around, although I can't remember in what context.

A woman's period signifies the ending of an old cycle and beginning of a new one. Period pains, the pain of ending one phase and beginning a new phase. The pain that comes from not being able to accept it, the body rejecting the change, rejecting to surrender and natural flow, rejecting to be comfortable with her feminine side. It is an exclusively female phenomena.

Birthday is the birth of a new consciousness. Perhaps this new consciousness is not analytical and sterile like Germans, and at the same time, not immature and superficial like a boy band. The birth of a new cycle of connection, flowing, life, the feminine aspects of the universe.

Arthur said to me when we agreed to separate that we were like two yarns of wool that had been knocking about inside a drawer together for so long, it would be near impossible to separate the two of us without cutting us into tiny bits.

He acts so disconnected from his feelings, he feels no loss, anger, or pain. I think it's me, my yarn of wool that is being cut into smithereens, while his one remains intact. It is so cold and frigid, it is not possible to cut his yarn, whereas mine is in bits. I feel betrayed by his lack of caring, lack of mourning, grieving, sadness.

I'm being tossed around in the grips of severe pain, regret. I question all my choices and decisions. I'm hurting badly. I feel devastated, shaken and so sad. I also feel angry, but I can't place where this anger is coming from. It seems universal, at the same time I believe I have directed my anger inwards, towards myself.

I told my dad that we had agreed to separate. He flippantly said "that didn't last long". My mother said "Oh, it's your loss, you have to get him back". My dad told me that I am a spoilt, difficult, calculating person. He said there was no point putting on this sad act, he was sure I knew what I was doing and it could not be good. The overall feeling they sent towards me during the conversation was that no one would want to be with me anyway, it had been a miracle that I had found Arthur and that he was willing to put up with me. No one else will, so I'd better get him back, it's my only chance. And also that my sadness and grief were a lie, I was not capable of feeling such emotions, I must be acting this way to gain something. I was insulted by them as usual, my feelings disregarded, my entire personality cursed.

I felt tiny and low after speaking to them, insignificant, dirty, valueless, bad.

I've been crying for days now. I seem to have a well of infinite sorrow and pain within me and no amount of crying relieves me, there's still too much more there. I can't imagine it will ever end, ever. Yet I can't survive much more, I simply can't. Why don't I just die. That would bring an end to all this suffering and pain. It would be such a release, but I'm still alive. I can't stand it any longer. I see no way out. I want to die, or erase the past year and go back to when I was happy, before everything collapsed. Why do my parents hate me so? Why do they think so little of me? Why do they believe I am the worst person alive? Why? What have I done? Yet they must know me, I am their child after all. Maybe they're right. Maybe I'm fighting a pointless battle. Maybe I should accept that I am the worse of the worst, I'm bad and worthless. No one can love me. They certainly don't. Neither do I.

I've cancelled all the arrangements I made to meet up with people over the next few days. I want to hide and cry. I don't want to see anybody. I want to bury myself, somewhere so deep I won't be found. I want to fall asleep and never wake up.

Broken, battered, fragmented
Crying, dying, dead

Lost, hopeless, lifeless
Floating, directionless

I miss Arthur. I can't imagine a life without him, and yet I have created my own destruction, I have drawn the path leading to a life without him and now there's no turning back. I love and miss him.

There's so much pain in my navel, it's unbearable, it's excruciating. I feel stupid. How could I have been so blind?

I'm so sorry, but I can't even say it. My life feels pointless and empty without him. Nothing. I'm left with nothing, a big fat zero, emptiness, hollowness and nothing. Just pain and desperation.

I have lost my partner, my best friend, my support and rock, the best thing that's ever happened to me, my love.

Fall forever, fall so low, so deep, so dark, so tired, so low. Hopeless!
I slept
I closed my eyes and I slept
I closed my eyes to reality
I shut it out
Switched off the lights
Plugged my ears
Let my soul die.

Did he kill it?
Or did I self destruct?
What life have I
That I battle through
What's it worth?
Nothing much.

He is my life
My family, my rock
He is my spark
My battery, my clock

My life is gone
My soul has died
No hope, no joy
No reason to survive

I'm trying, I'm trying
Clinging on to the vision
Phoenix rising out of the ashes
Yet I'm no Phoenix
And not in ashes
Just bogged down
In my own shit.

Why won't someone shoot me
Right here, right now
Put me out of my misery
Let me close my eyes

A new birth? I don't see it. I don't feel it. All I see is death. I'm told we need to die to be born again. I'm told a snake needs to shed its old skin, so that new skin can replace it. I'm told a caterpillar needs to die for the butterfly to emerge. But I can't imagine life or re-birth, all I feel is death, the painful, rotting, excruciating, screaming existence of death. Why so slow?

6 January 12

Natalie and Lucy are in a room. They're playing chat games. I take them strawberries and cherries. There's another girl there. I don't want that other girl there.

The place we're at is somewhere near the Bosphorous Bridge in Istanbul.

I leave them to go to Arthur's flat, although I don't really want to go anywhere because traffic is horrendous, it's typical Istanbul rush hour traffic, which means cars are not moving at all.

I make a pot of hot chocolate and a cup of green tea.

I've known Natalie and Lucy for years. I have a pretty good relationship with Lucy still, but my friendship with Natalie has been anything but smooth. I think there is an element of jealousy there on both sides. Also, I always felt our friendship was one-sided, Natalie can be quite selfish. She can't be a true friend, she has to always come first. There's no give in her and lots of take. I have felt hurt and betrayed by her many times over the years.

I have also always felt judged by Natalie. She has made derogatory comments about me a few times and I hold resentment towards her because of this. I have matured and changed over the years, but she still sees me the way I used to be at school and never withholds making negative remarks. I feel she's judgemental and rigid in her opinion of me.

Her negative feelings and comments about me coupled with the fact that she has never been a good friend to me led to me having the resentments built up for too long and the last time I saw her a few months ago I told her how I feel about her, how she's hurt me and betrayed me in the past and let me down so many times and I said I no longer wanted to be her friend. I thought I might regret the way I behaved after a while, but I have felt relief. The way I expressed myself was not ideal, but there were feelings of resentment that had been pent up and suppressed for nearly two decades and once I started letting them out they exploded. Her friendship was a negative one for me. She took and never gave. She drained and brought me down. It was an unhealthy friendship and I'm well to be rid of it.

Natalie and Lucy were both married at the time. Their relationships with their partners, in my view, lacked intimacy and honesty. Natalie's relationship with her husband has been abusive from the start. He always undermined her and cheated on her throughout their relationship. Lucy has on the outside a perfectly harmonious, functioning relationship, but it is in many ways an emotionally distant, logical relationship.

I am playing games with them, two people in supposedly long lasting, good relationships, but in truth quite unsatisfactory and lacking in many ways. The most important ingredients they both lack in their relationships is genuineness and emotional honesty, in fact in Natalie's case the relationship completely lacks honesty at all levels. She can't leave her husband due to her fears of being alone. She is afraid of not having someone in her life and she has never been with anyone else, so can't imagine anything different. She is unhappy, she no longer loves him, yet she won't break free. She takes comfort in the security being in a marriage provides her with, no matter how unhappy the marriage actually is.

In amongst all the stuff to do with relationships, especially intimate ones, there are still some things I don't want to face, personified as the girl whom I don't want there. There is stuff in the unconscious that needs to come out, but I don't want to see it, be with it.

I'm about to begin an uncomfortable, stressful, long journey. Rush hour traffic in Istanbul is shocking. Cars literally don't move. You can walk faster. I don't want to go on this journey to Arthur, but I have to. The journey of absolute honesty with Arthur, the ingredients that is missing in that room. As uncomfortable and painful as it might be, as much as I would like to avoid it, I need to go down that route. There is nothing more left to lose anyway. I have already lost him as my partner, but for my own sake and for the sake of our friendship, I need to bare my soul to him. I know I need to tell him everything.

If I don't take this journey, I will end up drinking a pot of hot chocolate. I don't like hot chocolate. People like hot chocolate as a comforting, soothing drink. It has a feeling of luxury for them. But it is high in sugar and calories with little nutritional value. It smells and tastes nice, yet it is not good for you. And on top of that, I have mild intolerance to milk, which would make a whole pot of hot chocolate even worse for me.

The pot of hot chocolate is me forever telling myself I am to blame, I am at fault. I can tell myself these are truths and I need to face them to be a better person, as if these thoughts will nurture me and help me grow. I can mask these voices with the mask of 'it's the truth, truth is good for you'. But they're not the truth and they are not good for me. They don't heal, they don't nurture.

It's time to stop blaming myself and carrying the weight of everything that ever went wrong in our relationship on my own shoulders. I can be honest, the truth will clear the baggage. The truth will not lead to him hating me, it might lead to him understanding me.

I fear opening my heart and soul, baring it all out. My heart will be left so fragile if I open it up and remove its defences. It is hard for me to speak my whole truth. But that is the only way that will lead to healing and growth.

Green tea is good, I like it and it's healthy. There's only a small cup of green tea but a large pot of hot chocolate in what I have prepared for myself so far. I deserve better.

I feel that through our breakup not only did I lose Arthur, I also lost myself, who I thought I was, where I thought I was and where I thought I was going. Everything that was valuable in my life seems to have vanished with him. There's only absolute emptiness. I loved and I lost. I believed and I failed. And I blame myself for the destruction, I blame myself for the breakup, but no relationship can be the doing of only one person, when it's going well, and when it deteriorates, it always takes two. All the blame cannot be mine. He must have played a part. All the bad, the shadow is not mine to carry. It never was or should have been.

I need to open up to him completely, face the challenge, be brave, overcome my fears. I know we talk about everything and we have always been honest with each other, but there's more in my soul, some of it I don't understand as yet, some of it I'm starting to see and recognise. It must all come out without fear of consequences, without holding anything back, without trying to smooth anything over.

7 January 12

God sends me a sign which I ignore.

There's a box with my rings in it on the table in a communal area. I think it might be a communal eating area. I see the box there. I think "I should take it up to my room", but instead I take the rings I'm wearing off and put them in the box as well and think "never mind". I leave the box there.

Next time I look over, the box has vanished. I panic. I search for it frantically.

I wake a guy who's snoozing in the room, so that he can help me search. He does help me. We search the clothes of two cleaners, who are looking suspicious, one is male, the other female. They have nothing on them. I know in my heart our search is pointless. I also doubt that the guy who's helping me is genuine. I feel he's putting on an act of helping me, but isn't really trying. He doesn't care.

Suddenly keeping anything seems pointless to me. Like a flash of lightning I'm rocked by the sensation that I don't want to keep anything anymore. I want to get rid of everything I have and own, absolutely everything.

I feel that familiar old ache in my navel brought on by my loss. That gnawing, scraping, knifing sensation.

It is a New Years Day party.

My box of rings, things that are valuable to me, they are personal and they are part of my personality. In spite of the personal, valuable aspect of these rings, I have left them out in a communal area, I've left them open and vulnerable, there for anyone to take, unprotected.

I don't protect the box or stand by it. Anyone can steal from it. It has no defences. It belongs in a safe place, in my room, but I leave it out in a common area. I don't value them enough, there's an element of nonchalance, as if I don't care, I can't be bothered. I'm distracted and not paying attention. I'm not connected to how valuable they are to me, I feel indifferent.

But then when they're gone, the loss causes me pain. I realise how valuable they were to me and I feel "disgusting" for having left them out there, unprotected. I blame myself for their loss. They should have been back in my room. I didn't own them, value them, take care of them. I didn't value and protect what was mine.

I should take ownership of what is mine, my personality, my dreams and thoughts, feelings and opinions, and my time and energy. Leaving them out there in communal areas only means that anybody can help themselves to them, steal from me, take what is rightfully mine. I shouldn't leave myself vulnerable for people to steal from me, for people to grab what they want. I am my own person. Yet I let people take. I give my time, emotions, trust, love freely, without protection. I don't value my time, my own feelings, myself, I leave them out for everybody. I feel indifferent to their taking. I believe I don't deserve better anyway.

I grew up hearing my parents tell me that I'm worthless, bad. I have believed them with all my heart and soul. As a child I had no choice, I couldn't have known better, but I'm no longer a child, I should know better by now. I should know by now that I am not worthless! I can take hold of myself and what I stand for. I am capable of protecting myself. I should value what's mine, take care of it, place it where it rightfully belongs, in my space, somewhere safe and not leave it for others to take from and abuse.

God has sent me many signs and I kept ignoring them. I can ignore them no longer, otherwise everything will be taken, there will be nothing left except for that horrible sensation in my navel, that feeling of loss and despair. I'm ready to stand up for myself, for myself as a whole, shadow and light, good and bad, all that I am, without disgust or embarrassment, embracing it instead. I'm not disgusting. Other people telling me I am should make no difference, but who I am has been left so open and defenceless, so far people have been able to affect the way I see myself, the way I feel about myself easily. It's time to own myself now, my whole personality, as it is and not leave it for others to judge and decide. I know who I am better than anyone else, yet I can't own myself, I let myself be influenced and swayed by others' opinions of me, their treatment of me, what they say. But I am mine, not theirs. I need to own myself.

The voices instilled in me by my parents, the ones that tell me I'm worthless and bad, these voices leave me vulnerable to the outside world. They can steal from me, because I don't own what's rightfully mine, what's valuable and personal to me, because I've never seen myself that way, I have not learned to protect and value myself. I can't see that I am worth protecting and owning.

Stop listening to the negative voices inside. Take heed of the signs God sends you.

I embody taking off the rings and placing them in the box. I embody the panic I felt when I realised the box had vanished. Then I embody the feeling "I don't want to keep anything anymore".

Taking the rings off is mechanical, devoid of any feeling or thought, like an act, a pantomime. I am completely detached from myself.

The panic is horrendous. I want to run, hide, not be seen, keep people away, search frantically. But there is no structure to my searching. It is frantic and aimless, my energy is diffused, disconnected.

When I embody the sensations of not wanting to keep anything anymore, I become full of anger. It feels like a knee jerk reaction against the world. An unconscious reaction that stems from denial and refusal, rather than a genuine letting go. I want to break and destroy. But none of these feelings are healthy, they are the subconscious acting out without awareness or understanding. The blame I place on myself for leaving the rings out is overwhelming, I want to destroy myself completely, destroy everything that was mine and had to do with me. I know I will then be left with absolutely nothing, but that feels right, I feel I deserve nothing more.

I find panic the hardest feeling to be with and face. I focus on that further. The opposite of panic is confidence, a calmness and serenity that comes from knowing I'll be okay and that I'm doing the right thing. Confidence that I can allow things to come to me, welcome them and then let them flow off me without affecting me, without letting them rock my core and destabilise me. The panic comes from lacking that trust and confidence in myself and the world. It comes from not being able to let go, from wanting to control, driven by my fear.

102

I move impulsively and start to let things in. My arms open up and out. I am even able to gather the energy from my surroundings and welcome it into my heart. I can then let it go. It is free to either flow through me or off me. I can return it, like an offering. I know inside that everything will be okay.

I think of people like Cara. With a sense of duty I take care of her needs. She's an addict and a very difficult person to get on with. She manages to alienate those who come near her. But over the years I have willingly done things for her, given her my time and affection. And she willingly sucked all she could out of me. I think of people like her as vampires. They suck your blood until you're completely dry, unless you come to your senses and break free. I have had a few of these vampires in my life. 'I don't mind, of course I'll do it', 'Of course I'll spend my limited time off work running your errands', 'of course I'll keep you company, be there for you' and all of this with a desire to help, to be good. There's no enjoyment to be had out of spending time with vampires, no gratification or pay-off. They just take. I did these selfless acts of giving from myself for years. I let them use my time, take from me whatever energy they could, and abuse my goodwill. I drew no boundaries. I invited people like her to take from me, something in me told them "I'm open and giving, take from me whatever you want. I don't matter, I have no value, nothing worth protecting or treasuring, take all you want". That was my inner message shining brightly outwards, attracting to me the vampires of this world.

Well, I'm done with them. I have no desire left to be taken from like that. I'm finished, sucked dry. I'm not an open, infinite resource, there for everyone to use. My time is just as valuable as anybody else's. So are my feelings. I will share only when I want to, with whom I choose. No more of this everyone's good underneath, give to all and sundry. Everyone is good underneath, but my resources are limited. I have spread them out so thin, I can't find myself anymore. I am also good underneath and deserve the same amount of compassion and care, time and energy, yet to myself I give none.

I have beauty inside and I have worth just like my rings. I'm gathering my energy back in. I need to heal my wounds, find my truth and choose who's worthy of my friendship and help. I am not there for everyone to use and abuse.

9 January 12

I'm travelling with Persephone. We're sitting on a bench. She's distressed. She lost her hand luggage, which apparently consists of a plastic bag and she couldn't be bothered to pick up her black zipped bag at the airport after landing, which she had checked in for the flight.

I say "Don't worry Persephone, I'll go and get it". My heart is warm towards her, full of compassion. I kiss her tenderly on her forehead.

She gives me her toothbrush for safe keeping. It is the only thing she has left on her. I put it in my burgundy handbag, my favourite bag, but the zip's broken. I struggle to close it. Eventually I manage to zip the bag shut by opening it to the end and re-closing it. The zip's rotten.

I pick up my bag to go back to the airport to get Persephone's bags.

She smells and looks more like her old, pre-alcohol, pre-addiction self.

I show real tenderness, love and care towards Persephone. Not only the flesh and blood real one, but also the Persephone, who is a shadow figure, one that is not accepted by the outer world. The one that is judged, criticised and seen as a failure. Through my tenderness, acceptance and love she becomes her old self again. The person she was before all the suffering, pain and self-destruction she inflicted on herself through her addiction.

Persephone is lost in the world, she has lost her way, she is drifting. Persephone, who had so much potential, a loyal, caring friend, an extremely intelligent young lady. Persephone who had her whole life in front of her, intelligent and loved by all who knew her. Persephone who threw it all away, without awareness, without understanding of what was happening.

Her possessions, all in her bags, are lost. She didn't even value her checked-in possessions enough to pick them up. Her immediate possessions are kept in a plastic bag, a run-of-the-mill plastic bag. All she has left is an intimate item used daily to cleanse, one that is not shared between people, her toothbrush. She doesn't trust herself even with that item, which she gives to me for safe keeping.

She is lost and forlorn, destitute. She comes across as broken, abandoned. My heart flows with so much love and compassion for her, I feel so much sorrow in my heart and the simple act of showing my love, kissing her on the forehead, restores her back to her youth, to the days of promise, to the days of potential, when she had so much waiting for her, so much to look forward to, so many options, so much living to do.

She is also a part of me, the part crushed and broken by my parents. The part of me that was full of life and joy, naivety and optimism, hope and promise. I have learned to shut that part of me down, close it up, it is locked away.

My zip is rotten, it won't work properly. A zip is used to hold things together. Mine needs to be replaced. Perhaps my bag needs to be replaced, at the very least my zip needs replacing, otherwise I cannot carry and protect my immediate possessions, things I need with me to face the world daily, to deal and interact with people, to live in society.

Although she chose to leave her bag at the airport, she is now feeling the loss. She is sad. There is calm in her sadness, it's not passionate, yet it is full to the brim. At the same time she feels powerless and hopeless. She can't find the energy or will within herself to go back and retrieve her things, or search for her plastic bag. She just sits there, not even asking for help. I offer to take care of things for her. I don't judge her or tell her off for being careless, I show love and compassion. This simple acceptance and love heals her, so that all the damage caused by her addictions, in fact even the traumas leading to them, are healed.

We are on a journey, travelling together and we have made it this far. We've lost some things, but we are still together and alive and with all the sadness, there is also love and deep compassion. There is hope and warmth.

I love Persephone, I love her for who she is. I love her gentleness, buried under so many years of abuse, covered with the passions and angers bursting out of her from the unconscious, uncontrolled, not

106

understood. And I'm willing to help her, to try to find for her some of what she has lost.

We both lost so much as children. We lost our ability to receive and accept love, to nurture and be nurtured, to accept, to have confidence in ourselves and others, to value ourselves as human beings, for who we are. We lost the purity in ourselves, our hope and joy. Her luggage is mine also. She is alive within me every day of my life. I feel her pain deeply. I feel her hopeless, helpless fight against life. She has given up, but dares not pull the plug. Perhaps there's just enough left in her to want to hold on. I've felt that way myself recently. When the whole world seems like a dark, hostile place. When life becomes synonymous with war. Where every step is a struggle and worst of all where belief and hope have gone, so that each struggle seems pointless. There's no light in that world, no reason to get up in the mornings, no point in trying. There's also no will or energy to die. At times like that I wish I could simply fade away, lose consciousness and never wake up. I can't go on, yet I can't end it either.

I think of Persephone every day, I wonder if there's anything I can do to help her, apart from being there for her should she need me. I think of ways of making her life better. I worry about her and pray for her.

Whether I find her bag or not, we will continue our journey. I will help her and love her. We will manage. The things in the bag were old anyway, worn out, no longer useful. We can find new things to replace them. There's always a sense of loss when things come to end, when people leave us, when we leave them, but we can move on. The sun still rises the next day and life goes on.

Healing is always possible. Human beings are incredible, our bodies, emotions, thoughts, souls function in a way that is beyond our logical understanding. Our capacity to heal and move on, to adapt is unlimited. I'm searching for healing within myself. Part of my healing will be hers too. As I understand myself, my pain and my process better, I will also learn how best to help her. The Persephone inside of me needs to heal for me to become complete and happy. The poor, abandoned, betrayed, shunned, damaged soul within myself. The part of me unaccepted, undermined and abused. We are in this together, all three of us.

I embody Persephone. I embody the old Persephone pre-addictions. I become overwhelmed by a great big empty hole inside of me. I know that this hole can be filled with self-love, acceptance and connection. I feel this to be possible. I also know that this hole was there because of lack of love from her parents, because of years of their taking from her, scraping her hollow, but never feeding her.

As Persephone I feel that I don't care about other people, I've grown indifferent to their existence and their needs. I don't even care for them when they reach out to me and when they show me love. I certainly don't care for their suffering. I can't care about anyone else, because I'm lost, I don't know how to care for myself, I've forgotten what caring is.

I have no aims, no desires, no destination. I'm just rambling along, directionless. I feel so listless. I don't really want to die, but I don't have the will to live either. I understand it's so much easier to lose consciousness in addictions, be oblivious to the world, and maybe die without even feeling pain, in a cloud of non-existence.

As her, I feel I have an erratic heart, mostly cold, but when I connect to love I feel angry, very very angry, overwhelmed throughout my body with raging anger.

That dream I had a while ago, it seems like it was centuries ago, but it's only been a year since I started off on this journey. In it I went down 22 levels, down into a dark cave, where the earth was shifting, crumbling all around us, caving in on us. I went down supposedly to save my friend Persephone and through her, the unconscious side of me, the side that didn't want to come out, but needed to. I went down to bring it out into the open, into sunlight. The earth caved in, we had to wait, we were faced with death, threatened by suffocation under tonnes of earth, dark, damp earth.

It's the dark hole I just felt within her, which is within me as well, that needed to come out to light. And all the things around that hole, what caused it and what can heal it. The emptiness, the lack of self-love and acceptance, the inability to take in nurturing, to receive love, the darkness that is a heavy burden, dragging us down, all these things that are born of that hole, that live off it, are a part of it.

I had just enough hope and belief in me not to kill a part of myself and not to leave her there to die. Just enough conviction and energy to be able to reassure her. And that strength, that hope and belief, that reassurance is what is saving us now.

I feel that hole within me. It's overwhelming. At times it is the only thing that I am aware of. It is so dark and deep, it seems nothing can fill it, nothing would ever be able to heal it. I feel empty, emptied of all that I was, that I had. I can understand Persephone. I can understand the feeling of "Why bother? Life is so hard and without any hope, what's the point?" I don't even know what I'm striving towards. My steps are heavy and dragging. There's no light anywhere, not even a glimpse of light. Life is a burden, a heavy sack of damp, dark earth. I'm struggling. Yet I know I will come out the other end. Somewhere inside of me there must be hope. That sympathy, that love I feel for Persephone, I deserve some of that too. If only I could learn how to give myself some of that acceptance, love and forgiveness. If only I could hold myself and believe, not just tell myself but really believe, everything will be okay. At times it seems impossible, then there are moments when I know in my heart it will all work out in the end.

The part of myself I hate so much, the part that is shunned, judged, the part I have no forgiveness for, although I am ready to forgive anyone else in the world of any crime they might commit. For myself I have no compassion, I do not know how to nurture myself, I don't know how to, I can't feel I deserve it, I was taught I don't. All of this, because I can't, hating me was instilled in me at such an early age, so strongly and repeatedly. But that hatred needs to leave. I am not bad or evil. I deserve warmth and compassion. I take care of everyone around me, friends and family, even towards people I hardly know I give so much. Yet to myself nothing.

I imagine kissing the wounded part of my soul the way I kissed Persephone, with compassion and love. I feel warm inside, the warmth spreads into my heart and then out of it into every cell of my body. My cells feel alive, vibrating.

I am able to smile. So much warmth emanating, and it didn't come from the outside, I didn't need it from anyone else, it came from me, I have it within me to share with myself. That life-giving, beautiful warmth. The hole recedes into the background...

10 January 12

I'm on Bagdat Caddesi, in the Goztepe area, an upmarket, rich part of Istanbul. I want to buy ice-cream, but the queue at the store is too long and I don't want to wait, I can't be bothered. I go into the store next door. I order two bottles of sparkling water and a hot cheese sandwich from there. It's like a fast-food bistro. They take the cheese out of the freezer, it's a tiny portion. The guy serving me microwaves the cheese and mixes it in a blender with other stuff that looks unhealthy and odd. The whole thing looks like some sort of low quality, manufactured, unnatural hot melted mix with herbs. He spreads it on a roll.

I ask him how that tiny piece of frozen cheese turned into spreadable cheese like that. He said "What a question, it's obvious. They used the right chemicals".

I'm surprised "you mean it's made of chemicals?"

"Well, of course"

When I was very young, the first flat we moved into in Istanbul was not far from Bagdat Caddesi. We were renting a flat near the train tracks. My sister and I shared a room. We had run down, old furniture and the flat itself was run down too, but it was home. We left that flat when I was ten years old. The flat belongs to a time I lived my life without questioning my parents in any way. I lived the life my dad laid before me. It never occurred to me to wonder whether what he wanted was what I wanted. I never had the slightest doubt that everything he said was true, that he was infallible, he was always right and he was good, pure good and strong. I went to his choice of schools, I studied hard because I was told to. Everything they said was the absolute truth, unquestionable law. It never even occurred to me to question them. I did as I was told. I never thought about what I might want, I just did as my parents wanted. I took it for granted that that was the right way, the only way and that my

111

dad was always right and knew everything. My dad was perfect. He was successful at work, I believed he was loved and respected by his colleagues and friends. I knew he was exceptionally intelligent and I believed him to have a pure, golden heart. He could do no wrong. He was God-like in my eyes.

My instinct wanted ice cream, but the queue was too long, so I left what I wanted through impatience and lack of determination, although in fairness what I wanted was not nutritious, healthy food.

I decided to go for something that seemed to be more wholesome. It is the logical choice if you're hungry and it appears to be healthier. But it turns out that what gives the impression to be healthy, good and nutritious is not wholesome after all. It is full of medications, chemicals, poison. It is fake and unnatural. It is not good for me at all.

What my parents instilled in me and I simply assumed to be true and good for me during those years, has also turned out to be toxic, full of unnatural stuff, things that are not good for me after all. At the time I believed it all and followed unquestioningly. I was even in awe of it in a way, thinking all I was told and led to believe by my parents was the absolute truth. It had to be good for me, they must be telling me these truths so that I can better myself and learn. What I believe to be good for me, turns out not to be, it's full of poison, it's fake. Logically a good career, my dad's chosen path in work and life, a life full of heavy responsibilities are what I should follow, what are good for me, but intuitively they are not. My dad also always told me that he criticised me so that I could see my faults and become a better person, I believed this to be true, but he didn't point out my faults in a loving, nurturing, helping way. In fact most of the time he didn't point out my faults at all, he just relieved his own anger, stress and hatred. He insulted me and psychologically and emotionally abused me. He pumped me with poison under the guise of giving me something wholesome.

I believed he was right. I had so much to change about myself. I was such a terrible person. I had to try hard to make myself better. But nothing I ever did was good enough. I never received acceptance, I never got a compliment no matter what I did. And the abuse continued and got worse over the years. All the while with me believing that that was what I deserved. I was getting only what I deserved, nothing worse and it would all help me to better myself somehow.

These beliefs are wrong. They are poisonous. What my dad said he was doing for my own good, was not good. No goodness can come of his treatment of me, just deep wounds.

Just like that time when I was fifteen years old. My dad had come into my room. The room was dark, I was lying on my bed. And my dad lectured me on how evil, unloveable, unlikeable I was. He was sure I could never possibly have any friends, I was too horrible for that. I had friends, but I believed what he said and doubted my friendships. I assumed that they probably didn't like me. I was super-sensitive to anything they said. I took offence easily and always doubted myself. Surely they weren't really my friends. Surely they didn't like me, they just put up with me. Surely they hate me really.

It's so hard to change these deep, embedded tracks, even after we realise how far from the truth they are and how damaging. They have become so much a part of us, so deeply ingrained in our being, we fall into those tracks all the time without even noticing it. Those tracks lead to darkness. They are a dead end.

15 January 12

Mick, Tim and I are sitting round a table, playing a game. Mick tells me to leave so that he can go to the toilet. I say "surely you're not going to make the whole house smell so much that I need to leave it?"

I look at Tim. He nods, implying that it's best I leave.

I say I need to go and get a female pad out of my bag first. The bag is a plastic bag which is positioned at my feet. I find what I'm looking for and leave.

After that I go to the yoga room. There are yoga mats lined up in rows there. There's a glass door along the front wall and yoga mats lined up vertically along it and then another row behind those. My yoga mat's placed in the centre, right by the glass doors. I have to step over my things to be able to close the glass doors, which is what I do.

Mick, the sensitive, to an extent immature part of me is going to relieve himself. There is an understanding that this is going to smell bad. Anyone who remains in the room will be able to smell it and Mick is uncomfortable with other people smelling his shit. Obviously the sensitive part of me is not that happy about letting all my shit get smelt by everyone, but to an extent the whole dream indicates that I realise that's part of life and I'm accepting of that. Tim has an easy-going, accepting type of personality. He doesn't try to change things or people, he takes things as they come. He is also quite a private person. He tends not to talk about his problems or feelings. This accepting side of me, the side of me that can take life as it comes and doesn't get overly stressed about things, the side that is private, nods, agreeing that the smell will be unpleasant and is not for everyone to experience.

I leave the room taking something with me that only women need and only when they are at the end of a cycle, which is also the beginning of a new one. I feel okay about leaving. I go. My feminine, accepting side is okay with not being there and accepting of the fact that there will be a smell.

Yoga is all about connection of the body, mind and soul, deeper awareness of the body and what's going on inside of us and acceptance of ourselves as we are, the yin side of existence, accepting what is as it is. The yoga room is surrounded by glass walls. Yoga is a very intimate, personal practise, however here it is practised in a very public way, in an open, public environment, that doesn't allow for intimacy or privacy.

By closing the door I'm leaving the draught out, preventing circulation and clearing of the air inside. I'm allowing the smell to remain inside, rather than letting it out, as unpleasant as it might be. And to be able to do this I have to step on my own space, in a way walking over it, the space where I practise connecting and uniting my body with my mind and soul. My privacy needs to some extent to be walked over, if acceptance of myself, shadow and all, is to happen.

My life is at the brink of huge changes at the moment. My entire life as I have known it so far, everything I have built towards has come crushing down. I am leaving my husband, a relationship of twelve years, I am moving out not only to a different city, but also different country. I will need to find work and a new place to live. All my relationships are under scrutiny, some are already changing. The way I see myself and my life, my place in the world is also having to change. It is the end of an old cycle and the beginning of a new one. I am equipped with what I need to get through this time of turmoil and pain.

I am accepting of these changes, however this does not mean that my private life and my feelings should be paraded for all to see and smell. It is okay to keep them hidden and private. Sometimes what comes up is unpleasant, but that is a part of life, that is how things are. We don't always come out smelling of roses. I can accept the shadow, the bad, the smelly, it is part of being human. This doesn't mean I need to share all of that with everyone. I can accept it and keep it private. It is private after all.

Some people, Dell, Tim and a couple of others, took it upon

themselves to gossip about me and talk behind my back. Dell even made up stories and spread lies to make me look bad. He said pointless and absolutely nonsensical things, all with a view to harm me. He created lies just to make me the bad one, led by the poison in his own veins, his own complexes, resentments and unhappiness. He had hopes for himself and when Arthur and I separated he thought he had a chance with me. When I turned him down, he turned sour and made me into the enemy, the bad person.

I'm already inclined to think I'm bad and take on any blame there is going, so at first I got crushed by his lies and stories. I felt betrayed, I had thought of him as a close friend. It hurts badly to be betrayed and let down by someone you care about and trust. But that time has passed. I no longer feel anything towards him. He wasn't worth my friendship and loyalty and his bitterness and lies are not worth me crying over. My private life is not for people like him to step on and smear. My feelings aren't there to be tossed around and dragged through the mud.

I'm feeling so low and lonely. I feel like I have been stranded on a deserted island, with hardly any tools to survive. The emptiness and loneliness is washing through me like waves against the rocks. I feel like I've been dropped into a dark isolated cave and I'm lying there, afraid, miserable and utterly alone.

I'm going to find my way out myself. No one can help me here. But sometimes I completely lose confidence in myself and I drop into desperate darkness and hopelessness. I'm sure I'm going to die here, doubled over in pain, a lake of tears around me and stranded in immense loneliness, abandoned and betrayed by everyone and especially myself.

Something bad is happening in the office. It seems to be a supernatural occurrence. My boss's character changes due to this. A consultant hired to solve the problem asks for my help in a very rude manner. I agree to help, but tell him "I'm helping you only because something bad is happening, I can feel it is. If you can do something to help against whatever is going on, then I'm happy to help you in this endeavour. Something definitely needs to be done. In fact it's crucial that something gets done. But you should have asked me nicely anyway, there's no point in being rude, it's unnecessary and inappropriate".

He realises he's underestimated and not fully appreciated me. He thought he could boss me around and walk all over me, but he can't, I stand up for myself and make it clear I'm not going to accept bad treatment from him.

I throw away leftover food and rubbish that is lying around and clean the place up to ease my anger until I'm ready to help him. I don't feel like helping him while I'm still angry, I need to dissipate the anger first.

I bring him coffee in the morning.

Normally my boss is a confident, loud, vocal, charismatic, efficient, intelligent person, but he angers easily. He has a sense of humour and he's a perfectionist.

There is an outsider, an objective consultant who can help me work things out, help me solve the problem that has taken over life at the office. The consultant is an inner figure. He is at first dismissive of me, he underestimates me, but then he realises his mistake. I stand up to him and tell him he can't treat me badly, but I do work together with him to solve the problem in spite of my anger.

The problem comes from the outside and is out of my control. It feels supernatural. But we work together to solve it. We do this to re-find the energetic, charismatic, intelligent, efficient boss, the one with a sense of humour, the one that is also a part of me. He is overwhelmed by these supernatural energies and has been taken over by them. He is no longer acting himself and cannot work efficiently.

The boss reminds me of my banking days. He is efficient, logical and achieves. Even the set up is similar to large bulge-bracket banks. The office is open plan and is surrounded by glass walls and windows. It is a clear, open, clean area with lots of light and space.

The forces that have taken over are so powerful, I have lost sense of myself. At the moment I'm in a place where I can't achieve anything. I've lost my sense of humour, my efficiency, my energy and charisma. I feel lost and powerless. A part of me has come in to help find these qualities within me again. But this same part of me wants to dismiss me, it thinks it can walk all over me, it takes me for granted and wants to order me around.

But I am no longer willing to put up with this kind of treatment. I stand up for myself. I value myself and demand to be treated with the respect and courtesy I deserve. The dismissive side of me can no longer ignore me, it has to pay attention and treat me decently.

I know I need to work with this consultant to solve the problem and in spite of my anger, I do. Solving the problem is much more important to me than any attack on my pride. I clean up rubbish, relieving myself of my anger so that I can work with him properly, rather than under the negative influence of anger.

It's important that I stand up for myself, that I appreciate my own value and demand decent treatment, respect and value from others. This is a positive step for me. I have noticed this to be increasingly the case in my life. I'm no longer letting people push and shove me, use me, mistreat me. I have a higher sense of inner worth and can hold my own against those who try to undermine me. There is more strength and wholeness within me.

I was looking at old photos and came across photos of Persephone from the wedding. She seems together and present in them. She does care about me, otherwise she would not have made such a big effort to be there for me in every way she could on that day. "What a waste". A beautiful, intelligent woman in her prime, full of energy, but she is now faded and dying. Is it the search for a higher, deeper spiritual meaning that has taken her down this route? The spark and energy in her face and eyes have gone compared to photos from ten years ago. It's as if an internal light has gone out. The energy has faded. She's a foggy shadow of her former self. Can the light be rekindled? I hope so with all my heart.

No rebirth can be experienced without death. Inanna's descent to find Ereshkigal was a journey into death. She had to leave everything behind to undertake this journey. She was stripped even of her clothes. She was left on a hook to rot to death. But then, just as all hope had gone and she had accepted her end, two minions allow Ereshkigal to mourn by mirroring her. Once her feelings have been released and seen, she feels better and allows the minions to take Inanna back up. Inanna returns having found and owned her own shadow. She returns to the world whole.

I'm on way down. I'm being stripped of my clothes and possessions. The path is not easy. I am afraid, it's dark, cold, damp. I don't know if I'll survive. I'm overwhelmed with inner turmoil and pain. Each step I take deeper down, new suffering awaits me. Each time I feel I cannot possibly take another step, it's too much, I find myself placing a foot forwards again. It's dark down here and stifling. But without taking this journey I can never be whole, I would only live as a faded shadow of myself, a part of me left unconscious, unknown, unseen, a part of me not acknowledged and owned.

Persephone had to die to experience womanhood, to have her femininity awakened. This is my spiritual quest. Without death we cannot awaken to our deeper spirituality, we cannot be reborn. Birth demands death.

It's my time now. Only God knows why. I feel empty. I don't feel I can go on. I am so lost in this darkness. I have no energy, no will, no hope. I see no light to guide me. Just utter darkness. I can't breathe. I'm experiencing the death of me as I have known myself so far. Everything I thought I was, the life I built, the friendships, the beliefs and hopes I held, me as I've known myself and my life as I have known it are dying.

I find myself fighting against this journey. I'm afraid of being swallowed up in the damp darkness. I want to fight back, run back up and out into the sunlight. So many times I think, I don't care about my shadow, about spirituality, about wholeness, just let me go back to the way things once were. But this struggle only makes things worse. Part of me walks on down and part of me fights against it, so much energy wasted in my internal conflict, in my uncertainties and fears. If only I could let go of trying to control, direct, if I could let go of the fear and believe, then I might be able to experience everything as it happens. I might find my steps are lighter and the darkness not so stifling. But I fail, I fail even in letting go. I'm running from it while I walk towards it. I can't continue like this. I'm killing myself. It's too much. Help me live it God, help me be with it, feel it, accept it, flow with it, please. And if not, please get me out of here, because I have no strength left. I don't understand anything anymore. Nothing makes sense to me.

Why did I have to end a twelve year relationship for this journey, for rebirth? At times, most times, it seems like such utter nonsense. Could I not have undergone this journey with him? Why did I have to destroy absolutely everything? Why couldn't Inanna have kept at least some of her clothes on? Why would they not let her carry a flame to guide her, comfort her, show her the way?

So much destruction, all the walls caving in and infinite darkness. Who could survive this? What have I done? I want to go back, I can't continue. I can't breathe. I want to lie down and die.

I question everything. I try to tell myself a greater understanding will come from all of this suffering, a growth and spirituality, but all I really feel is regret. All I see is destruction. And I'm the destroyer, I'm the killer, the murderer. I have no one else to blame. I threw myself into the darkness, it was deeper than I thought and I broke every single limb in my body when I hit the ground. Now I can't get up, I can't move. What was I thinking? It was nice up there, sunshine, trees, flowers, streams. What am I doing in this darkness? Why can I no longer find a way out?

God help me please, I'm begging you, I'm on my knees, I'm in too much pain, I'm hurting too much, I can't go on, help me please, hear me, help me.

20 January 12

I close my eyes and feel inwards. I try to connect to what is inside of me, to what wants to come out, be expressed. I feel and wait. But nothing comes. All I feel is darkness, all I see is black, nothing else.

I want to protect myself from the darkness, I want to close up into a tiny, tight ball, I want to cover my head, throat and heart with my arms. It's suffocating me. I can't keep it out. The darkness is forcing its way in. I can't breathe. It's heavy. I can't keep it out. Stay out, please. It's taking over.

I start to panic. I want to cut through the darkness. I want to cut it away. I start making cutting movements in front of me. I feel desperate; my movements are fast and sharp, directed by the fear and panic inside of me. But the darkness won't budge. You can't cut darkness. It remains. I'm getting tired. I want to protect myself from it, but there is no protection. I want to get rid of it, but I can't.

It's like a black fog, a dark mist. It won't allow for any visibility. It won't let through any light, not even a glimmer. I want to see through it. The blindness I'm experiencing because of it scares me. I'm trying to cut a way through, but it's impossible.

And then all emotion leaves me, as if it's been drained away. I feel nothing now, just the darkness. I feel no more pain, no anger, just a blanket, all-encompassing darkness. My instinct still wants to cut it, but I'm too drained of energy to try anything.

I drop down on my knees. I can no longer protect myself. I feel the darkness envelope me tighter, taking over my body, seeping through into every organ, every cell of my body. Now it's just darkness, I am pure darkness. Inside and out, nothing but darkness. And I can no longer protect, I no longer try to. I just stay there in stillness, on my knees, devoid of any emotion, blank and in empty darkness.

It's pointless trying to cut darkness, trying to cut away at fog or mist. It's not possible. They lift of their own accord, when the time is right, when the sun is up high enough to burn them out, they slowly lift, then light and visibility return.

But I'm trying to fight the darkness. I'm afraid of it. I don't believe it will ever lift. I believe it will suffocate me. Eventually I lose all energy, I realise I have no chance against it and give up, wearied from my struggle, left empty and motionless.

A big dark hole, a blank
I see no possibility of filling it

I miss Arthur so desperately much. He's here, yet already gone. So distant. From my partner, the closest person to me in the world, to whom? Who is he now? So cold and distant, he might as well be a stranger.

My life is unbearable. My body, my torment feels unbearable. It's unbearable to exist, to be living and yet dead.

I can't believe, have faith and allow the darkness, the fog and mist to lift. I can't be at peace with it. I struggle and tire myself out. I lose and am on my knees, desperation taking over.

28 January 12

I'm with Jerome. We're at the cinema. There are many individual toilets, most of them are men's toilets. I need to go urgently and am searching for one for women. It takes me a while to find one.
   I eat something.
   Miles leans in to me, way too close for comfort, and says "Arthur's conversation with Mick is long since over, I can see light on the phone. He's faking the conversation".
   The film starts at 1:30. It's now 3:30. I'm annoyed we're late. I'm trying to get them to move faster so that we can watch the film.

Jerome is a friend of mine. I actually fancied him for a while when we were at school together, but suppressed any such feelings I had for him, because I didn't think they were reciprocated and I didn't want to ruin our friendship or bring any unease into it. He is very sensitive and sensual, a deep, understanding friend with whom it is easy and natural to have intimate conversations. He is also very good looking. His work is artistic, he has worked in his family's design and marketing business, he has made and released a music album and is currently a music producer. He is lots of fun to be around. Although he has been a friend for nearly two decades, my feelings for him were more complicated and involved at one stage of our friendship, although this lasted for only about a year or so. So the relationship is not entirely clear cut and straight forward.
   I want to release myself, express myself in some way, but there doesn't seem to be a female outlet for doing this. I am surrounded by male toilets, male energies. I eat something to nourish myself. The male way is logical, it is analytical and thought through. It is based on action, doing, moving forwards. The female way is felt, acknowledged, accepted as it is, allowing for what is. It is based on being and allowing to be. There has been much logic, analysis,

action and determination in my life. My life has been based on doing, acting and moving forwards in one direction or another. So little of the feminine way has been allowed, not much of nourishing, healing, accepting, holding, being. But I am searching for this now, searching for a way of releasing and expressing my feelings as they are, a way of accepting myself, being with myself as I am.

There's so much around deception in this dream. The not so clear relationship with Miles, which was also a close friendship I thought, but ended in violation. Arthur, the person I trust most in the world deceiving me about being on the phone and conducting an entirely fake conversation with someone I in turn have deceived him with. Mick, another complicated relationship, once again a friendship that became more involved and complicated emotionally. Arthur, we're still close, very much connected, but no longer together. I have never understood where I stand with him. Even in the past, when he said he loved me, I was never sure. All those years we spent together, I kept expecting him to leave. There was so much uncertainty emotionally.

Miles was one of my best friends at school, or so I thought he was. We were very close and kept no secrets from each other. He knew me inside out, and in spite of what he did to me in the end, I think he cared for me as a friend too. He trusted me. He told me things he didn't tell others and counted on my friendship.

At the same time, he abused my feelings for him. At times he would treat me badly, but then he'd come back to me and I would forgive him and still be there for him as a close friend, without judgement or resentment. During our last year at school, although he knew I had no experience at all in such things and he knew I wouldn't be able to speak up, protect or defend myself or tell anybody else, he sexually violated me. It took me years to be able to face what had happened and work on unravelling the betrayal, hurt and pain around the incident. My work around trying to heal the deep trauma caused by the incident is still continuing. What happened then has barely been acknowledged by me, I'm still delving into it step by step, the trauma was too great to be able to face then or even in its fullness now. He certainly never did acknowledge what happened, or any wrong doing. When he was finished he got up and condescendingly mocked me: "you're so stupid, why are you so afraid?"

I have never understood why he did what he did. There was no need. I was a good, loyal friend, why ruin that? I felt for years he could not have valued me as a person, as a young woman or as a friend to have been able to treat me like that. He had a girlfriend at the time and was popular amongst girls, he was never short of affairs, he did not need me for sexual release. And yet he used me, he betrayed my friendship and trust and then he made fun of me, belittled my fear and pain.

I could not show weakness or vulnerability, it had been engrained in me never to. I got up and acted as if nothing had happened. I did not acknowledge even to myself what had happened for years. I still don't remember large chunks of the event. Most of it is alive in my memory in the form of flashbacks, static pictures taken intermittently. The film won't roll. Just pictures. But the entire event and all the pain, hurt, betrayal, worthlessness I felt from it are still stored in my body.

It's way too late for the film now. By this time the film is over. Film symbolises projection and all projecting has been done. It can no longer be changed or watched. It is in the past. I want to be able to go back to it, but that is no longer possible. It's too late for my worries and regrets, the film has already been played out. There's no point worrying about it now, no point regretting. I might as well accept the fact and move on. Unfortunately I'm still living in the past, what was, what could have been, regrets, feelings of loss.

What holds me back from being able to move on? A fear of being judged, misunderstood, laughed at, made fun of, criticised. Fear of making myself vulnerable. Fear of being used and abused. Fear of not being understood. Fear of regret. Fear of all these deceptive forces and ideas that keep getting played out within me.

The fear results in an inability to express my feelings, they get stuck in my throat and won't come out. When I want to talk to Arthur about my deepest, darkest feelings, the ones buried under so much earth, the ones I'm starting to dig up now, I find I can't form the sentences, my mind goes blank. I can't express myself. I'm afraid of losing him completely, losing even the small something we have left, the friendship I treasure so much, the little connection we are still holding on to. I'm afraid he'll judge me, hate me. I can't accept my own feelings. I'm my worst enemy, my greatest critic. I judge myself so harshly, I expect the same severe judgement from others. But it's time to express myself in the feminine way, express my feelings as they are with acceptance, not driven by logic and analysis, not coming from the head. Instead express them as they come from the heart, with acceptance. After all, there is deception in holding things back, it is hiding part of who I am. Complete honesty and speaking the truth, in all its complexity, with its black and grey as well as its white, without making excuses or placing blame, is the only way forwards, the only way to be able to nourish and feed my soul, to be whole, letting the shadow live and breathe together with the light. After all none of us are black or white, we are all shades of grey.

The thought of total emotional expression scares me, my chest, shoulders and neck become tight. I can't let go of the tension, I can't let go of the fear. I block my own energy, my own flow with all that constriction. How can energy flow and heal if it's all dammed up.

I suddenly experience fear of falling. It's as if I'm at the top of a mountain and if I let go of control, if I let go of logic, I will plunge to my death. I'm afraid of that fall. I cannot trust. I'm afraid of losing control, I grip the reigns so tight, there's no blood flow, nothing can move, yet I can't soften my grip. I fear the reigns will fall out of my hands and I'll be lost on a galloping horse, going who knows where.

I'm afraid of life, letting go into life's ebb and flow, ups and downs, life's natural breath in and out. I'm trying to hold still, but I'm stagnating, freezing. I can't move. Life moves on around me, without me. I'm afraid that if I let go I will get carried away. The unknown scares me. And yet life is in the letting go, in the flow, in the trust. I'm not living.

I'm afraid of being happy. I have lived so long believing that I don't deserve it, I'm afraid of grabbing it even when it's there for me to have. In a way, to be happy is to stand up to my parents, to defy them. I fear the punishment that will follow. Whenever I've been happy in the past, the happiness has been followed by a fall, all the more painful for its contrast. When I've trusted, I've been betrayed, when I've loved, I've been walked away from. I cannot trust the good, it brings with it a price too great, a bad that follows which is simply too unbearable to experience. I expect the fall while I'm still at the top, before there's even any sign of it, I'm so sure it will come. I expect it, and in my own way I invite it. I beckon it. I receive it openly when it comes, because I know I deserve no better, I knew it was coming, this is what I, rotten as I am, deserve. I fear feeling too good, it's overwhelming and I don't deserve it, it will end anyway.

I have been deceived in the past, but I'm my greatest deceiver. I have deceived myself into believing that I deserve nothing good, happiness is not my lot, I cannot be loved, I have no value, that I will destroy whatever I touch and the destruction is mine to keep.

Perhaps this realisation comes too late to change my past regrets and replay them in a better way. It's too late to change the past and watch the film that has already been played and finished. But there will be other films. I can be honest and on time for those.

30 January 12

Mick refuses to take a newspaper from me He says he can't take it, because it's feminine and therefore polluted.

I have listened to the feminine voice inside of me, felt deeply into myself with as much truth and acceptance as I am capable of. I have opened myself, made myself vulnerable, loved, these are all feminine aspects. And I now feel rejected, the feminine in me has been rejected.

Newspapers are the voice of the masses to the masses, driven by the values and norms of the masses, as well as what will sell, make money and cause sensation. They are a symbol of society and the masses, its morals, thoughts and views. The critical part of me, the male, analytical, logical part that doesn't accept and allow, the one guided by the common voice of the masses, is now rejecting what is genuine and feminine in me. It is labelling my feelings, my vulnerability as polluted, dirty. And in the process, it is also rejecting what is naturally in sink with it.

The side of me that's hard on myself is now again being hard on me, rejecting me for having acted in this feminine way, opened myself up.

I learned to view feelings as a weakness when I was younger. That not only showing feelings, but to even feel them is a weakness. Life must be logical, not based on emotion. I was not allowed to show feelings, good or bad, as I grew up. My parents never showed any emotion accept for anger and even that was masked under the pretence that it was necessary to make me a better person, to discipline me and guide me. Feelings had to buried and were shunned.

I have grown since then, I have been recognising my feelings and allowing them to come out more and more. I have been trying to accept and welcome them. And at the moment I feel rejected and abandoned. A voice in me says "I told you so, you stupid girl. What were you thinking? Feeling means pain, showing emotion invites hurt and rejection." I see these emotions, what are part of me, rightfully mine, as polluted and bad. They need to be gotten rid of, I must be cleansed of them.

I opened up to Arthur about what I needed, how I felt, what I felt was wrong in our relationship, what I felt was missing. And he told me that was it, that these problems could not be resolved, that our relationship was over. He rejected me. He betrayed me in a way. And my anger, instead of turning outwards, being directed where it should, towards him, has been directed inwards, towards myself. I'm angry with myself for having laid myself vulnerable, for having opened myself up to hurt and rejection. I see it as my fault. As a result, I want the feelings out, they're polluted, bad, I don't want them in me, I don't want to experience them, they bring nothing but pain and grief, nothing but embarrassment and self-punishment.

I should be more accepting of myself, feelings and all, whatever they are, they are mine, a part of me and they are no less valuable than any part of any other person. I value others' feelings, I don't judge them, yet myself I judge and berate harshly, I don't accept or forgive, I beat myself up at every opportunity.

It makes no sense that a newspaper would be polluted because it's feminine. It makes no sense that something feminine should be labelled polluted anyway, let alone an inanimate object which is neither male nor female. And yet that is what I'm doing. My precious, feminine side is being shunned by myself, rejected, labelled as bad, dirty, when it simply is, just is, not good, bad, dirty, clean, but is as it is. But this is what I do to myself. I'm so used to it, it's hard for me to see the nonsense hidden behind it. I act as if that's the right way, the only way. I laugh at the dream figure's response, but I take my self-directed anger and resentment seriously, I feed it and let it thrive. It has no more truth to it than a newspaper that is feminine and therefore polluted.

1 February 12

I wake up in panic. My teeth are falling out. They are broken and rotten. They're all falling out, my mouth is empty, it has become a wasteland.

I've lost my ability to grip, bite, to stick my teeth into life, to chew and digest. It feels like I've lost touch with what is, with life and reality. It's a time to draw in, to nurture myself, to recollect inwardly, direct my energy towards myself and let it work within me.

I'm feeling disconnected from life, as if I'm somewhere else, up in the clouds, watching 'me' live this everyday life from afar, from above, disconnected, not me myself walking on earth. I feel nothing, I'm not involved. I'm just watching.

I feel sad and needy. I'm depressed. I can find no reason to get up in the mornings. The start of a new day brings me anguish, the horrible knowledge that I am going to somehow have to make it through yet another day. It used to be different. No matter what was going on in my life, I always woke up with energy and expectation. The mornings were the best part of the day for me. There was so much to do, so much to look forward to. Now I just want to hide. I can't face it. I can't get up and start the day, because it doesn't end, it brings nothing but darkness, unhappiness, depression, heaviness. I feel like I can't go on.

I feel so utterly, despondently alone. I've lost everything. Everything in my life I cared about or meant something to me. Everything, including the will to live, the desire and energy to be alive. I'm an ungrateful bitch who's incapable of appreciating what she has, incapable of loving and receiving love, a tormented soul who can never be happy or satisfied, who has to poison everything she touches. A witch who has to ruin everything, destroy all that comes her way.

Oh to be able to sleep forever, blissful unconsciousness.

I have no hope, I feel so lonely, I'm so unhappy and afraid. I'm hurting, badly. My heart, my chest, my navel, they're all in pain, they're screaming with pain and hurt. It's unbearable, yet somehow I'm still alive. Why?

I feel deep into my navel, trying to connect to the hole, the darkness and the pain. I start thrusting my arms outwards in all directions as if I'm throwing things away, as far as I am capable of throwing. The movement and the strength are coming from my navel. I'm swaying back and forth, then my whole body starts to swoon and sway.

My heart is trying to break out, but it's too constricted and it can't. I want to tear my heart and my chest out, the pain in them is too much for me to bear. I want to get rid of them, hoping they'll leave, taking my pain with them. I'm beating myself up with so much self hatred, pure, fierce hatred, all directed at myself by myself. I hate the pain, I hate the cause of the pain and I blame myself for the pain, so I hate myself further. No matter how vigorously I beat and thrust out, I can't get rid of my heart or the pain it carries. I want to die.

I fall to the floor. I can feel a connection with the earth, with Mother Nature, with nourishment and food, with healing. I need it desperately. I need to feel that connection and draw from the earth. I want to gather from the earth into my body, into my heart. I want to feel the earth. I feel healing can and will occur through that connection.

The source of healing, connection to nature and to earth, to what is solid and material, to what is yin and accepting. I feel it can heal me. Trying to throw the pain out, trying to get rid of my heart won't help. The movement of trying to get rid of what is, what's in me is frantic, it gets me nowhere. I get more and more frantic as I try and I keep failing. Yet when I drop to my knees, in some sort of surrender, in acceptance, I connect to the earth, the comforting feel of wood. I feel a sense of warmth and healing. Earth is nurturing, it is accepting, it is non-judgemental, it does not pick and choose who can stand on it and eat from it. It does not choose what can grow in it and how. It is and let's be. It is Mother Nature, it is a whole. I imagine her brown and green, the colours of forests and flowers, arms wide open waiting to embrace and hold, to rock gently and

131

soothe. I see her face with a warm wide smile playing on her lips. She beckons to satisfaction, wholeness, acceptance of all, and most of all, to happiness.

My healing will not come from analysis, thinking and logic. My healing will come from nature, from the earth. It will come from learning to accept myself as I am, with all I am. Learning to love myself with all the light and all the shadow. Learning not to constantly try to get rid of the shadow, change it, lighten it, not to constantly beat myself up and punish myself for every thought and feeling, every action. It will come from soothing myself by holding myself with love and acceptance in my arms and rocking myself gently, rhythmically. My healing will not come from reading books and deciphering messages and images, it will come from feeling the images, from being with them, feeling them, letting them be alive within me, allowing them the flow of life, allowing them the freedom to change, grow. It will come from simply being with what comes up, without judging, without trying to control or change.

Healing will come from appreciating life, the little things in life, the feel of a gentle breeze on my face, the brightness of a flower, the scent of a lily, the sound of water against sand, the flutter of a bird's wing, the immense wisdom and peace to be found in a forest, the magnificence of the peak of a climb up a mountain. My healing will come from connection, connection to earth and nature, but also connection to my body and feelings, an accepting connection that does not hate, dismiss or criticise, one that loves, the way God is said to love all without judgement, without favourites.

For a moment, I could feel the healing take place. I felt wounds within me fill with blood and oxygen. I felt them draw in and come alive, rather than bleeding or rotting in oblivion.

For a moment I knew in my heart that healing would come. For a moment I felt confidence and hope. For a moment there was light in my body. For a moment I believed.

4 February 12

I'm walking in a spiritual dessert, trudging along. I'm so dry and thirsty, so tired and hot, so depleted. There's no shelter, no water, nothing as far as the eye can see except sand, never-ending, never-changing, constant sand. Sand forever and ever. Scorching, unforgiving sun beating down from above. I'm so tired I can't continue. I drop to my knees, but the sun is too hot, there's no shelter, so even that provides no relief. Staying inactive seems to burn more. I begin to crawl.

The constant, unforgiving criticism I turn on myself is burning me like the harsh, unforgiving sun. Nothing to shelter me from its fierce glare or to help quench my thirst. I don't allow anything to, I burn, moving on, scorching myself with bitter resentment. I'm exposed to the harshness of my own sun, I berate myself for exposing myself, burning myself further, I placed myself in that desert, I am the harsh sun and at the same time the one crawling, suffering under its glare. I've opened myself up to judgement and it's burning me even more. I feel inadequate, unworthy, I refuse myself a drop of water.

Where does all this self hatred come from? How deep it is rooted, how savagely it tears me apart, limb from limb, tearing the skin off, chewing the bones. Is it really just my parents? Are they capable of inflicting so much pain and suffering, causing so much damage and destruction?

I play tough, keep going, keep crawling if necessary, instead of asking for help, begging for water. Vulnerability in my mind is associated with powerlessness, weakness, being used and abused and being left hurt and broken. I live with the fear of being hurt, of having my heart broken. And fear is like a beacon of light at sea, beckoning the ships in, I bring all these upon myself whenever I can. I accept my path, the one that takes me crawling through unforgiving deserts as my lot, I crawl willingly, it is after all all I deserve. I would not stop at a lake if I stumbled on it. I don't deserve relief, water, shade, I deserve my suffering and pain, so I take it all on, invite it, place myself in a desert with no water or shade and then I crawl, feeling sorry for myself.

I see so many parallels between Persephone and me. Some people run for total self-destruction, embrace it. Self judgement creates the desire for self destruction, the desire to destroy everything good that might be in their lives. The belief that you're not worth any better is so deep, it overrides all other thoughts and feelings. You are also driven by the instinct and need to fulfil your parents' expectations of you as being worthless, a failure, bad to the core. It runs so deep. How can one love themselves if they were never loved by their own parents, if they never experienced love, caring, acceptance, compassion as a child, if all they ever got from them were insults, abuse, undermining, hatred, criticism, resentment? You learn to live up to your parents' expectations so that they might accept you instead of resenting and punishing you and also because you can't imagine them being wrong, they are always right when you're a child, they are the only authority when you are small, the ones who are there, supposed to protect you, keep you alive. You cannot realise they come with their own baggage, their complexes and deficiencies, their own internal dark shadows, unrecognised, unconscious, that drive their actions and their words. But their expectation results in them punishing you, and punishment will continue no matter what you do, good or bad. Good is punished by condescension, criticism, resentment, withholding; bad by anger, shouting, hitting, withholding. And you take on their role even after you've left home. You punish yourself, that's all you know, that is what's safe and familiar.

What really matters to me? What lights me up inside? What gives me joy, fills me with warmth? I light up when I teach, when I interact with people, when I feel warmth from people, spend time with friends, take time in nature, listen to music, especially live music, see a good play, spend time in my beautiful flat, my home and sanctuary, place flowers around it and watch them bloom.

What used to matter to me so much in the past was poison in disguise. I wanted to be good, that always mattered to me, but I've realised I look for perfection, not just good and then I use not being perfect as an excuse for further punishment. I can't accept and love myself. Judgement results in unhappiness. What's important now is not to be 'good' whatever that means, but to love and accept myself as I am. Those who love and value themselves, easily love and value others, it can be no other way. I don't mean in a selfish, narcissistic way, but in a genuine, heart-felt way. Those who cannot love themselves, cannot really love others. They might spend a life time trying to please, trying to make up for what they think they lack, but they cannot really love, not if it's not available within themselves to give to themselves.

The only way we can help others, help them heal themselves, love them, value them, be compassionate and forgiving is if we can first heal ourselves, love ourselves, be compassionate towards and forgive ourselves, value ourselves.

It's essential to me to live my life as my heart directs, live it genuinely, honestly, not driven by others views and priorities, others judgements and rights and wrongs. To live it intuitively, the way that feels right to me. In my heart I know how to live and how to be. I want to be guided by that intuition, the one that blossoms from the heart. But I question it, because I don't trust myself, I belittle it, ignore it, try to suppress it, although it has never mislead me. I don't yet know how to trust it, but I know now that I need to learn how to. I know I have my own wisdom, just as the universe has its own wisdom, which I also need to learn to trust. That's where acceptance and flowing with the energy of life rather than fighting against it will come from: trusting the wisdom of life, of the universe and letting go into it, being guided by it.

An image appears of a dark-brown skinned girl swimming in dark black and navy waters downwards into the depths of the ocean. She's wearing a golden bangle on her arm. The bangle is sparkling and sun rays are glittering through the water, lighting her way and lighting all around her.

The image gives me joy and hope. She seems to me to be at peace with herself and her surroundings. She's swimming on with no hint of fear or hurry. She's glowing. She's pure and radiant. She is swimming down, to retrieve her treasure from the depths of the waters, yet she's not worried about what she might encounter or whether she will find it, or even whether she has enough breath in her to survive. She's happy to swim on and feel the water on her skin, she trusts the light and her intuition guiding her way. She is not carrying stress, tension and the heavy weight of questioning. She is following her intuition and light and trusting they will lead her where she needs to go. She's happy and content in a childlike, pure, joyful way.

I think of the little girl I used to be. I hate her for being weak, for having cried, for having let people hurt her. I hate her for not being stronger. I hate her for caring about what others did, said, thought, I hate her for caring about what her parents told her day in, day out. Poor girl. Even I hate her. Love the little girl, have compassion for her. Don't hate her for being weak as your parents did. She was only a little girl. She was weak and vulnerable, because that's what children are. What happened to her, the way she was treated, wanting love and acceptance wasn't her fault, it was your parents' fault for mistreating her, not hers, she didn't deserve that. But then, they didn't know any better, they were not able to treat her any other way. If you can, forgive them too.

I have spent a life-time using everything as an excuse for self-criticism. It's human to cry and hurt, to shout, to feel, to make mistakes, yet I have not accepted any of these in myself. I forgive others anything, yet forgive myself nothing. Forgive the little girl and forgive yourself for being the little girl.

It's not my fault. A parent abusing a child when she is only five is not the child's fault. A man raping a virgin is not her fault.

I feel so scared I want to run.

8 February 12

I imagine myself as I was before, about a year ago, and as I am now. I close my eyes and feel inside of me. I try to become empty, spacious and receptive, so that I can allow whatever wants to come in space to enter.

An image comes up of the way I was before. I can see lots of space. It's like a cell without its skin. There are bits of light and shade. Sun rays are flowing in and out. There's movement in this space. It feels free and light. In fact it's quite bright. But it's not contained at all. It has no protection, no outer walls, no boundaries. It is left completely open and vulnerable to its surroundings. It doesn't have much density, substance. It could be pushed over, moved around, broken into, torn apart so easily. There's no solidity or strength to it.

I see myself as I am now. The image is that of a very dense tree trunk. I'm not yet rooted and I don't feel solid either. The surrounding bark is only fine and thin. And yet the structure is much stronger and denser than what it used to be. It seems to be built of hundreds of stalks of hay held together. Not too dense, but just dense enough to not be broken so easily. Not much light is able to go in, out or through. It's darker. But it is much more contained.

I feel it can get denser still, stronger. It can root down into the earth and grow up to connect with the sky. Most importantly it can choose to give out or take in, it's not just an open, unprotected structure, one that anyone can take from, anyone can use or enter into, it has protection and boundaries.

I'm comforted by these images. I feel better and stronger as the second structure, less vulnerable, more contained, more whole somehow.

I'm not as happy and free as I used to be, not at the moment, at least not at the conscious level, although I have a feeling at the unconscious level there is much more light now in the darkness than there was before, much more space and freedom. Previously, outwardly I was open, happy and light, but the depths were not recognised or seen and they were dark. Where as now, the outside is denser and stronger, but the inside is no longer pitch black, there is movement there and space, light is penetrating into the darkness.

I don't feel I have as much to give to people at the moment either. I don't feel as open, but I feel stronger. I'm learning to set my boundaries and protect myself. I'm no longer there for people to take from and use. I feel more whole and aware, more conscious. I won't be as easy to hurt, invade, break, push over. I am more myself, as I am, not labelled with good or bad, simply myself.

For the first time ever last December when in Istanbul, I was not self conscious, I was myself. I didn't care what others might think. I have always been so self-conscious in Istanbul. People there are so judgemental. They judge you by who your friends are, what you wear, where you go, where you're seen, by everything. I was a shy girl and was extremely self-conscious growing up. I didn't feel comfortable in my own skin.

Those worries were left behind when I left Istanbul. I have been more confident since. I feel free, I don't worry about what I do, where I go, what I wear. But for some reason, as soon as I'd cross the border and step back into Istanbul, my self-consciousness would return.

This time, for the first time ever, it didn't. I was perfectly comfortable as I was, with who I was. I was me. It felt like a miracle, a huge step, a new lease of life. It was amazing. It came from the denser outer structure and the increased recognition and acceptance of the darker, inner shadow.

11 February 12

The caves
I've stopped bashing my head
Against the walls of the caves
What's the point, I lay bleeding
And no one dressed my wounds

I've stopped drowning myself
In tears, regret and questions
What's the point, I screamed for answers
No one heard my screams

I've stopped breaking my bones
In anger and hatred
What's the point, I suffered
People laughed at me as I lay naked

I'm moving on in life
Giving up the fight against me
I'm laughing at the crowds
They can no longer hurt me

I live!!!

Life. I feel alive again. I'm backpacking around Brazil and travelling
has enlivened me, I feel full of joy. There's distance between me and
my depression and all my troubles. Every day is new and different,
there's so much to explore and see, so much to smell and breathe
and taste. I feel completely separated from all that has been
happening and all I've felt.

I need to remember this, when I'm lying there broken and

hopeless, when I can't find a single reason to carry on, I could always pack up and leave. There's so much to life, so much the world has to offer, I can always start a new journey and leave the past behind.

But I can't leave myself behind. I catch up with myself. Unless I stop the ongoing war within me, it will end up catching up with me wherever I go. But here I feel I can succeed. Here I have the energy and will to try, to live, to smile. I've found some peace, or maybe the distraction is great enough for me to be able to ignore the darkness for a while. I'm grateful for this moment of hope and life. I'm grateful to feel I still have it in me, that I'm not completely dead.

Shocking how we are able
To pick up fragments of our lives
Our heart and soul broken to pieces
And yet somehow we survive

We burn and break, destroy and kill
Yet we rise from the ashes
And have life in us still

We move and forget
Ignore, repeat and turn
Are we more whole as a person
Have we at all learned?

Or do we stumble through life
And strive mainly to survive
The mist we draw over our eyes
To move on is to lie

And yet we still feel whole
We hang on to hopes and dreams
We let past experiences go
They're just memories it seems

We ride on through the night
We build tunnels in our spite
We dig and we scramble
Our next life's preamble

How else could we love
Believe and trust
Then break it all apart
And see light in the dark

How else could we smash
Everything we ever loved
Break it all to pieces
From our loved ones part

How else could we dance
Sing and dream in romance
When we have killed
Our own belief in love

It's a mystery for sure
But so important to know
That even when we think we're dead
Each breath proves we're alive yet.

I'm in a large rectangular room. It has big windows and is very light. At the upper end of the room, there is a sectioned off part, which is the breakfast room. It is parted from the rest of the room with the use of a curtain. There are stairs and a path on the left leading up to the middle of the room before the curtain. There's more breakfast stuff on a long table on the right. I'm standing in the middle of the room.

I'm standing there because this is where I've come to get dressed. I've been lying on the floor on my side with my left arm tucked underneath my head in the breakfast room, but people started to come in with their breakfast, so I had to leave. I was sleeping naked, with only a white sheet to cover me. I had to leave to find a more secluded place where I could get dressed. I didn't want to leave, I was resistant and moved slowly. I didn't have the energy, but more and more people were coming in. They hadn't noticed me yet. I knew I had to get up. The action required a lot of effort. I felt drained, unwilling, and resentful that I had to move. I slowly gathered the sheet around me and slipped behind the curtain, arriving at the point I am now standing.

At first I stand there dazed, feeling confused and out of sorts, like someone not yet fully awake. There are three pairs of jeans left lying around for me to choose from. They are all new, blue jeans. I put the first one that grabbed my attention on. I drop the sheet to be able to do this. It is a perfect fit, comfortable and it looks good on me. But I feel the need to try the others on as well, to see what they are like, just in case one of the other ones is a better fit or more to my liking. I feel uncomfortable making a decision without testing all of my options first.

I try all three of them on. The first one turns out to be the best fit after all. I make my decision and just as I am putting the first pair of jeans back on, a man walks in from the breakfast room. A cheer rises as the curtain parts. After that, one after the other, loads of men start coming through and then returning to the breakfast room. Each time the curtain is lifted all the men in the breakfast room can see my bare bum as I am trying to get dressed. I feel naked, bare, uncomfortable, vulnerable and on show.

Someone along the path on the left calls at me saying something about the jeans being too expensive for me. He is poor and looks South American. He is my father. My judging, 'you're not worth it' father. The father who would not buy me clothes, because I wasn't worth the money spent on them. The father that withheld from me.

Growing up I never had many clothes and certainly no nice ones. I had to make do with one pair of jeans throughout my teenage years, and even them I had to beg for. By the time I left home, before I bought another pair, they had so many tears and holes in them, I had to wear tights underneath. For the seven years spent at school, I only ever had two school skirts. One was the cheap school design, which my parents bought me. None of my friends wore that skirt, it was so horrible. We could wear any skirt we wanted just as long as it was grey and not too short. I begged my parents for a non-uniform grey skirt, but they wouldn't buy me one, because the school one was "perfectly fine and still in good condition". My friends made fun of me, because I wore that skirt. My dear aunt took pity on me in the end and she sewed a grey skirt for me for Christmas. She took it in, let it out, shortened or lengthened it throughout my school years so that it continued to fit and it was my saving grace.

It was the same with all clothes. I was allowed two jumpers, a few shirts, one set of weekend clothes and that was pretty much it. Unless one of them was falling apart, it could not be replaced. We weren't that poor. I was always made to feel that spending any money on me was a waste of money. I wasn't worth it. I would probably spoil good clothes anyway, although to this day it takes me years to wear out clothes, I don't seem to ever 'spoil' them.

The last week at school was activities week and we were all allowed to go in casual clothes. I dreaded that week every year. I hated it, although everyone else loved it. It was a week of outings, fun and no classes. I dreaded it because I had nothing to wear. I prayed nobody would notice I was wearing the same pair of jeans every day and the same t-shirt every other day. My friends were all wearing what seemed to me to be such wonderful clothes, and I never could.

The wound goes deep. I still have tremendous trouble spending money on myself. Even when I was earning well, I never bought myself a branded item of clothing. I like simple things and can get them for cheap, that's what I still do. I don't wear them out easily, so my spending on clothes is laughably miniscule. I feel uncomfortable wearing anything new or that looks nice or smart. I feel out of place in it. I don't feel I'm worth it. Clothes like that are not for me, they're for 'better' people, people who dress smart, who look good, not me.

I have made new years resolution after new years resolution to make an effort to dress better, to put more effort into my clothing and to buy nice things for myself once in a while. It's one of the only new years resolutions I have yet to fulfil.

Clothes symbolise the persona. I'm lying in a vulnerable position, with no defences in a public place and I'm naked there, stripped of my persona, stripped of any defences.

Nakedness can also symbolise birth and even the position I'm lying in is similar to one a baby would take to sleep. Breakfast time is the start of a new day, the birth of a new day. It is also food, nutrition, sustenance.

The whole dream has the flavour of new beginnings, a light large room, breakfast, nakedness, white sheet, new jeans.

People come in. I cover myself, defend and remove myself away from the public space. I retreat into a more private area. However my privacy is disturbed, it is not respected. I am intruded upon.

Jeans are functional items, they are comfortable, they can be dressed up or down, they last a long time and they also happen to be my favourite item of clothing. I pretty much live in them. I feel comfortable in jeans, they sit naturally with me, on me.

My instincts turn out to be right. Although I try the other two pairs on as well, the first one is the best fit and the one I want. In spite of my instincts and the first one turning out to be perfect, I still have to compare it with the others first. I don't feel comfortable making a decision without having all the facts.

The male figures, my animus, appreciate my naked body, they

cheer it, but at the same time they are intruding on me, they are not allowing me my space and privacy. They like my body, they're not criticising it or making fun of it, they're enjoying it, but simultaneously they are not respecting me. They're jovial, but trespassing my personal space, my boundaries. They make me feel uncomfortable, self-conscious, vulnerable.

The father figure is an alien one, from a distant, foreign country. He's my father, but looks or sounds nothing like him, he feels unrelated. He is the voice of the judgemental wider group, of my parents, of society, of rigid morals that lack understanding and a deeper awareness. My parents' ideas have been engraved in me, yet somehow they feel distant here, they are not as effective, not as hurtful. He tells me my choice is bad only because it is too expensive for me, I am not worthy of such extravagance. I'm not worthy even of the price of a pair of jeans. Yet he is poor, he cannot afford them himself. It smacks of sour grapes. He can't have them, so I shouldn't either, because I don't deserve them. He can't be happy seeing them on me, or appreciate them for me, if he can't have them, they're no good for me either.

Is that why I was not allowed happiness? Maybe that's why my parents couldn't imagine me having friends. How could they have none while I had so many? Impossible in their mind, so my friends couldn't be real, either they were fake, or I was lying. They were poor growing up, so I had to be brought up poor too. We didn't have a lot of money, but I was denied very simple things, not just clothes. I was denied a carton of juice I might ask for, because it was unnecessary, I didn't need it. I was denied food I might fancy. In fact denying us things was very much the way we were brought up and 'taught morals' in our household. I think often they said no before they had even taken in the question. If we asked for something, it didn't matter what it was, whether something to wear or something we wanted to do, the answer had to be a no. They gave us all we needed, didn't they? If we were asking for something it was purely out of greed or being spoilt, attitudes that need correction, correction can only come through punishment. Asking for something resulted in insults or punishment.

But here at last I ignore him. I am worth it! I will wear the jeans.

I can afford them. I take no notice of him at all. I remain untouched by his lies. It feels like a turning point in my life. No matter how much I have analysed my parents and their treatment of me, no matter how much I think I have understood and learned, their words and actions were still able to have the same effects on me as they did when I was young. But here at last they have no effect at all. They float pass me like the pointless words of a bitter stranger that they are.

I'm in Correas, in Brazil. A scientist is conducting some high brow experiments. In my mind I decide to join his team. I want to work on something scientific and do something good for the world. It all sounds fascinating and exciting.

Suddenly I'm in a room. I ask the cleaner what she placed in the doorway. There's a very small black box that's plugged into the socket. The box is in the middle of the room, the socket is the only thing on a pure, clean white wall. There is nothing in the room except for the plug in the wall, the wire running from it to the box and the box in the middle of the room. The room is completely white. The box is a simple, plain, velvety shiny black box, with nothing on it, no dials, no doors, no handles, nothing. It's heavy, made of lead or steel, very heavy and very dense. It's beautiful in its simplicity and its shining, glossy, deep black. It has no sharp edges or corners, they're rounded and flow smoothly.

The cleaner says she was asked to place it there and that she never knows what it is.

The box is gentle and soft to touch. It feels like if it moved, it would move in waves, subtly, gently, with no sudden, rigid movements. There is a softness to it, an acceptance, a naturalness to its existence. No rigidity at all. No strict separation from its surroundings, as if it flows into them and the surroundings into it. It can be anywhere and will have an effect on its surroundings. It's magical, sublime, beautiful, maybe even divine.

The box is solid, made of 100% of the same material throughout. No holes, no gaps, no scratches. It is grounded. It is perfect.

There is electrical energy flowing through it. It is alive. It feels alive, as if it's emanating a subtle warm energy.

Then suddenly the box vanishes. I can still see the wire that leads to the plug, but no more black box, the wire leads into nothing. As I'm staring at the emptiness there, just as suddenly a fridge appears in its place. A large, white, ugly fridge. It's a cheap looking, off-white colour. It has sharp edges and corners and the usual handles to open the doors.

The refrigerator is white with two doors. It has sharp contours and is rigid. As much the opposite of the black box in every way as is possible. It is functional, but cold inside and hollow. It is large and immobile. It is not pleasing to the eye. It is in your face, rigid, nothing subtle or natural about it. It sticks out in the room and doesn't seem to fit in, wouldn't fit in anywhere. It seems out of place, as if it's jarring against the environment. It has lots of sharp corners and edges. Nothing flows, neither its contours, nor itself into its surroundings, it seems static, frozen. It has set boundaries and is separated starkly from its surroundings.

The scientist, a creator, somewhat like a God, a Higher Power.

I become the box, subtle, beautiful, in a way perfect, simple, and so beautifully black, glossy and deep. No sharp edges, no corners, flowing, graceful. My corners and sides are rounded, polished to perfection. I naturally feel part of the universe, energy flowing though me, in and out of me, life feels natural and comfortable. I feel alive. I feel like I can be anything, become anything.

Black absorbs and integrates all the colours of nature without judgement, without leaving any out, without reflecting any colour, choosing or picking favourites. It takes them all in, accepts them, assimilates them. It is acceptance itself. It can become all and take in all.

The box has a lot of potential. It can become anything, be anything. This ability comes from the scientist, the Higher Power, and flows through the wire, the energy circuit. It has infinite potential. It is connected to a higher power, a higher force or energy. It is connected to creation and life.

I start moving and flowing in spirals, connecting to the earth and to the sky, gathering their energies in, moving like waves. I feel a part of the universe and full of potential, full of life's energies.

All life forms and grows in spirals: trees, plants, water, bones, DNA... Nothing in nature or in life exists in straight lines. Nothing natural has sharp corners or edges. Nothing is distinct from its surroundings, we absorb from our surroundings and emanate out to them.

148

Life is within me
Infinite potential
Join God's team
Join creation
Join life

If we block life's natural energy, if we refuse to absorb, if we shut down, if we freeze, we become like the refrigerator, cold, ugly, immobile, separated, rigid. We can be perfectly functional, but there is no beauty in our life, no movement or flow. Life is frozen, it is cold, rigid. The refrigerator seperates, it creates a harsh boundary between outside and inside. But if we can let go and flow with life, we have infinite potential. Through acceptance, gentleness, openness we can enjoy life and live it fully.

I feel I have been living so much of my life as the refrigerator. Functioning, but rigid, shut down, cold. And as I moved I felt the black box within me, the ability to accept, take in, feel, flow.

The dream is telling me to be the black box, the box with connection to the Divine, with life's energy flowing through it, welcoming all colours, receptive, open, accepting. It sent me the image of the refrigerator as a stark contrast, showing me what happens when we close down, freeze, try too hard to be functional above all and lose feeling and connection to nature and life.

I love the black box, its potential, its soft form. The refrigerator scares me. I can feel I am more the refrigerator right now. I also feel I have the potential of the black box within me.

Why can't I let life flow through me? What's stopping me? What is it that freezes my blood so that I cannot move and end up meeting the world with rigid and sharp edges and corners, instead of acceptance and love? I don't understand. I try so hard. And maybe the answer is in that short, simple statement. I try too hard. I'm trying, forcing, rather than allowing, flowing.

16 March 12

I fear being hurt, yet I get hurt all the time. I think that by closing myself up, I'm protecting myself, but I'm not. Pain still occurs, I just get frozen, unable to reach out and receive. I so deeply want to open myself to love and trust. I want to feel love, to feel safe in it. But I act out an unconscious knee-jerk reaction that pushes it away; the person, the care, the love offered. It happens no matter what I tell myself. I'm closed to receiving love.

I try not to care about people's opinions, but I do care. I think I'm protecting myself, but they have seeped into my being already, they're in there, then I shut down when it's already too late, they're inside. Two opposing energies within me, one aggressive and attacking to protect, the other wanting to receive, struggling against the attacker to stay open.

I take on the body of the attacker first and then the defender. They are both within me. I am attacking myself, blaming myself, accusing myself of all evil, and at the same time I am having to defend myself from the attack. I am at war within myself.

The experience is so intensely powerful, I feel I can't repeat it. It feels too overwhelming. Yet I stay with the sensations and repeat taking them on.

The attacker is full of hate and anger, feelings that stem from its heart. Its hatred is powerful and it is directed at itself. It feels rigid, its whole body turns stone cold and rigid. It is full of accusation and blame.

The defender feels timid and weak, worthless, useless, as small as the eye of the needle. Its energy stems from its navel. It has been living on the back foot, constantly on alert, ready to flee, ready to defend and run. Its knees are bent and it wants to move backwards. Its navel is in pain, as if a knife is constantly being stuck into it and then turned, pulled out and then stuck in again at a slightly different point, driven in, turned around to cause maximum pain, pulled out and then again and again elsewhere and again,... The pain is visceral, so much pain, incredible pain.

Then I embody each in turn. The defender wants to communicate.

The defender: "Please don't hate me. Why do you hate me? Please don't hate me. What have I done? Please don't"

Accuser: "I don't know why I hate you. I just do. You're weak. You're despicable. I hate weakness. I hate you"

Defender: "What can I do so that you stop hating me?"

Accuser: "Maybe hit back. Defend yourself. Stand up straight. Be strong"

The defender tries to do so. He straightens his legs as best he can, but still feels weak. He doesn't want to fight.

Accuser: "I still hate you. There's nothing you can do. I just hate you. I want to kill you"

Defender: "I want to die too. I want to vanish. I wish I could. My life is so worthless anyway. A burden on others. A waste of space. A disgrace"

The defender starts to feel numb. The pain is too much, so he loses all sense, until he is completely numb. "Can I give you a hug?"

The accuser shrugs. The defender walks over and hugs the accuser. As soon as he does, he feels warmth spread over his heart, he feels comforted. But the accuser doesn't want the hug and doesn't like it. He doesn't reciprocate. His arms remain by his sides. His body remains frozen and rigid. He pushes the defender away from him, turns his back and walks away. The defender stands there broken, abandoned, hurt and feeling lost.

Weakness, vulnerability for me meant punishment, hurt, resentment and anger. My dad hated to see weakness more than anything and any sign of weakness invited the worse punishment, even when I was a tiny, vulnerable child. I learned to despise weakness. It meant punishment and pain. I hated myself for getting hurt or upset, I hated myself for caring. I hated myself for being weak. These feelings, these natural ways of living, learning, growing had to be shut out.

My parents wanted me to vanish. They hated me for existing. I wanted to hug them, I wanted their love and acceptance. Even if they hated me, even if they didn't hug back, any contact with them would have given me warmth, they were my parents after all. But they walked away again and again and again.

When you're attacked your body responds in fight or flight mode. As children we can't fight back. We can't place any negative on the parents, especially both of them. We depend on them, we need them, we love them, we desire their acceptance and love. I couldn't shout at my parents or hit them and I couldn't run anywhere. There was nowhere to go. So I froze. It's a natural animal response. Fight or flight and if that doesn't work or it's too much for the body to take, freeze.

Emotional pain can be excruciating. Abandonment and rejection by parents is horrendously painful and the wounds cut deep. The pain becomes intolerable and the body shuts down, it cuts off circulation in a way, we become dissociated from parts of our body, our energy no longer flows freely. We freeze, emotionally and energetically.

Any time in our lives some event, sound, smell or word can trigger the same freeze motion in the body. The body remembers. Freeze is an instinctive defence. We find ourselves freezing when we're faced with being hurt, when someone is walking away from us, when the tone of voice someone uses triggers somatic memories. Our body freezes whenever it faces danger or threat. It can no longer function harmoniously, efficiently, comfortably. Like a car that is old and breaking down, it jerk starts, then comes to an abrupt halt, it fights when we try to change gear, it has a mind of its own and that mind won't flow, won't drive smoothly.

We can re-harmonise our bodies, retrain it, unlearn what was engraved in us so long ago and is so incredibly destructive. We can unfreeze all the inherent tensions in our bodies and bring down the barriers, walls, blockages so that energy can flow smoothly again, so that we can live wholly and joyfully again. But this takes so much time, so much undoing, re-learning, so much facing of old pains, re-bleeding of old wounds. It's a hard, hard path, and yet it is the only way.

There are the two voices in me, the two energies, personalities, beings. One is strong and unforgiving. It cannot stand pain or weakness. In its mind these invite abuse and pain. It would crush anyone or any being that shows weakness, it despises seeing weakness because weakness is where it started, from where it built its defences and strengths, a place that is so bare and vulnerable, going there is too big a risk to take, best to bury it, hide it and reject it. Then there is the other being, the one that feels the pain, feels abandoned and rejected, feels weak and hurt. It screams and is crushed by its stronger other half. They are at war and this war rages within my very own body, in my soul. Every step I take is a battle between the opposing two. One wants love and is afraid, the other fears hurt and therefore hates love. How can I move on when a great war is raging within me? How can I have any energy left to live, love and dance? All my energy goes to the battlefield. I reject myself at all levels. The fighter is rejected for its harshness and cruelty, the giver is rejected for its weakness and vulnerability. Ultimately I reject myself and I reach an impasse. I freeze.

I do feel rejected at the moment. And worse than that, somewhere deep inside I believe that is my lot. Some part of me thinks that no matter whom I encounter, what situation I am in, I will end up being rejected and abandoned. And at the same time I hate myself for placing myself in a position that leaves me open to rejection and abandonment. Why did I care? Why was I not stronger? Why did I open myself to pain? What's wrong with me? Hatred and pain, suffering and abuse, all going on simultaneously. I am the criminal and the victim at the same time. I hate them both, so what's left for me? What am I beyond the two at war? How can I make peace? How does one learn to love and accept themselves? Is it even possible?

I need some light, some inspiration.

29 March 12

Broken and lost
Damaged
Need to be returned
To my old neighbourhoods

I'm a pain, a responsibility
A nuisance
Broken eggs
Rotting as we speak

No hope, no light
Persephone went down like this
She crashed and burned
Never resurfaced

I'm drowning, sinking
And all I believed in
I've left behind
No hope, no resurrection

Mistakes, wrong decisions
Wrong turns along the way
One or two
And now I've gone too far
No way to put things right, to restart

My world has completely fallen apart. I am so depressed, I can't find a reason to get out of bed, I can't find a reason to breathe. I want to die, but can't end it myself. Why not? Oh God, some mercy please, why won't You let me?

I had a total breakdown today. I thought of divorce, of taking off my wedding ring and suddenly I felt physically sick. I started looking at cars passing by, wondering if I had the courage to throw myself in front of one of them. But then what if I didn't die? What if I was hurt beyond repair? What if I ended up crippled? What if I turned into a vegetable, unable to communicate, unable to ask them to turn off the machines that kept me alive, but I was still able to see, hear, think and worst of all feel? There'd be no escape. I would be trapped with my thoughts and feelings forever. I would want to die, but I wouldn't be able to do anything about it. What if I was comatosed and was never able to move a muscle again and yet I could still feel? I'm not strong enough for that, I know I'm not. I'll happily die, as long as there's a guarantee that I will. But without an assurance that I will die then and there, I can't make the move, I'm too scared. Not of dying, I'm terrified of surviving and suffering even more.

Then I crumpled up in a heap on the sidewalk and started to cry, uncontrollably, in hysterics, so forcefully, my ribs were hurting. I couldn't stop. I cried for ages. Eventually I managed to call a friend. She talked to me for an hour until I calmed down. I managed to get up and make my way home and hid under the covers, feeling so desperately utterly despondent and miserable.

When the light goes out
And all is dark
A candle light
Would be enough to spark
A lantern, a belief
Some joy in life
But my life has been deserted
By all candles and light

I'm so lost my Lord
So please help me see
Cause I've gone blind
I'm groping, falling
I'm on my knees

I'm strangling not the devil
But my very own soul
Can You not show me
Some way out of this hole?

Warm me, provide a light
Don't forsake me
Cause then I will die.

I could write
But all joy has gone
No belief left in me, no hope
Write about what?

I could dance
But life has gone
Music muted
Dance to what

I could run
But my legs feel flaky
They wriggle and squirm
Run with what

I could talk
But words are worthless
Speech full of lies
Talk of what

Arthur held me
He shook me when need be
He laughed and supported
He was my strength

I'm sinking, sinking
Throw me a float

I can't breathe or see
Darkness all around me

Self inflicted, no one but me to blame
And yet I can't pull myself out
I can see no shore or guiding light
Only painful death awaiting me

I seem to go down, ever lower. I keep thinking there is no way I could ever feel worse than this, things simply can't get worse, I think I'm at the bottom, but to my amazement, there always is further down to go, lower and lower, into deeper and deeper darkness, that damp soil, that smell of putrid decay. I sink further, I think I can't take any more, I can't bare it. And yet somehow I do. I'm still breathing, but God why, I'm still suffering and in pain and I know now that it can get worse. It always does. It won't stop. My suffering won't end. There is no end. There will never be any light again. Yet I'm not allowed to die, I'm not allowed to escape, I must endure and suffer, but why? How much more can I take? How much darker can my life become? Why am I still alive? This poor heart of mine, how can I bare so much pain, what could possibly be keeping it beating?

I can't imagine ever feeling happy again, smiling, laughing, dancing with joy. My life is over, so why am I still breathing? What makes my heart continue to beat? Why won't my body give up? The pain is too much for me. I can't go on. Please let me be. Let me die quietly and peacefully.

2 April 12

I feel like I'm in a holding room. Like a caterpillar that has entered its cocoon, waiting. Like a seed planted underground, no visible sign of life, yet it needs this time of quiet to be able to grow when spring comes. Huge changes have been taking place in my life. My life is now unrecognisable compared to what it was a couple of years ago. My everyday life has changed, I have separated from my partner, my friendships have changed, even my relationships with family members have changed. What I do, how I earn my living, how I live, everything is changing. And so much is changing and transforming inside of me, my understanding of myself, who I am, who I thought myself to be, what I want from life, my place in the world, my role in life, absolutely everything.

All these changes need to be integrated. My soul isn't letting me engage in normal life until I've integrated them. It's too much to be able to just take in and move on with the click of a finger. Integration takes time, so do growth and transformation. The field has been planted, now it needs to be fallow. It needs stillness. All the work is happening underground. From above, it looks like nothing's happening, the earth is still, no sign of life, of sprouting vegetation, but imperceptibly, at a deeply significant level, growth and transformation are taking place.

Plutonium needs to be broken down to transform into energy. The caterpillar needs to die to be reborn as a butterfly. The snake needs to shed its old skin for the new one to grow in its place. Growth needs not only the spring, but also the still winter. Inanna had to lose everything and rot on a stake for days to find Ereshkigal and through that rescue herself and return to light whole.

This time of stillness is not useless or a waste of time, it is absolutely necessary. During the stillness energies gather, understanding can come, integration occurs, healing can happen.

I am fighting the stillness. I find it hard. I'm used to doing, being active, moving on. Death feels final, I can't see the rebirth, I can't imagine it, feel it, but I need to believe, otherwise despair and depression set in. I find it so hard to be, to accept, but this is exactly the time for just being and accepting. I beat myself up, I hate myself for not moving forwards, I hate myself for being trapped in darkness. I am frozen, dead. Only death and hatred reign, all directed towards me. I cannot feel compassion towards myself.

I am finding a whole new way to be with myself in the world. Arthur used to be my root, rock, base. Now I have to provide those qualities for myself. My way of life is being reformulated. Everything I believed in, I am now questioning, some I keep, some are getting thrown out, they are either no longer valid, or they never were valid or good. The way I see myself in society and the person I used to be, have been changing. I'm more in touch with the real me, the one hidden under layers of abuse, defence and survival. I am living more from my heart, although at the moment it is a tormented heart, very much in pain, yet I am living the pain. I am not ignoring it, burying it, shunning it. I am feeling it and letting everything come up, nothing is getting turned away.

In its own way, all this is quite profound. It feels like something quite subtle, yet fundamental is happening. I can feel it in my whole being. There are times I wish I could just turn back the clock and remain ignorant. Connection to the heart is connection to the essence, to the true core of our being, to the divine in us all, but it is also connection to our fears and pains, our wounds and sufferings. They are built around the heart like walls, defences. We must wade through them if we want to free our heart and let it be what it truly is.

Experiencing the pain, suffering, loss and discomfort of re-orientation is difficult. My instinct is to run away, to hide, to ignore. To bury it, not feel it. But it is part of life, I must remember that it is not pathological.

I place tremendous pressure on myself to make everything okay, to have everything fixed internally right away. I've always placed a huge amount of pressure on myself to do my best, to get things right, to be good, to achieve. As a child nothing I ever did was good enough. My parents criticised no matter what, they wondered why I couldn't do better, they asked why I was such a failure. And I kept trying. Maybe if I do this, I succeed in that, I excel in this, then they'll accept me. They never did. Nothing I could ever do could have ever been good enough for them. And I continue to carry that pressure with me. I work so hard at everything, I try so hard and I'm never satisfied.

And even now I am doing this. 'There must be something wrong with me. Why am I depressed? Why can't I get over it? What's wrong with me?" It's my fault for being depressed and not leaping up and moving on. It's my fault that everything that's happened to me has happened to me. It's all my fault, always. I feel like a failure because I'm not happy, because I can't be happy, because I'm miserable and I haven't been able to leap out of the dark hole I'm finding myself buried in. I carry the guilt and the blame as well as the pain.

I tell myself it's not going to pass over night. What I've been through is pretty huge and pretty bad. I need to go easier on myself and stop pushing, stop beating myself up.

I need to reach out, feel and communicate with this presence, this stillness, this waiting, the suffering and pain, rather than thrashing about and fighting it, wearing myself out in the process.

I'm feeling lost and alone, desolate, but even though I'm not feeling held, there is something that is containing me. Somehow I'm still alive, I'm still functioning to a large extent. I'm still working, thinking, feeling, trying to understand, peeling layer after layer, going down level after level, ever deeper. We feel powerless and lost in the middle of a storm out at sea, but even then there is something that contains us, even through all the thrashing around and fighting.

It feels terrifying and like hell to be in this situation. I have spent my life working and controlling, building a life, making things 'good' and suddenly I am absolutely powerless, being thrown from side to side, in the dark, no visibility, no helm.

I'm told to pray, to connect to something greater than me, greater than my little ego. I don't need to believe in a classical 'God' for this. The universe, nature, the energy that connects us all with each other and with earth, I could pray to that. I could pray to the wisdom of the universe. I didn't want to. I thought it would be hypocritical. She who doesn't believe, prays when she needs, how cheap. And yet prayer is raw, it's not intellectual, or disciplined. Prayer can be a scream for help from the heart and that scream is so honest and true, there is nothing hypocritical about it.

There have been times when I have prayed, begged, cried for help. My heart and soul in anguish, feeling hopeless, on my knees, wanting to die. My heart was screaming and that scream was a prayer. I realise how honest that prayer was, how clean and pure in its simplicity. It was not hypocritical.

I realise how rich those people are who do believe. There is always hope then, always comfort. You are never alone. It was hopelessness that killed me most. How can you go on when there is no hope? What's the point? Hopelessness is true darkness of the soul.

I have prayed, many times recently. I have prayed for light, even a tiny one, for hope, for help, for strength, for direction. I feel my prayers were heard. How else could I have survived. Every time I felt I could not possibly go on, something happened to give me just enough to survive, to carry on, even if for that minute, it kept me alive. I'm still alive, working, surviving, communicating, trying.

I analyse too much. I criticise, judge, label all my thoughts and actions, even my feelings. But feelings are feelings, they simply are. They are not good or bad, right or wrong, our actions can be, but feelings are not, they are just what they are. I've been letting my feelings in more, without filtering them, analysing them, judging them, criticising them, just feeling them and letting them be.

Saraswati told me to allow myself to find comfort in my suffering, Allow myself to live it. I have been living it, as fully as I am capable, but I find no comfort in it. I don't even understand how that is possible. Experiencing the suffering is just as important as experiencing the joy itself I am told, but I shun that thought somewhere deep inside. I want no suffering. It's always too much, too painful, too raw.

It's time to allow myself to feel joy, but I cannot face pure joy and happiness either. I feel I am not worthy. Yet I have not sinned beyond redemption. I am not bad, evil, undeserving of what is good, unworthy. I do deserve it, I can embrace it.

I feel like I need to hibernate, to hide away, to sleep. I tell myself that's wrong, bad, I force myself to go out there, get things done, to work, to live, but maybe I should trust my impulses more. It's okay not to do anything for a while. It's okay to let the seed grow. For now it's okay to be still and feel miserable, to cry and hide. This is all part of the journey, of going deep down, far enough down, so that I can find Ereshkigal and come back up again.

Seeds once planted, need to become cold, immobile, lie in darkness, so that they're ready to grow and blossom in the spring. Without that dark, cold, still period, seeds would not be able to grow. I'm in the winter phase of my life. I need to go cold, be still and immobile. I know I do. I know and understand it in my head, but as ever I fight the impulse. I tell myself I'm a loser, worthless if I don't get over it, get up and live, do, be. I rot with the earth and that really is my own doing. That thought is probably my biggest enemy. Those who can accept grief, loss and suffering genuinely, as part of life, with calm, are those who can learn and grow from their experiences and still live and love and be alive when they are ready. Those though who fight every inch of it, will die with every inch. I am still fighting. As yet I still have not found out how to stop fighting myself. I am fighting. All those wounds in me... How do I stop this self declared war upon myself? How?

9 April 12

I feel like I'm not standing, I'm continuously falling. There's no ground beneath me, holding me, supporting me.
   It's so hard to shift the intensity of the feeling, to shift the energy. It feels impossible to forgive myself. I feel so much anger towards myself, I'm consumed by it. It's so intense, it's preventing me from living, from being, from loving.

The natural impulse I have is to block off my feelings. I block my feelings of abandonment and rejection out, but with the bad, the uncomfortable and destructive, the good also get blocked out. This natural impulse helped me survive for years, but it is now impeding me. It is only exacerbating the problem.

My life was built on a lie, the lie that I was worthless, unloveable, bad, evil. It is so hard to dismantle this lie, because I lived with it for so long as God's given truth, the unquestioned truth, as implanted and ever engrained into my soul by my parents, my all-knowing, dependable parents.

I'm starting to dismantle the lies. The truth wants to come forward and I am struggling. I am reassessing and getting rid of stale, poisonous baggage. It takes so much energy to hold up something that is not true. Energy stops flowing, everything gets blocked up. If we can always be honest and true with each other, about our feelings, if we can move from the heart, we will keep renewing ourselves, our relationships will stay alive. As soon as we become unable to do this, energy, love, feeling, truth, genuinety and life get stifled, blocked, suffocated, we become poison to ourselves.

I can't force happiness or care-freeness. I try, but I find can't. Now for me is a time for remorse, for allowing my grief, sadness and loss to be felt, to come out, not to battle it and force some assumed, fake happiness. But I cannot accept even my grief. I feel like a failure for even feeling loss and sadness. I fight myself because of even these most basic, human emotions. Everything's a battle for me, everything I think or feel or do must be wrong. It's so tiring, so utterly draining and all-consuming.

'I get bored' is a kind of self defence, a way of handling or avoiding difficult emotions. It creates disassociation, makes it easier to walk away, provides the excuse to disengage.

The belief that I don't deserve to have what it is that brings me my own way of happiness is a strong, destructive voice that lives within me and is so powerful. The diabolical voice that takes over, sometimes without me even noticing it's there. It wants to step on and tear everything that might stop me from seeing myself as unloveable, undeserving, from seeing my life as hopeless. It is these diabolical elements that are preventing me from experiencing myself in a different way. In the past it protected me, saved my life, but now it's harming me, destroying me.

Something is diabolical when it separates parts of our own being from the rest, so that we cannot be whole. It keeps us from experiencing inner peace and wholeness.

I remember the black box. The box that had infinite potential and full acceptance. In fact the black box was the opposite of this rejection I feel, leaving no potential. And yet the rejecting, hating forces are the ones that take over me. The only way to undo the damage is to be with that box, be surrounded by it, be of it, become it and let go of the refrigerator. In that box lies the accepting, living, loving, flowing truth.

I need to learn to separate those voices that are within me from the actual me. They are so integrated in me, so much a part of me, I don't always see them for what they are. But they are a dark cloud hovering over me, they are not me. They are a destructive dark cloud. They are my parents' cloud, not mine, yet I own them. They are not mine!

The dark, suffocating, heavy cloud, grinning sarcastically, thinking "you poor stupid little thing"

And this is the cloud that takes over everything, my whole being and soul. A stupid black ridiculous cloud. It takes over so that I cannot move forwards and be the infinite potential that lies within me.

Those parental voices that discredited my existence after bringing me into the world, those voices dominate. But those voices are nothing but a stupid dark cloud, one that will eventually evaporate into nothingness. I must remember that. They have no substance, no real life, they are not me, not mine.

And through all this, with it all, in spite of it all, there is another energy, another voice that is working very hard to move through all this darkness, to shift the dark, damning energy, to disintegrate the cloud. The voice that brings to light the positive influences in my life and I can be drawn towards them instead of the dark cloud, but only if I let myself. I can embrace the positive energies no matter what form they come in; a smile, a walk, a breeze, music, a yoga practise, a compliment, a flower, whatever. They are there, otherwise I would not be alive now, I wouldn't be searching and going down deeper still, I wouldn't be trying, I wouldn't have survived. Where does this energy that keeps me descending come from? I don't feel it is there. I cannot see it. Yet I am still going on. Is that God's gift to me? The positive energies are there, let them be the louder voice within, let them guide.

My father overstepped boundaries with what he said and did. He did not honour me as a person, did not honour my autonomy, he did not respect me. He called me evil. He placed that belief in me, although it belongs with him. He made me carry it, although it should have been part of his bag to investigate.

"A young woman will struggle to have a relationship with a man if they weren't the twinkle in their dad's eye" Well, I certainly never was... And I most certainly do struggle to have deep, accepting, loving, trusting relationships with men.

My father did not know how to respond to my mother's insecurities, her resentment, he had to push me away to protect my mother's feelings and demands of him, to protect their relationship. This was all deeply unconscious, but nonetheless they guided his actions.

The voice in me that wants to rip everything apart, even life itself, is so strong, critical and harsh, and yet it is not my own voice. It has become my voice from years of taking it on, owning it and being trained to do so. It belongs elsewhere though, not with me. That voice also cut me off, helped me survive, prevented me from feeling things that could have been too overwhelming and life threatening for me to feel at the time.

Perhaps I want to destroy myself to be able to get rid of these thoughts. The thoughts themselves are inherently of the nature that try to destroy me. They have come from my parents and I have taken them on. Every 'bad' I do is an added bonus for these thoughts, 'aha, you're bad, see' and further punishment follows, I have proven my parents were right. This only feeds the poison, the poison gets stronger and I continue to drink it, feeding it further, it strengthens, and on and on and on... I'm tired. I'm depleted. I'm nearly dead.

Feelings can't kill, they want to be heard, they want to be felt and recognised. Shunning them only makes them angrier, makes them want to try harder. Acceptance, acknowledgement, living their truth eventually takes away their power.

Yet I'm so confused and overwhelmed. I can no longer tell when I'm poisoning myself, when I'm drowning myself, when I'm feeding the negative sources and when I'm learning, understanding, feeling. All is entangled and in the middle of a strong, tight knot is my neck. I can no longer breathe. But I am still trying. I'm fighting for life, real life, not just to stay physically alive, but to live a genuine, heartfelt life.

I'm correcting a presentation I need to hand in. I go to the beer hall, where Arthur is doing something. There's music playing in the background. I leave the presentation unfinished, although it still needs some work and corrections, so that I can get to the beer hall before it's too late. I get Persephone to come with me.

For once I'm not forcing myself to do what I 'should'. I work on the presentation for a while, but then I let myself go out to have a good time, to enjoy being alive. I'm giving myself internal space to relax. Music is the language of the soul. Deeper conflicts, painful situations have not yet been resolved, they still need work, however I can still allow myself to go out and enjoy life.

Somehow in the dream the flow of life is more accessible to me. Rather than forcing myself to work, to get something done, I allow myself to relax and have fun. It seems like a turning point. As if I've suddenly realised that it's okay, I don't have to have everything perfectly ready, totally prepared. I'm letting go of some of the super-responsible me. I can be in the moment and relax. For the time being the voice in me that is so demanding has backed off. I can be less hard on myself.

The inner voice in me that is so destructive is strong, but it is not the truth. It uses someone like Dell to back it up, someone who will label me for wrong reasons, who will spread lies and gossip about me and I take it all on, I own what he says, although it doesn't belong to me. His actions stem from his own complexes. But the influences these have on me are beginning to crumble. Something's opening up inside of me, so that music, the song of life, can play through me. I'm not acting so constrained and self-condemning.

I am connecting to Persephone, whom I take with me. She is the one who defies the norms of society, who can take a more light hearted approach to life. I'm also going to connect to my inner Arthur, my rock, strength and sun.

4 May 12

A huge structure is pulling me towards it. It's as if there's a vortex in the centre wanting to suck me in. The structure is shaped like an ear or old style gramophone. It is made of a smooth, bronze-gold coloured metal. It is filled with a creamy coloured moss or mould, which is dense and spongy. The moss is death. In the centre there is an entrance to a pipe. The end of the pipe is broken and jagged around all around. It has ragged edges and is sharp and rusted with thin spikes poking out. It doesn't seem to lead anywhere. No light comes through it. Inside is just darkness. The pipe doesn't have an opening on the other side of the structure. The front of the ear structure, where the opening is, is surrounded by the smooth metal, filled with the moss with the pipe in the centre, but all around on the sides and the back you can only see the smooth, rounded metal.

An energy like a vacuum is pulling me in towards the centre of the pipe with huge strength and force. It's like a vortex.

I feel fear. Overwhelming fear, nearing panic. I know I need to let go, stop fighting against it and let it pull me in, but I'm afraid. If I resist and struggle, I will end up in the mould which will take over me, it will spread through me and numb me into death. It is so dense, there's no space, no air.

But the pipe is tiny, it's only the size of the width of my fist and my body could never fit through it. As soon as I reach it, the sharp rusty edges of the pipe will cut me, it will hurt me and make me bleed.

But deep inside I know that I need to let it pull me in. I need to let go of my fear. I need to believe that it's fine to let it cut me and it's okay for me to hurt and bleed. It's the only way. I need to trust...

The pipe's hollow. I don't know where it goes, where it leads, if anywhere. It's dark, but I know in my heart that's where I need to go.

I try to let go, I feel myself being pulled towards it and then fear takes over. I start to resist and feel myself move towards the mould, the moss. It's soft and comfortable, it's numbing. Like moss spreading over a rock, gradually it takes over. Like mould spreading over cheese, moving deeper and deeper and wider, until the whole block of cheese goes mouldy, dead. If I cling onto the sides, I

168

will go comfortably numb, the fear will diminish, I can fall asleep, become unconscious, but I will gradually die. I need to take the risk, let go of my fear and allow the vortex to draw me where it will, into the darkness and unknown of the pipe. I need to trust that even though it might hurt and cut, I will make it through and my path lies through there. There must be light somewhere.

It's so hard to let go. The impulse to control, the overwhelming fear, the need to hold on to what I know and can see keep me struggling against the pull. I close my eyes and imagine myself getting sucked into the pipe. I feel myself letting go.

There's a saying, for a camel to pass through the eye of a needle, it needs to get rid of all of its baggage first. I have 35 years worth of baggage on my back. All my complexes, inhibitions, fears, hurts, wounds, they're all weighing on me. I can only pass into the pipe if I shed all my baggage. And if I let go and trust. Rather than trying to control and understand, the masculine side of life, to let go, be and feel, the feminine side of life.

A gramophone should emit music, but the mould muffles all sound and kills music. No sound emanates from this gramophone. An ear should hear, but there is no sound to be heard. Everything is muffled, suffocated in this structure, it asks for death, yet it itself is alive.

I have a fear of bleeding, of getting hurt, of having my heart broken, of failure and making wrong decisions, of the unknown, of regret and letting go of what I know... These fears hold me back, they freeze my actions, they cut off my instincts and feelings. My instincts know I need to let go, but I cannot trust them.

I enter my cave and lie in a foetal position. Images of friends flash through my mind and the image of the gramophone appears. Then I come out of the cave and move from my heart. I create a cocoon around myself for protection, an enclosure, but with space. I lie there for a while, not thinking, just letting myself be, eyes closed. Eventually I cut a slit in the enclosure and exit. I feel the sun on my face. I feel its welcoming warmth, the warmth of life.

My life is in turmoil at the moment. Everything is changing. So many endings are taking place and I'm afraid. My fear causes stress

169

and pain. It makes me rigid. I'm ruled by my presumptions, that I'm not worth anything, I'm not good enough, that I'll always ultimately fail and that I'm unloveable. I need to let go of these, as comfortable and known as they are. I need to let go of my life with Arthur, as comfortable, known as it was with its sense of certainty and security. Nothing new can come in if we keep hanging on to the old, but it is so difficult to let go of the old. We are afraid of the unknown, afraid of big changes, what we might find if we enter a dark cave. If we don't take the risk though, we die every day in stagnation, like being covered in moss, every day we die a little more, a little more of us becomes rigid, moss-like, frozen, incapacitated. We need to let go of our fears and take the plunge.

I need to let go into the pull of the universe. I need to learn to trust in God, in the energy of the universe, its intrinsic intelligence.

He who can't take the risk of destructing himself is not fully alive.

I'm constantly trying to control, but I need to let go to be able to live and move on. As long as I'm clinging to the old, I become frozen stagnant, I can't move. There is no life in that. I need to believe in myself, in my instincts, in the way the universe and life flow. Only then can I live.

Goodbye my love
My strength, my rock
Goodbye my inspiration
My best friend
My companion
Goodbye my life
As I've wished and planned it
Goodbye

Welcome my new path
Rugged and alone
But mine
With flowers to plant
Trees to climb
Mountains to explore

170

This image proved to be a source of inspiration for me for many months to come. Whenever I felt stuck and afraid, I brought to mind this image and felt myself letting go into the pull of the pipe, letting go, being pulled in, trusting. It felt right, it relaxed my body, released tension. I felt my grip loosen, blood flow return, courage grow. I could then move on again.

9 May 12

I'm going to stay at some kind of retreat, I've just arrived. I'm sharing a room with seven other people. There are eight single beds lined up in the room. I want to take the bed closest to the door, but Miles also wants that one. I say "Okay, fine, it doesn't really matter to me, I'll take the one by the window instead" But then I realise that the radiator is right under the window and is on full blast, which makes that side of the room way too hot for me. I don't like sleeping in warm rooms, I prefer a cool room with the window open. I feel very uncomfortable, but I don't want to turn the radiator off. There are seven other people there to share the room and they may prefer sleeping in a warm room. I don't want to take charge and have a negative effect on their comfort. But eventually I can't stand it any longer and turn the radiator off.

Various conversations are going on. I'm going in and out of the room, doing things. Miles is saying some macho male stuff, making comments and asking questions. I feel I really couldn't care less. I'm barely responding. When I do answer a question, my replies are short and delivered coldly. I feel huge inner strength, I feel unshakable.

I get the feeling my responses to Miles' questions and comments are good and that he is impressed. He thinks I've become much stronger over the years and more interesting. I feel independent.

After a while Miles and I start talking. There's a ladder there with hundreds of bits of black ribbons hanging from it. While we're talking I'm playing with them and stroking them.

I gather, as the conversation moves on, that he wants to have sex with me. I ask him "You want to go all the way?" He says "yes". I tell him I'm not sure I want to. I feel indifferent. He asks me if I have a boyfriend. I say "yes" and inwardly think "but he loved me".

I wake up first with a feeling of warmth and love, which is then very quickly replaced with resentment and irritability.

Miles is not a a supportive character in my life. In the dream I manage to keep my emotional distance. I feel indifferent throughout. I don't agree to have sex with Miles, because I don't want to. I feel strong and independent and like the way I am responding. A sign of growing self-confidence, valuing myself and loving myself as I am.

Going all the way can mean becoming intimate and understanding of who someone is more deeply, perhaps even going all the way in spite of what he said. Miles embodies violator and abuser. Perhaps he is inviting me to understand better what it means to be the abuser, who an abuser is, what goes in their minds and souls. Forgiveness can only come out of deeper and better understanding of the other and what drove him to his actions.

I stood up for myself. I felt strong and independent, and yet there is also a blind spot around who he is. Feeling indifferent doesn't necessarily mean I'm not affected, it can also mean he needs to be dealt with more squarely, more logically, with less emotion. Indifference towards violation is not normal or healthy. Violation in a healthy and balanced person will result in anger, outrage, defence. The resentment, anger and hatred that has been created in me through the act of violation, instead of being directed towards Miles, where it belongs, gets displaced. Playing and fidgeting with black ribbons means I'm not really indifferent, I'm anxious, stressed, uncomfortable. Black is also the colour for grieving and death.

The day he violated me, he also killed a part of me. He killed the trusting, loving, naive girl in me. In fact, he killed the girl in me. He created a woman who did not understand what love and passion could mean, for her sex became intertwined with abuse, pain, being used and not caring, instead of a deeper connection, part of a loving relationship.

A part of me died, because I couldn't understand, face, deal with, feel the pain, hurt, betrayal that had been awoken in me. I had to freeze, forget, deny, cut off. I froze and couldn't move, I couldn't defend or protect myself. I forgot most of what happened. In fact I forgot the entire event for years and then gradually remembered pieces of it. I denied myself, my rights as a girl, a woman to say no, to not be violated, to report what had happened and have him punished. I cut off my emotions, the natural energy flow in my body, so that I became disconnected, so that I wouldn't feel, because if I felt the full extent of my pain, I feared I would not have survived.

My dream is suggesting that perhaps the time has come to face some of these buried traumas, the suffering and pain, to let the grieving process begin, to mourn. Also to understand the violator better, to get to know him. To mourn the death that was caused and then hopefully to let go. Not to bury or deny, but to actually release it all to light and out into the air, let it go, let it leave my body and my soul.

I don't as yet know how I'm supposed to do any of this, but I trust my soul, my subconscious that speaks to me through dreams and bodily sensations. I trust the law of the universe, which has brought me here and knows when I'm ready. I trust my body, which would not bring these up for me if I wasn't ready to face them. It will also guide me in the right direction as and when...

I'm playing with the idea of grieving and death. I'm engaging with it. Ribbons make things more noticeable, bring something to our awareness. Maybe I'm getting closer to the grieving and darkness that happened around this abuse.

Miles and the events that surround him are at last coming into my consciousness. They are there and I am aware of them and engaging with them. It does need to be dealt with, I know; how, I'm not yet clear. There is much pain and trauma around it all and I have already spent a lot of energy trying to deal with it. It has not reached closure though, there is still more.

The extent of violation: sexual, physical and emotional, is huge. My best friend, turns out not to be a friend at all. I trusted and believed him, but he forced me down, held me down and sexually violated me. It's not an easy thing to come to terms with. I felt disgusting and damaged, I felt it was all my fault, I must have done something to bring about these events. I have carried these feelings with me for the past twenty years of my life. What did I say or do, in what way did I act that made him feel he could, that it was okay to do what he did. Why wasn't I able to stop him? And enveloping it all, the feeling that I am damaged, rotten and irrevocably dirty for life.

But it wasn't my fault and nobody deserves to live through what I did, no matter who they are and what they have done. Yet I don't hate Miles. I don't feel anger or hatred towards him. It's all directed towards myself and always has been.

9 May 12

It's my first day at my new job in a massive building. The building looks like my high school. I'm completely unprepared. I don't even have the name of the person I'm meant to be meeting, or the presentation I'm supposed to be talking to, with me.

I come across the people I'm going to be working for and tell them I am lost. They take me where I need to go.

I'm helping my boss, when suddenly two rich, spoilt women and their helpers come in. One of them introduces herself. I'm stunned, I freeze and say nothing. My boss places his hands on my shoulders, turns me around and marches me out of the room. Once outside he says to me in a kind, warm, but firm voice "this is no time to be shy". I go back in and introduce myself to all of them.

I want to go to the toilet. There are six doors in the toilet area, three on one side and three opposite. The three on the right turn out to all be showers. I try the third one on the left. Instead of a toilet, there are steps inside, going down somewhere. I start walking down the steps. They're covered with honey. My socks get sticky with honey.

I find a therapy room downstairs, but no toilets.

I have to take all my clothes off, everything on me has become sticky with honey. Luckily I have clean underwear and socks with me.

I appear completely unprepared for a new beginning, new life, new work, but I have helpers who take me to the right place. I also have a champion in the figure of my boss, who guides me and helps me save face. When I freeze and am unable to move, he takes me aside and reminds me that this is "no time to be shy". My boss is a positive animus figure inside of me, helping me confront things and stand my ground, to be myself and unfreeze.

I don't like the women. They symbolise attributes I dislike in people, for example being spoilt and driven by monetary gain and comfort. They are anima figures in me, perhaps they show aspects within myself I need to meet, face and understand more, things that I don't like and am judgemental about. I freeze in front of them, but now it's time to face them, not freeze.

I keep telling myself "How can I complain when I had everything. I have no right to suffer, I have so much. I'm bad and a failure because I'm suffering, I have no right to disintegrate. I should be happy and grateful", as if my suffering is insignificant because of all I've had in life. But my suffering is suffering, it is real and not insignificant.

I have been violated, this creates tremendous suffering and deep wounds. It's okay for me to acknowledge that. It's okay for me to feel pain and suffer. It is unrealistic of me to expect superhuman strengths of myself. It would be unhealthy and destructive if I did not acknowledge my pain and tried to bury it, brush it under the carpet. The pain would still be there, however it would remain unrecognised. Instead of being experienced and dealt with, faced and released, it would remain like a tumour within me. In spite of knowing this to be true, I still beat myself up about not being carefree and happy, picking myself off the ground and skipping along as if all was well.

Honey is sweet and sticky. It's sticking to me, all over me. Perhaps it is an idea that I have, that seems sweet and good, it is stuck to me, it is all over me. But it's not good. It's not good to believe that "It's not okay to have rage or express anger". Overriding, stifling these feelings can be destructive. I don't need to be 'sweet' and good by never expressing anger, never even acknowledging it's there. Anger is okay when it's directed against the proper source, when its felt in its pure honest form and not acted out unconsciously.

Underwear is intimate. Even my underwear is covered in honey. I feel I need to be 'sweet', never be angry or upset even in my most intimate relationships in order to be loved and accepted. But this is false sweetness. It is not appropriate. Honey on clothes is misplaced, it doesn't belong there. The feeling that I can't express anger and outrage is misplaced.

It was never okay to express emotions with my parents. I still can't accept having anger or resentment towards them. It feels wrong, as if I'm a bad person to feel that way. All children should love and respect their parents and be grateful, that's the overriding instinct within me and I punish myself for feeling anger towards them. I believe I'm evil because of it. I punish myself for not being able to forgive them, I believe I'm bad. I force myself to be sweet and good, I try to override the negative emotions I feel towards them and try to replace them with positive ones. It feels so wrong to not be able to do this. But this desire to muffle my resentment, to override it is not appropriate. I was abused by them as a child and feeling anger is appropriate and right, trying to suffocate that feeling is not. I'm not evil because I'm angry with them. I have a right to be angry. I need to allow myself to feel angry towards them rather than turning it against myself. This does not mean acting out and hurting them. It simply means allowing myself to feel what I feel, giving myself that right, and experiencing the feelings I have without labelling and judging them as evil.

It's okay to feel that outrage. I need to release it. I'm looking for the toilet to be able to release the feelings, express them, let go of them, let them flow out. But I can't find the ability to do so, I find no toilet, instead I find a treatment room. These feelings need treatment, going back and facing these emotions, dealing with them, letting them come to the surface, and eventually finding the ability and the right way to express them.

The curse that my parents imposed on me that I am bad and worthless is stifling me. It sticks all over me and on everything that I do, every relationship I enter, even very intimate ones.

Not only my parents, but I expressed no outrage at Miles for his actions either. Even rape produced no anger within me towards the abuser. Instead I hated myself, I blamed myself. I felt dirty, damaged, disgusting. But I didn't hate him. I still don't feel angry towards him. All emotion seems blocked. I still can't find the toilet to express myself. Perhaps after some treatment…

I need to acknowledge the violation that occurred both from my parents and from Miles and allow my emotions expression. Anger needs to be directed towards the right place, not inwards.

The violation that was perpetrated by my parents from childhood continues to be perpetrated, but now by me. I devalue myself. I'm hard on myself and in the process I violate myself, my nature, my soul, my instincts and all that is good and worthy in me.

It's the first day of school. I see the guy I used to like and say to Natalie "I forgot how good looking he was. I really like him". She tells me "it will pass". And it does. I forget all about him very quickly.

It will pass, it is superficial and has no significance. The superficial relatedness that was attractive, but didn't serve a deeper purpose will pass. I need to find a deeper way of being in relationship.

7 July 12

Every human being reaches the point in their life when they realise that they are utterly alone. This tends to happen when we lose our parents, or the parent we were closest to and relied on most. It is sad when we lose that person through death, but it is a tragedy when we lose them or realise they have never been there, while they are still alive, because then there is no memory that keeps the flame within us burning, no voice in us that assures us "you were loved". The truth is a slap in the face, one that burns and echoes through all eternity. "Even your parents did not love you, who in the world possibly could, if those whose flesh and blood you are, who brought you into this world, can't?" The answer becomes engraved deep within our soul as "no one".

But is that true? A parent may not be able to love, not because the child is unloveable, but because they themselves are incapable. Someone capable of love will be able to, but the scar is so deep. It is so easy to break the scab and the old wound starts bleeding again, it gushes out blood. And in all that loneliness, we find friends who care, who support, listen, love, hold. We are in essence alone, but somehow with so many by our sides.

When Emily's mum died, she said it had been so terribly hard for her, not just because she had lost someone she loved and was close to, but also because she had lost her rock in life, the person she could always turn to and count on, who was always there for her. I know now what she meant. Yet my parents are still alive. But I have no rock, no anchor, no safety shore, no home of acceptance and love. I have realised they never took on these forms for me and never will.

My mother is an eccentric character, one of the most narcissistic people I have ever met. She is incapable of genuine love and whatever she is capable of, she has given my dad. She had nothing else to give, and not only that, her children were a threat to her. Her husbands' love might be divided, they might get some of it, she might cease to be the centre of his universe, the most important person in his life. The threat was unbearable for her, so she resented us. She blocked us out, withheld love, care and acceptance, at times hated us and subtly, unconsciously forced my dad to do the same.

They took so much from me. They had no right to. They wounded me deeply. I was only a child, dependent on them and they withheld, abused, criticised, punished, hated. I was defenceless, my only defence was to shut down, close up, freeze, so I did.

I'm peeling layer after layer of my being. At each layer I find more wounds and suffering, more painful memories. Yet I will continue to peel until I reach my core, the unblemished pure heart, the light that shines within. The light that was crushed, the heart that was broken, buried under sand, brick and steel. They may have wounded me badly, but no one can destroy a person's soul completely. Under all those layers I will find my soul; beautiful, radiant, alive. I will continue my descent, until I save my shadow and bring her out into the light.

26 July 12

I'm at a retreat centre, similar to ones I've been to for yoga retreats. I'm sharing a room with someone. There are many communal spaces. Mick has been visiting me there and he leaves to go home. He sends me a text message not too long afterwards saying "Arrived home. Good night baby. X"

I reply "so soon?"

"I got the 10:02. Only 11 min train ride"

But 15 minutes after I receive the text message I walk out to buy some bread and he's there, sitting on a bench. I ask him what he's doing there. For the moment I have forgotten about the text messages he sent me minutes ago. He says he needed to sit down for a minute. He kisses me and leaves.

Half an hour later, after trying many times, I manage to get through to him on the phone. I ask if he's arrived home safe. He says "Yes". There are Turkish voices in the background. I am furious "You're still here, aren't you?"

He gets angry in turn "What are you doing? You have no right to follow me"

"I wasn't. I heard Turkish voices in the background and guessed"

He hangs up. I try calling him again a few times, but he won't pick up. I leave a message saying that I need an explanation and beg him to meet me.

I feel despair, I'm hurt, I feel betrayed, there's a horrible pain in my navel. I am crying, thinking "he's sick of me. He doesn't love me anymore"

I tell a friend and as I'm telling her I remember the texts he sent me saying he'd arrived and even which train he took and how long the journey was. Those texts came from him without promting or any questions. I suddenly realise, I know within me, he's cheating on me. I run to my room to check my phone, but those text messages have vanished.

The images in the dream and the feelings they create in me stand out strongly as belonging to my relationship and feelings around Arthur. The pain in the navel, loss, betrayal, anger, hurt, inability to get an honest response from him, lack of genuine, honest communication.

I'm at a yoga retreat centre, yoga is to unite, to join. This is a place where the conscious and unconscious are united, as they are in sacred marriage. The main thing happening in my life right now, my main task at the moment is to join together my conscious and unconscious, to bring the unconscious out into the light. I keep myself from feeling complete and whole with the voice that tells me I've done wrong, that I don't deserve to have anything, I'm to blame, I'm to suffer.

Mick cheating on me symbolises me cheating myself out of being able to be in a proper, loving, fulfilling relationship. I cheat myself out of accepting that love. I cheat myself out of feeling that love for myself, accepting myself as I am, cherishing myself and being whole.

The process I'm going through is to learn how to create that love, to give it to myself and to be able to receive it.

There is deeply rooted fear of abandonment in me and that's what triggers that excruciating pain in my navel. Each time I'm rejected, walked away from, abandoned, it reignites those deep wounds I carry in my navel, wounds created when I was small, wounds created by my parents' rejection and abandonment. The pain comes to life even when there is no real rejection or abandonment, but just the fear of it.

I think, wrongly, that if I don't open up, if I don't allow myself to become vulnerable, if I don't love and care, I won't be hurt. But I will, in fact I constantly am, because I can't protect myself from caring, I can't numb my emotions completely. I try not to love, I unconsciously reject any love offered me, in the fear it might be taken away and the pain caused would be unbearable. But I fail, because I do care, I do feel, try as hard as I do, I can't stop myself from feeling, I can only bury my feelings and ignore them, but they are still there and the pain is real. I need to dismantle that rooted belief coming from my past and is so wrong. I need to allow my feelings to be felt, the blocks and barriers to be released, love to flow in and out freely.

I feel like I had made a terrible, irreparable error and the wrong could not be righted. I start to hyperventilate. I am filled with panic and fear. Suddenly there is nothing to look forward to. I wake up with these feelings alive in me, overwhelming me. I feel the need to run, to scream, but I freeze, sitting there full of panic, pain and remorse.

It's not true that a wrong cannot be righted, no situation is irredeemable. Mistakes are lessons we learn from, some can be intense, but we grow with their help. They are on our path to help us.

At my core I feel the pure terror of abandonment. A feeling and fear so painful as a child, especially as when we are young we are so powerless to do anything about it. We are weak and vulnerable and our life source is snatched from us. But what's past is in the past, it should no longer dictate my everyday life. I am no longer weak and vulnerable. I am no longer dependent on my parents or anyone else for survival. I can love and be loved and survive with or without. The wounds are old, they don't belong to now. What happens now only reignites old pains.

My parents abandoned me. All my life I struggled to be accepted by them, to be included, appreciated, acknowledged, loved. But I never was, even on my wedding day they withheld from me, they criticised me, shouted at me and did their best to ruin my day. They were not able to upset me because I was surrounded by my partner who loved and cherished me and many wonderful friends, who joined in to make that day special and beautiful for me. My parents taught me that I don't deserve anything good, that I have no value, that I don't deserve to be treated well, that all I can expect from life is to be kicked in the face. But my life since has shown me otherwise. I have struggled to see the love around me, to receive it, because I have not been taught how. I've learned to defend myself and close myself down, but I have so much to open to now. My life has been so full of beauty and genuine, loving friends. My parents were wrong about me.

The greatest abandoning that is happening now is the one I am doing to myself by refusing my own worth and value.

The strength of my will around some issues is causing stagnation and an impasse in my life. I am so determined to survive, to be strong, to do right, I block out the voice of instincts, the music of my feelings. I try to force myself down paths that are not meant for me, racing towards places I don't belong to.

I need to learn to trust myself, my inner voice. For years Arthur was the container for me, but I can move without him, I can trust and live and be without him, I have that ability within me. That is the lesson I'm learning, however painful it might be, however lost I might feel after our separation, I am learning to be whole within myself, to find strength in my vulnerability, beauty in my feelings. I am learning to walk with my head erect, proud of who I am and what's within.

We are all, none of us, perfect. We re-incarnate to heal old wounds, to learn and through our experiences grow and blossom. Wounds are not there to punish us, but to help us evolve. It is not a case of bandaging the wounds up, covering them, ignoring them. Strength is not the ability to crush and endure. Real strength lies in being able to let a wound breathe, nurture it, heal it, recognise it. We can't force healing, we need to allow for space, time and the body to work its own healing. We can be proud of our wounds, they show we have lived, we have felt and that we are strong enough to have survived, we are not afraid of them. They are not a source of embarrassment, needing to be hidden. They are an essential part of who we are. Any beauty there is within us has developed thanks at least partly to our wounds and suffering. The ability to sympathise, empathise, care for others, help others comes from our ability to see our own wounds, nurture them and let them heal.

Hope and light
You sank me into darkness
I could not breathe or see
But as soon as I let go of your hand
To the surface and light, I floated up free.

Your prison walls may be infused with love
Your presence full of care
But your prison gives me no light
And in it I'm devoid of air.

12 August 12

Arthur, Louise, Arthur's sister, and Arthur's parents are in some house. I turn up there and Arthur tells me he's going out with Louise. I tell him that's sick. They are acting like a couple and doing things together as a couple. They plan to cook for the family later.

Arthur is lying on a double bed. I lie down next to him and I cry. I cry and cry and cry, my tears seem to have no ending. It's so hard for me to see him with someone else, it hurts so much.

Also I'm wondering if there's something truly wrong with him. It seems so twisted, wrong and sick for him to be with his sister, for him to be living and sleeping and having sex with her, to be in a romantic relationship with her.

I find it all so terribly hard to accept. It hurts, it's baffling and confusing.

If he really did get together with his sister, he would be considered sick by society. Interbreeding leads to degeneration and is considered immoral. There is also something sick about a man and woman of the same blood, brought up together as family, brother and sister, ending up in a romantic, sexual relationship together.

Somehow this all has to do with what happened in my relationship with Arthur. He was, in some way, not able to extend beyond what was completely known, absolutely safe and secure. The ability to risk something in intimacy, something like the potential to be hurt, the ability to be vulnerable, was impeded in our relationship. For years this would have been impossible for me as well and we continued together happily and harmoniously for a long time. But over time something opened in me and I wanted a deeper intimacy, an emotional, sexual intimacy we didn't share. He was not able to provide that for me or go down the path leading to it, exploring deeper feelings with me.

In some ways I suppose our relationship was like one a brother and sister would have. We shared everything, we were close, we talked about everything, there was a deep bond there, but it lacked passion, an emotional vulnerability and honesty.

As an inner figure Arthur symbolises the resistance and impediment to a full opening up for intimacy. It opens up the core dynamic of what needs to be seen, which is the deep fear around real intimacy, allowing for vulnerability. There is a fear of betrayal and abandonment. He's with someone where the relationship can be completely safe, but it's not healthy. He avoids a healthy, life generating relationship and takes a safe and secure option instead. He knows his sister well, there is no unknown there, no finding out, exploring, learning, no surprises, just the comfort and security of what is known. But the relationship can't create healthy new life, any children would result in serious problems. There is also no space for an enquiring, an exploration of the other, a discovery of something different and courage to move into a risky place, one where hurt, pain, betrayal and abandonment are possible.

What came between me and Arthur was our inability to let go and open up at a deeply intimate level. We were both strong and independent in our relationship. We didn't go into 'mushy' things like saying 'I love you' or 'I need you'. We went on in life as close, independent companions, lacking vulnerability and passion.

In the dream I do open up though, I am lying on a double bed, a place of intimate communion and I am crying uncontrollably, honestly. I'm completely vulnerable and open. I admit to him how hard it is for me to see him with someone else. I care enough about him to feel that way and to even let him see it.

But before that opening up, everything is matter of fact and practical, as it always was in our relationship. The emotional side was too scary and threatening to broach, so we never did.

How does a healthy union get formed? How can we allow ourselves to find a way to that?

Arthur's entire family is emotionally closed, they are practical and never show or talk about emotions, they are functioning, but lack deeper intimacy and honesty in their relationships, they have possibly never connected to their feelings. But feelings are a part of the human being, you can't leave them out. You can ignore them and suppress them, but they are still there, they don't vanish just because they haven't been acknowledged.

Real truth in a person can only manifest when the person is also truthful about feelings.

What came in-between me and Arthur was a longing, yearning for that honesty, intimacy, vulnerability, emotional opening. It needed to be recognised and my whole being went for it one hundred percent.

Arthur did betray me. He betrayed the emotional side of me and of our relationship. Feeling is still lacking from his side. He still has not shown any signs of remorse, hurt, pain or loss from the break-up. He has moved on, seemingly indifferent. That is a betrayal of our marriage, of the relationship we shared, of my feelings. It is also a stark reminder of how things always were. He never showed emotion. I did. I had passionate outbursts of anger, hurt, or joy. He would tell me to pull myself together, which I inevitably did and we went back to the unemotional and logical. That is how we lived and shared. But feelings are a part of us and instead of carrying them as a weakness, as an attribute to be ashamed of, to be hidden, I can allow myself to hold them as a part of me, a valuable, real, honest part of me.

I know I can't go back to the way things were with him, my rock and security, everything I wanted him to be though he was, I can't go back to a relationship where I feel 'less than', not good enough, insecure about the others' feelings. A relationship that is unsatisfactory emotionally, one where I don't feel loved and cherished. A relationship in which I feel alone. The only way forward is to recreate the relationship, building it on what we have, the friendship, trust, companionship, sharing, but also bringing in the emotions, feelings, vulnerability. But this can only happen if both sides are willing and want to work together. He doesn't, so it can't happen and I need to let go of 'what ifs' and regrets.

Arthur is a container, a rock, a logical existence, but lacks emotion, sensuality. The feminine side, that of raw emotions have opened up to me, I can no longer shut them down and Arthur's pure analytical, logical existence can no longer fulfil me.

An image of a child wondering around alone in a large open field appears. Golden wheat is bending in the wind. The wheat is so high, it reaches the child's shoulders. The child is a little girl, with long brown hair in pleats. The girl is lost and feeling so completely alone. She has been abandoned and she is afraid. But at the same time she can feel the sun's warmth on her face and the wheat strokes her arms and hands as she walks on. She is welcomed by the field, but her soul feels barren. She wants to be received by the field, but she fears rejection and she can't let go. She keeps wandering on, hoping she'll come across someone who will open their arms to her and envelope her little frail body in their strong warm arms. Then she will be accepted. She will be taken care of and loved.

This poor abandoned, lonely child is wondering around in my psyche. She is waiting for acceptance and love. She is lost and confused and until she has been welcomed and acknowledged, taken in, fed and loved, she will continue to wonder around lost.

Why is it we feel ashamed of our wounds? Are they not proof we can feel, that we are human, that we are alive? Are we to blame for others' actions that have created these wounds in us? And yet we try to cover our wounds up as if they show some kind of weakness, as if they are a fault within us.

The only way to heal is to reach out to that little child, take her hand and lead her to warmth, to a welcoming home and loving arms. To show her that she will not be abandoned or rejected by everyone. The only way healing can occur is if the child is acknowledged and accepted. If I can love that little girl; fragility, weakness, fear and all, if I can love myself, the little girl I was, the one who was despised by my parents and in turn learned to despise herself, the one who was abused, hurt and betrayed, I ended up hating her for her weakness and for not being able to defend herself, then maybe the dark, painful hole within me will heal. Then maybe I'll be able to feel the warmth of the sun, to let it into my soul and maybe I'll be able to lie in the wheat field, happy, content, at home and no longer afraid or alone.

Remember, that child, although she suffered so much, she turned out to be very strong. She survived all the abuse and grew up to be a lovely, successful, warm person, one that is loved by many. Remember that that child must have had immense internal strength to be able to survive the darkness and the void. Cherish her. Love her. Accept her. Welcome her.

Remember that that poor child could not have defended herself against the abuse. She defended herself the only way she was capable of, by shutting down, freezing. It is not her fault she was abused, she was only a little girl. Stop blaming her and hating her for what happened. Welcome her, nurture her, tell her it's okay, tell her she's okay.

Despair, emptiness, loneliness
I see no way out
Been like this
Will always be like this
Help me out, please help me out!

Hole in my abdomen
Craving for love
Want to be held
Warm and close
But all I get is distance
All I know is to push people away
I can't be held, I can't be held

Reach out to me
Grab hold of me
Love me, kiss me, want me
I know I kick and push and cry
But please share your warmth with me

22 August 12

I had planned to travel by plane, but I end up taking the train instead. It was meant to be an afternoon flight, but my parents tell us we will be served breakfast on the flight. I cooked dinner the night before and we're all going to have red wine.

We're at the train station. Mick's running backwards. He runs past me and jumps backwards into the open arms of two guys. It turns out they are old friends of his, who will come on the trip with us.

A bit later Mick does the running backwards and jumping into the arms of the guys again, this time he's laughing.

I'm on the train now, but decide I need to get off. The train doors won't open. I rush to the doors mid-carriage to try those and jump out. The train has started moving. I get stuck in the doors and struggle to free myself. Eventually I manage to pull myself free. I've forgotten my shoes on the train.

The battery of my phone is lost, so my phone is not working. I search for the battery in golden sand. A couple shout out at me "The sun makes the sand look golden, don't touch it, it's coconut sand, it's poisonous". Coconut sand is meant to be green.

A little train passes on the track next to us. I shout at Mick to look out. If he doesn't move out of the way, he'll get hit by the train.

Everything's working against arriving at a real resolution. Things that need to happen for me to be able to move forwards are not happening, or going wrong. There is no progress, just stagnation and even going backwards. Everything seems to be working against me. Travelling somewhere is moving from one place to another, it means progress. But I can't catch the flight. Things are the wrong way round with the flight anyway, they are going to be serving breakfast in the afternoon. I want to use the train instead, but even the train doesn't get me to my destination. I have to leave the train and that proves to be a struggle. This journey, this direction cannot happen with the way things are at the moment. I have to jump out. I forget my shoes, which are necessary for walking. So no flight, no train, no walking: travelling is for the time made impossible for me.

Mick's going backwards. Everything seems to be working against the natural current of things. Nothing helps me move forwards on this journey. Everything's working against me.

In the sand is written "Things are not what they seem!" The sun is consciousness. I trust it and believe that the bright light of consciousness will shed light on truth and show things in their true light, in their true colours. The couple are warning me that there is hidden danger in that assumption, and in my intrinsic trust that assumes all is exactly as the consciousness shows and sees it to be. I think I'm conscious, I think I see reality as it is, and that I am being my true self, while in fact I am not. I'm tricking myself. What seems to be golden sand is in actual fact poisonous coconut sand and it is the sun itself that is tricking me.

I do trick myself with rationality and logic. I logically find ways to make myself bad and wrong and to take on all the blame. I logically analyse things and come to the conclusion that my instincts, my feelings are wrong or bad. I supposedly shed light on the unconscious, but come up with only negative, destructive conclusions, all pointing in the direction of my lack of value and worth. In fact, in spite of all the thinking and analysing I have done and all the faith I place in my conscious efforts, I am tricking myself and seeing something that's not true.

Watch out for the little old train! The train has something to do with childhood. It's the force driving all of these wrong implications. I'm seeing things as a child sees them, as the child in me has learned to see them. The child in me needs to be recognised. A childlike manner in seeing things is not the full, true picture of the way things are. It is a view that is not yet fully developed. To take it as the full truth will be misleading.

I'm running from hope and enthusiasm without even realising I'm doing it. I might see these attitudes as too naive, yet when tempered, they can get me through anything. Cynicism says watch out. The cynical one who sees coconut sand as gold sand is the one that is saying watch out. It is telling me to be mature and realistic, and hence not to trust, to be on my guard. I am tricked by the fake sun, but at the expense of the hope, enthusiasm, vitality, naivety and joy of a child.

In archetypes, eternal youth sees hope and faith. It can recreate life out of nothing, but it never lands, is never able to manifest the ideas. The old woman is responsible, but too responsible, she is wise, she knows how to get things done, but she has lost the ability to live lightly, to laugh, to enjoy life and the things it has to offer. In her hands everything turns to stone, there is no creative life or spark. The task is to balance the two, to let the spirit live and at the same time have maturity, thought, structure and limits.

Mick is running backwards, he is laughing with childlike enthusiasm and a carefree spirit. He is caught by friends, held in their arms. But he can't get anywhere, he is repeating short bursts of running backwards.

The mature, cynical, tricked one is telling him to watch out. He could be hit by the little train. The little train from childhood, that is the source of the lies that trick me, but is also the source of his carefree, happy attitude.

What I analyse and decide, no matter how well thought out, is not necessarily the truth. My thinking has been poisoned by my past. I can trust my feelings, although I never allow myself to. I can learn to run and laugh. The journey is not possible at the moment, maybe it's time to stop forcing it on myself. Maybe I'm aiming for the wrong destination anyway. Maybe it's time to stop, play and laugh for a while and just be.

I am full of so much anger at the moment. Anger mainly towards myself, but it shines on to all around me as well. There is so much resentment in me, for what I have done, choices I have made, towards my parents for causing so much pain, for moulding a me I don't like, one that creates unhappiness for herself. I feel resentment towards others as well, sometimes for no obvious reason at all.

I feel so utterly despondent and lonely. Nothing in my life seems worth living for. Life itself doesn't seem to be worth all this struggle and suffering. I see no point to it all. No point to my suffering and ultimately I see no reason to live.

I miss Arthur desperately, fully, overwhelmingly. I feel so depressed, I can't imagine sinking any lower and I hate myself for my depression. I feel it's my fault and weakness that I am not able to shake it off. But no matter what I do, I can't seem to shake it off. It's stuck to me. I'm stuck and I blame myself for this. I can't just accept and be, let time take its time, let my body feel, heal, rest, allow the stagnation and emptiness to be. I fight with myself instead and make things harder for myself.

I feel stuck in deep boggy mud, in quicksand pulling me in. I'm drowning in my own mud, in my shit. I'm angry with myself. I feel like a complete failure.

I don't know what to do. I can't breathe. I can't move. I can't see. I can't free myself of the pain. I'm drowning and I can't even imagine a way out.

31 August 12

Persephone, Alice, and I are sitting in a cafe. I want to order something to eat.
Persephone says "no". I get up and go for a wander. I find free coffee. I bring
the coffee back to the table. Persephone adds water to it. I try to pour myself a
cup, but she won't let me. She spills coffee on my bag. So I go off to find some
more coffee. Persephone's acting bossy. She's harsh and strict. Alice is her usual
tell-tale, gossipy self.

My parents arrive. My mother tries to order chocolate biscuits for me. My
father says "We've heard that's what our daughter wants" in a self assured
manner, which is very typical of him. He always knows best. He knows
everything and no one can tell him otherwise. He's always sure he's right. I
try to explain that chocolate biscuits are not what I want. I want some decent,
proper, nourishing food. My mother keeps speaking over me. She doesn't hear
anything I say. She's not interested. She's excited, animated, happy and loud.
I can barely get a word in. It's impossible to find a gap in her monologue and
I can't speak over her.

Eventually I shout "Shut up!" Everyone in the cafe goes silent. There's
a sudden stillness. I tell my mother what happened.

It's funny that in the dream my mother and father are exactly the way
they are in real life. My father is authority. He is sure he knows best
and will not listen to others' views. He is even sure that he knows
what's best for others. My mother is uninterested in anybody else,
she is self-absorbed, lost in a made-up, theatrical world of her own,
mainly built from novels she has read. She has no connection to her
surroundings, other people, or reality. She's often flustered and over-
excited, she speaks too loud and too fast, as if she's worried someone
else might try to put a word in. She always has to be centre stage. Even
her choice of words and the way she sees things are not real, they are
like bits taken out of the books she's read. She lives in a world of
drama and theatrics and she sees the world through tainted glasses.

Persephone in my dream is not the way she really is. I feel betrayed and cheated by her.

I love coffee and I start my day with a coffee. It is important to me, yet Persephone prevents me from fulfilling this basic desire. I keep trying though.

Persephone overrides my needs and wants. She adds water to the coffee without asking me, even though I like my coffee strong. Then she won't even let me have any of it. She also spills some on my personal things.

I don't like biscuits or chocolate, yet my father orders these for me, sure of himself and his 'knowledge' that that is what I want. He won't hear otherwise.

This is typical of my parents. They have never been able to hear me, even when I have gone to great lengths and effort to explain myself. They are deaf to my voice. They are sure they know me. I am the evil one, the bad one. They are sure I have no friends. Even when many of my friends travelled all the way from different countries to be at my wedding, they still told me that those people weren't my friends, they were Arthur's friends. They were so sure no one would come for me. It was impossible for them to see otherwise. They always think they know me better than I know myself and they know what I want. But they are wrong, they have hardly ever been right about who I am, what I need and what I want.

For my parents I don't exist. What exists for them is their projection of me, their idea of me, not the real me. They can't look at me and see me the way I am, they have to keep their projection alive, otherwise they would have to question everything they have done so far, the way they have always treated me, the things they have blamed me for and that would be too much for them to face. They are rigid in their approach, driven by compulsion. This leaves no options open for me. Their attitude towards me, their demands on me, their insults and abuses all create ever deeper wounds. Nothing I do or that I am was, is or ever will be good enough for them.

Yet there must be so much unacknowledged pain trapped within them for them to have been able to treat me so badly. By labelling me bad, unworthy, faulty, damaged, wrong, they protect themselves. They place the shadow on me to carry, thus freeing themselves of it, at least on the surface.

It is not mine to carry. I don't want biscuits and that doesn't make me wrong or bad, it's simply not what I want.

Alice is somewhat peripheral. She is there, as her usual self, but plays no significant part, has no effect on anyone. She is part of the wider family dynamic, the one that sees, watches, labels and then gossips and smears.

1 October 12

Self destruct!
Break my heart with my own hands
Kill my soul, so that I can never fly
Strangle life out of me and forever cry
Pain stays with me forever
Sinking deeper and deeper and deeper.

Semi conscious dream of being on a massive motorway with roads winding, crossing under and over each other and I am crossing it as a pedestrian. I make a dash for it. I reach the half way point and realise I cannot go any further. So I consciously imagine traffic lights a bit further up. Cars stop there and I cross the remainder of the motorway safely.

Motorways, modern ways that lead from one place to another, they provide a route to travel down, to get somewhere. But I am lost. There are so many routes and so many cars and it all seems to be going on around me at such high speed. I make a dash for it, leave the safety of the sidewalk and find myself in the midst of whizzing cars and intertwining motorways. I am lost and have no idea how to continue. It is too dangerous to make another dash for it to reach the other side. The cars are passing too fast.

But I don't give up. I believe and imagine a solution. I create traffic lights a bit further up, so that I can proceed safely. It is such a positive image, with belief, strength, motivation and an ability to create a solution that gets me safely to the other side.

At the moment I feel that I am stuck in the middle. My life is like a walking catastrophe and I feel completely lost. But the image reminds me I have the solution within me and I can reach the other side in one piece as long as I believe in myself and create a safe way to continue on my journey.

Find a place of peace and beauty, a place in nature, somewhere that will feed your soul. Let nature shift you out of this bog that has descended upon you from the outside. You know that mud is your anger towards yourself, planted by your parents. Stop feeding the bog. Go somewhere where there is sun that can dry it out, where you can hear birds sing and feel the wind as a breeze on your face. Don't drown in this, let the beauty of nature help you, let it soothe your soul.

2 October 12

I bring up the image of the gramophone in my meditation. I let go to the pull coming from its centre. I allow my heart to fill with faith and hope.

And then I see that above me light appears. Bright light. And I am being pulled upwards. The light is shining white, then gold, then all the colours of the rainbow. I am surrounded by endless light and a bright blue cloudless sky. The sky, the light, the rainbow, it all feels endless and I feel blissfully happy, content and at peace.

I let go, letting myself get drawn further and further towards it, into that glorious blue sky with so much bright, welcoming light.

I have started a new career, set on a completely new path. This also means I am able to provide for myself once again. It's exciting and it's a new beginning. I am learning a lot and have met interesting people. It is new, brand new. And it came because I let go, I stopped trying to get on one of my old paths and thought about what I would really like to do instead. I had all options open to me. I allowed myself to believe. I knew what I wanted, so I set about trying to find a way to get there. And I did.

Letting go into the flow of the universe... and suddenly new opportunities appear, seemingly out of nowhere. I don't feel stuck any longer, things are moving. I am starting to live again, rather than being squashed in the ground, made immobile by the weight I placed on myself.

I'm at San Francisco Airport.

    Once I reached the airport I realised I hadn't done any of the things I wanted to do in San Francisco. I had planned to wander round the streets aimlessly and do some shopping. But in the end I did none of these. Today I went straight to the airport for check-in and the day before I had done nothing and gone to bed at 8pm. I feel like I have totally wasted my time. It feels like a lost opportunity, one that I have thrown away and can not get back. It feels like a loss and I feel regret and a cloud hanging over me created by my inability to change something that I have done, which was 'wrong' or 'bad'.

    I need to join one of the visa queues. Many long queues have been formed. A new one opens. I follow that one. We are led through numerous doors, and eventually we stop in an office. Lots of people are congregating there, but nobody's forming a queue. I'm looking around, wondering what to do. I don't have much time left until my flight is due to leave, I need to be quick, but am unsure of the best way.

    A tall, thin lady with short blonde hair, a long nose and glasses walks in. She says to me "You've beat me here. As you know my speciality is elsewhere, but I thought I'd help anyway". She's standing right in front of me. So I say "Should I have got my boarding pass first?"

    She says "Oh no! Yes, you should have. You get passes downstairs." She adds "Show me what you have". I spend ages looking through my red bag. I find the confirmation print-out, but they've already torn half of it off to let me through into the visa queue. She looks at it and asks what time my flight is. The part that shows the time on the conformation has been torn off.

    I fumble around in my bag for ages looking for the paper I have written all my travel details on. I eventually find it.

I am on a journey and am frustrated that I haven't done the things I wanted to do. I feel like I have lost the opportunity now and am angry with myself for throwing it away and wasting my time.

I am stressed, because I don't have everything ready and prepared. I wasn't prepared for the journey in the first place, I didn't accomplish what I wanted to while in the city, I wasn't ready to leave and now I don't have the right documents in place.

I feel anxious that I might not be accepted on the flight. My path has been derailed. In my life I feel that I have lost my path, gone off the right one, the one I had planned and aimed for, the one I was on. I have left where I was, but I had not done or achieved the things I had thought I would while I was there. I feel the loss of that life and I feel I have wasted it, wasted what I had and the opportunities it presented. I feel I took a wrong turn and regret my actions and choices. I feel I have lost my spirituality, my morals.

A woman, an anima figure, who seems to know what she's doing, who comes across as intelligent, mature, knowledgeable, is trying to help me.

There is tension in me stemming from the constraint there is on my time. I worry that I might miss my flight.

I feel unprepared for the journey, yet I have just enough with me to be able to make it. I don't give up. I'm trying to get hold of the documents I'm missing. I'm accepting help when it comes.

Overall there is a feeling of regret and loss, but this is the start of a new journey, one that will take me somewhere else. There is no point regretting what has already passed. There is no point beating myself up about it. I can accept what has happened and still move on.

The visa, which allows me to enter the new destination, is missing, but I can get one and I have help within me. Help comes from a female aspect of me, which is by nature accepting, nurturing, feeling, but this figure, when she appears, has male attributes as well. She is intelligent and ordered in her thinking. She is a doer, she is logical and pragmatic. Both aspects are within this figure, which is a part of me and accessible to me. She will help me get on the flight and start this new journey.

In spite of the overall feeling of not being prepared, I am still putting things in order, getting together the documents I need so that I can travel. I have not given up. All is not lost, but the sense of loss and regret is unnecessary and unhelpful and yet very strongly present. I'm just about functioning and moving on, but there is a sense of being lost, there is a lot of uncertainty.

21 October 12

Mick and I are going to see a film at the film festival with Brad and Fi. The film's at 6:30pm. However we wake up at 5:30pm, and we can't get hold of Brad or Fi to let them know we will be late. We're rushing around, trying to make it there on time. We're somewhere that might be Euston. There is a quality of anxiety and franticness to the whole experience.

I am lying next to Mick. A spirit comes and pulls the cover over us. Mick is digging his nails into me. I dig back very strongly. I'm screaming "Mick, Mick, Mick", but no sound at all is coming out.

I feel utter, heavy despair, exactly the same way I felt when I was a child and dreamt a recurring nightmare. In that nightmare I was being chased by people, cars, helicopters and I was running, running, sometimes along motorways, sometimes along the sea, forever running, being chased, not gaining any distance between myself and my followers. I felt terrible despair, fear and panic. There was nowhere to hide, I couldn't get away and they kept on chasing me.

I feel claustrophobic. I want to run away and escape. I'm terrified.

I am going to take a shower. I'm in a communal place. As soon as you enter the hallway, there's a very large, open plan office on the right. The showers are through the first door on the left and still on the left, further on, are other rooms. I take off all my clothes and realise I have forgotten something, so I leave the shower room to go and get it. When I come back to the shower room, my clothes have vanished. I grab a towel and run into the office. I'm furious. I try telling the girl at reception what has happened, but no words come out of my mouth, in fact they don't even form. I end up spluttering and uttering weird noises. The girl is upset and angry and shouts at me "what the hell are you doing naked in here". Then she realises I'm trying to say something, but can't, so she passes me a pen and paper and I write down what's happened. She turns to someone else and tells her what's happened too.

Someone's killed someone and stolen some things off of them. Police come in to search everyone. We are in adjoining rooms, the floors are completely covered in yoga mats. Obviously a yoga course is going to take place there. My teacher and his wife are there in the room, but my teacher's wife is pregnant and although I know it's her, she doesn't look like her at all. In fact she doesn't look like anyone. She's ugly, although my teacher's wife is beautiful. She has dyed blond straight hair and an angry, nasty look on her face. I see a girl hide an envelope under some things and I know she's the guilty one and that's what she's stolen off the person she killed. But I don't say anything. I search for a place to set up my yoga mat. I try a few locations, but the spaces I try are never big enough. Eventually I manage to place my mat down by the door between two adjoining rooms. Space is tight there and it's not a good place for me, but it's the only one I can find. People are chatting with each other, but I'm withdrawn, I don't speak to anyone, I just hear what others are saying, barely listening, not paying any attention.

I'm haunted by old emotional ghosts. They are invading my private, intimate space and life. They want to hide something from view. I am overwhelmed by the old voices telling me what's right or wrong, good or bad. These voices want to cover up my truth and hide it away from view, because they say it's bad and should be hidden. I should be embarrassed of it. These old ghosts cause despair, claustrophobia and fear in me. I want to run away from them. I want to scream and shout, but no sound comes out, my throat is blocked, I can't express myself or let out the old emotions. Nothing comes out at all, no sound, no expression in any form.

My teacher is someone I respect and trust infinitely. His wife is also an incredible person. She has a pure, beautiful soul, she is strong and full of life. A year ago my teacher told me that I would be making a huge mistake if I left Arthur, that I would regret it and I was driven by wrong motivations. I could not stand by my actions and beliefs faced with such a strong force. He knows so much, he is so advanced in his spiritual practise and I trust and respect him immensely. Then there's also the old blaming voices, "you're bad and wrong" which take over so easily. I feel stifled by them, invaded, yet I can't run or scream. The force is too overwhelming, I freeze.

I wasn't able to defend myself against my teacher. I couldn't explain why I was making the choices I was making. I wasn't able to voice my feelings. Something's screaming inside of me, wanting to be heard, but I can't let it out, I can't release myself from the old influences.

When emotions are intense and you're not able to release something, you dig nails into flesh. It shows frustration and creates pain, physical pain you hope will override the inner pain, the excrutiating sound of the soul screaming. I wasn't able to voice the frustration and pain, so I dug my nails into flesh and felt the other person doing the same, feeling physical pain to override the emotional one.

My persona has been stolen, my clothes are taken away at a time when I want to wash myself of old dirt, clean myself. I am naked for all to see with only a towel to protect me. But when I want to tell someone what happened and try to find my clothes, again I cannot speak. I cannot express myself, voice my feelings, voice the wrong done to me. Thankfully the girl at reception sees my distress and helps me by giving me a different way of expressing myself. I do and she reads it, understands and passes the message on.

There are various ways of releasing emotion. To scream it all out is not the only one. They can be released through writing or painting, or even bodywork and dance. These options are available to me and I should embrace them. I am shown how I can still make my voice heard, express my feelings and let out the old wrongs committed.

I'm sidelined in the yoga room. I can see the crime that has been committed and by whom, but I don't speak. I take a peripheral place in the room and listen. I am withdrawing and that's okay.

The murderer has killed a part of me, killed a part of my soul and I know what has been done and by whom, but I can't speak about it yet. I'm gathering myself, listening and being still.

I don't need to shout out everything I feel or express my trauma or my past verbally. It's okay to withdraw and keep it to myself for now. But I can still express these emotions. Not shouting them out does not mean repressing them.

I was robbed of my persona, of the way I meet people in the

world and I was not able to speak about it. Who I am, who I could have been were taken from me.

The thief and killer, she is determined, she wants to destroy. She is also within me and I hate her. She has a relentless energy that is determined to not let something in me live. She has her own agenda and she will not allow anything to make her deviate from it.

In all those images and dreams my boundaries are being broken and overpowered. My teacher's view invaded my own and took over. He had to be right, which made me wrong. I could not hold my own ground against it.

Even where I eventually place my mat is sidelined, but it is also in a space where everyone will need to tread on it to be able to get to or from the door. I'm withdrawn, unable to voice my views or feelings and open to everyone stepping over my personal space.

My clothes are stolen and I can't fight for them, I can't even tell people what's happened.

I can't act against the murderer and thief.

I can't scream against Mick or stop him.

I can't reach Brad and Fi.

A whole range of ways in which my emotions are not expressed, my boundaries are overridden, where I'm violated and hurt and there is nearly a complete lack of communication and expression on my side.

For no reason I can see
The emptiness surrounds me
The pointless pain and suffering
The hopeless crying in the night
So lost, so alone

Lost my love, my partner
Let myself down to the lowest low
Lost my faith in myself and all others
Now I'm drifting, drowning, suffocating
I can find no strength inside myself,
I see no hope anywhere outside

There is no light, no real scope
All feelings lost in eternal emptiness

I want to stand, to run, to laugh
I want to smile and hold and love
Yet the darkness is so vast
I have nothing to give to me or out

I cry, I cry, I cry and cry
No one hears me and my tears won't dry
I'm angry with myself, God gave me all
Everything I asked for He sent my way
Yet I smelt it, tasted it and spat it out
Turned my back and walked away
And now I yearn, I regret, I try
To find my way back, but the path is shut
For the likes of me there's no way out

I jumped off the cliff, seeing blue waters
And as I fall and near the end
I see it's all rock and it's going to hurt
But the fear is more painful than broken bones
I want to scream, to beg forgiveness
Of myself, not of others
I hurt myself more than anyone
And the pain, the pain, overwhelming pain
Regret and pain and hopelessness
When will it end, will it ever end?
And if it won't, how can I live
In darkness and damp, all is eternal darkness

My mother used to hit me a lot when I was very small. As I grew older, she passed on the responsibility of punishment to my dad. She would tell him I'd been bad and he would punish, without questioning her or without asking me what my side of the story was. My mother was the root of most punishment, even when it was no longer her hand that inflicted the pain.

I can barely remember the times she beat me. I was too young, but also the memories have been largely cut out, they are too painful to remember, even now.

In her world, everything was and always is about her. She has to be the centre of everything. She can see or hear nothing or no one, just herself.

So much pain was inflicted; I find it hard to believe anyone could be capable of inflicting so much of it, especially on their own children.

My mother has no sense of identity. She creates personas for herself from her books, novels and heroines. She lives in some kind of make believe world and fits us all into her worlds in her mind. She has no idea who I am and she doesn't want to know. She has created an image of me based on what she wants to see, mainly based on how she wants to see herself as a mother and how she can justify her treatment of me.

She uses others to help feed the dark, empty hole within herself. She tries to take what I have, be who I am, befriend my friends, take on my interests. She is like a vampire that sucks and sucks and sucks. She doesn't have relationships, she has victims she bites into and sucks the life out of. Either the victim manages to break free and save themselves, they run from her, or she will suck them dry, completely dry, until they are lifeless and bloodless.

I know my parents did their best, to their ability. It was their choice to bring us into this world, although a decision made for the wrong reasons. Neither of them wanted children, or are the type of people who should have children, but society and the norms they were brought up in demanded it, so they did. But they were unconscious, they could not love, they resented, rejected, abandoned and abused.

I feel so bad about hating them. Hating them feels so wrong. I end up hating myself for my feelings. I wish I could forgive them, really forgive them from my heart.

I'm noticing a similar dynamic to the one I had at home when growing up beginning to develop at work. My good work doesn't seem to be acknowledged by my manager. I get the feeling she's trying to put me down, make me feel 'not good enough', undermine me and everything that I do. But I'm learning to set boundaries with her gradually and I am also able to see more clearly the way the whole dynamic is acted out, my role in it as well as hers. And this experience is incredibly illuminating in terms of understanding the dynamic between my parents and myself.

I allow her to devalue me, because I don't value myself enough. I allow her to use me, by not respecting myself enough to keep my boundaries intact. She has her own issues that drive her to act the way she does, but I let her treat me badly. I let her undermine me. It's incredible to see this dynamic, to see that I play a role and although I can't change her, I can change the way I act, which in turn will change the way she treats me.

My grandmother died a few days ago. I didn't like her, my father's mother. She was a bitter old woman who poisoned anyone who came near her. She was evil. I imagine her heart as dark navy blue poison.

I didn't feel sad when I heard the news, but it brought up questions, followed by emotions, for me from other quarters. I wondered what I would feel if my own mother died. I am angry with her at this time of my life, in fact I hate her, but she is my mother and the reason for so much hatred is because there has been so much pain. We cannot suffer in the hands of someone who means nothing to us. Only those we love can cause us such depth of pain.

Would I miss her one day? Would I one day feel a loss? But then she has never been there for me as a positive, supportive figure even during her life, what could I possibly miss? What would I have lost?

Realising that in a way my parents were never there for me, I felt alone in the world. I felt so minuscule and the world felt so large and hostile around me. I felt confused.

9 November 12

I wake up and walk into my living room. Overnight a tall building has been erected right in front of my flat. The building is so close to mine, the two are practically touching.

My flat used to get so much light throughout the day, that was the reason I chose it and moved into it in the first place and it's the main reason I love it so much. But the tall building prevents any light from coming through. Even though the sun is up, my flat is left in darkness. I can see right into the rooms in the building opposite and they can see into my rooms. I have lost my light and my privacy.

I could have walked around naked in my flat with no curtains and no one would have seen me just a day ago, whereas now I can't even breathe fresh air, I'm breathing in the smells from the other flats, I'm looking into them, there's no light, no sun, no space, no privacy. It's all gone.

I cry. I scream. I consider calling a friend for help. I think of calling Arthur, but I don't, my pride prevents me from running to him with my problems. I need to be strong with him, so that he doesn't feel like I'm a burden on him. Anyway, there's no point, there's nothing anybody can do. No one can help me.

I start running around my flat devastated. I feel utterly devastated, it's unbearable. It's like my heart is breaking, and then gradually my whole body is disintegrating. The devastation is too much.

I think "I lost it, because I loved it too much". Everything I care about, love, cherish, value is eventually lost. I cannot love anything, because if I do, I will lose it, it will be taken away from me.

I think "This should be a lesson to you. Never value anything, otherwise you will lose it. Never care about anything, ever, otherwise you'll end up broken, devastated".

Once more there is a lot around the loss of boundaries and privacy. Loss of what I cherish and love and an inner voice telling me that all I ever care about will be taken away from me, so the only solution is to not care about anything, which in essence would be an emotional shut-down.

The skyscraper is shadowing everything I have built for myself, the life I have built, the flat I live in and love, who I am and I like to be, everything I value and care about, my private sanctuary, my home. A skyscraper houses hundreds of people. It is symbolic of the collective. The collective conscience devalues the very things I cherish and build my life on.

Underlying all is the feeling that I don't deserve to have anything good, anything that means a lot to me will be taken away. Anyone I love will leave. Anything I care about, cherish, love, count on will either be taken from me, will leave, or will be destroyed.

Don't let the untrue collective values overshadow your understanding of what is good and valuable. Don't let the fear of loss prevent you from having and cherishing, from loving and connecting.

I'm in Emily's massive mansion. It's an expensive, luxurious, posh place, nicely decorated with expensive furniture and it has a beautiful fireplace.

To start off with she is an overly caring host. She's there with a friend, getting on with what she was doing. She then eats some toast. There is very loud music playing in the background.

I feel trapped there and I want to leave, but she doesn't want me to go. I'm hungry and want to have smoked salmon. She says "We'll have it at three pm" and she tells me how she wants it prepared. She's nice and polite, but bossy.

She gets me to feed her baby. She tells me I have to fill a bamboo stick with milk and feed the baby from that. But when I start preparing the baby's food, I end up doing it a different way. I make a hole in the bread with my fingers and fill the milk into that hole.

There is a sense of materialism, luxury and opulence and yet all Emily is eating is toast. And in spite of having all this money, and taking on the persona of a caring host, she refuses to let me eat. She determines the exact time of when I should eat and how the food should be prepared. My needs are not met.

I'm bossed around and told what to do. I end up having to do Emily's job. She should be feeding her own baby, but she passes on her duty to me.

I'm trying to follow instructions, but somehow I do it differently. The problem is, my way could never work. The bread will soak up the milk, it won't hold it, it will disintegrate.

The whole set-up seems similar to the one I have at work. A manager that bosses me around and makes me do things that are her own responsibility. She uses me as a personal assistant and errand boy, although neither of these should be my role. There are much more valuable things I have to offer to the place, but I am undermined, not appreciated, in fact actively devalued.

I'm left feeding a baby, new life and potential, that is not even mine, in a way that won't even work.

26 December 12

I throw up in the toilet and a full, unbroken, undamaged, perfectly formed poached egg comes out and floats to the surface of the water.
  The toilet is blocked. It's leaking; shitty water's coming out at the point where the toilet meets the floor. It's clogged up with loads of toilet paper.

The egg is perfect and it is my favourite way of eating an egg. It is also the breakfast Arthur and I had when we had time to have breakfast together. It was like a ritual in a way. He always got it just right and I took care of toasting the bread.

The egg is poached to perfection and shaped perfectly. Egg symbolises potential life, the potential to create a new being. But it is cooked, so no life can emerge from it. It's dead. At the same time it is exactly the way I like it, it can still be nourishing for me. But for some reason, I can't digest it, I have to throw it out of my body. I can't use it. I cannot take in a nurturing life force; I can't integrate it into my system.

A mother is meant to nurture and feed her child, but mine did not and when she appeared to, the food was laced with poison. I want to eat the egg and integrate it, but my body won't accept it, something about it does not agree with my body and I need to get rid of it.

The whole situation is an impossible one. An egg can't come out perfectly formed and undamaged after having been eaten and thrown up. And yet here it is untouched in a way, perfect, unattainable. But the egg is there to be seen by me. Something about it needs to be looked at. Perhaps the impossibility of perfection and its indigestibility.

The dream is also a sign of moving forward, coming out of stagnation. At last I'm ready to look at what needs to be seen.

The toilet is where we eliminate unnecessary, unusable stuff from our bodies, where we purify. It symbolises expression. It can be a way of working with shadow material. It can have something to do with intimate relationships. To be able to be in an intimate relationship, you need to work through your own shit. Intimacy and love, feeling loved are good for me, they would nourish me, but for some reason I cannot accept them, digest them. I am rejecting something that is good for me. I'm rejecting love.

It shows lack of connection with mother. If a mother doesn't love and nurture us, we don't learn how to do it for ourselves and accept it from others. If we are taught very early on that love can be toxic, and in fact toxic love is the only kind of love we have known and recognise, we reject nurturing love, even when it is seemingly perfect.

The perfection is unrealistic though. Wanting things to be perfect can be toxic too, because things never are perfect. Perhaps I couldn't assimilate it because there is no such thing as perfection and my body knows that.

There is a huge demand on me, mainly coming from my father, that I need to be perfect, do things perfectly, get everything right, be white and pure in a way that's not even real or possible. He didn't just bring out imperfections in me, he placed non-existent ones on me as well. I learned to carry my darkness, his, my mother's, as well as their projections and unrecognised shadows. And anyway, a sense of perfectionism kills true life. It leads to self hatred and degeneration, because nothing we do can ever be good enough. Nothing is or can be perfect in the real world, perhaps only in imagination.

I saw Arthur as perfect and our relationship as perfect, but there is no such thing. I projected the demands of perfection onto Arthur and I carried the imperfections. I did not claim my own value. The spell had to be broken and it was. I couldn't digest his perfection and it was poisonous for me, because it meant I had to carry all the imperfection, the bad, the blame, the fault. It doesn't all belong with me and it is too much for one person to carry.

If something's perfect, it is on a pedestal, it is unreachable, untouchable. You can't be with it, you can't use it. There is no equality, no real connection.

I was surprised to see the egg there, but I didn't feel nauseous even when I saw it. I felt an element of curiosity within me, a desire to understand, to see, to analyse, maybe dissect. It was as if I was looking at a scientific experiment, someone else's thrown up matter, not mine. My body was disconnected. There was no bodily or emotional sensation that came with it.

An impossibly perfect egg, which can give no life any longer. It might be able to provide nourishment, but the body has rejected it, so it cannot do that either. It is useless, utterly useless, yet looking absolutely perfect in a toilet bowl... Useless and perfect, useless and indigestible...

My eyes

Those eyes
Infinitely deep
A well
You throw a stone in
And never hear it land

Those eyes
Infinitely sad
Carrying centuries of pain
Written in the lines and colours
Of those deep eyes

Those eyes
Infinitely green
Like water the depths of which
Is covered in moss and weed
Life and death entwined in one

Those eyes
Infinitely sad
Crying, crying, crying
They are screaming but unheard

In this world where hearing is only for lies
Those eyes
Infinite...
There's no trespassing, no seeing through
No going in
You look into them
You get lost

I am lost
I can't get in
I can't see
There's no sound
I can't touch
I'm out of reach
I don't know who I am
I don't know what I am
I don't know where I am
I don't know if I am

13 January 13

I have an overwhelming sense of loss. I have lost all hope and belief in myself and everything else. I seem to get what I want, yet I remain unhappy. I got the relationships I wanted and then ended up ruining them. I have a wonderful flat, yet still I'm not satisfied. I've found work, I have friends, yet I'm miserable. I can't see any way out. How can I possibly be happy? What's wrong with me? If I have everything, yet am still depressed, what hope is there for me, ever? I feel lost. I'm afraid I'm one of those people who will never be happy no matter what. What is wrong with me?

And yet I was so happy only a couple of years ago, and I threw it all away. Did I? It seems so. And now what?

I liked the person that I was when with Arthur. I don't like who I am now. It's not just that I miss Arthur and feel his absence in my life, it's also as if I've lost the best part of myself with him leaving. I miss the life I had and the person I was, or thought I was. Every area of my life has been affected and all changes have been for the negative. I should move on, yes, but to what?

My unhappiness is so deep and desperate, my body aches. I have no motivation, no will or energy. And even if I did, I don't know what I would use it for.

I am so blessed, so very lucky, yet I am miserable. What can I do? Will this ever change? Will the energy ever shift? Will I ever really laugh again?

17 January 13

I'm with someone, I can't remember who. There's a squirrel-like animal that is being cute and playful. I'm playing with it, stroking it, it's nuzzling its nose into my hand. But then suddenly it grabs my hand with its paws and bites my knuckles. It's digging its front paws into my hands and fingers.

I try to throw it off, push it away, get rid of it, but its clasp is so tight, it pulls at my skin and I can't get rid of it. I struggle for ages. It's hurting me a lot. Eventually I manage to get it off my hand. But then it grabs me again. I struggle once more, but as soon as I manage to get it off my hand, it grabs it again. This whole process repeats itself many times until it claws its back legs into my waist on my left side while still grabbing my hand with its front paws and clawing into my skin and fingers. It's excruciatingly painful. I struggle like mad, as if my whole life depends on it.

I manage to get it off me, but it grabs me again. Again the whole process repeats itself and then a few more times.

Finally I throw the animal across the room with a lot of force, with all my strength and more. My action creates even more fear in me. I feel terrible fear at my potential to be able to use such force and throw an animal with so much brute strength. The fear of what I have done is much greater than the fear I feel of the animal. I'm also petrified that through my actions I have made the animal even angrier and it will come back at me with renewed force. I'm afraid of the animal's potential too.

I wake up. I check my hand and there are claw and bite marks all over it. I'm in tremendous pain. I check my waist and there are claw marks there too. The pain is horrendous. I'm wondering whether the whole thing really did happen in a parallel universe. Or maybe a non-physical being clawed and bit into me in my sleep, a being that is invisible when awake, but still present. I'm in pain and I feel utter horror and fear spread through me.

I must have still been within the dream, because I wake up from this as well, but my left waist and right hand are still in pain. I still feel horror, pain and fear. There are no marks though, at least none visible to my eyes.

221

An animal, one that first appears friendly and cute, but is then suddenly overtaken by a demonic presence, which seems to come from nowhere. It's suddenly possessed. It attacks me with huge strength and nastiness.

This is a process similar to the one going on inside of me. I am attacking myself with huge brute force: "What have I done? I'm so bad. I'm unworthy. I'm evil. What's wrong with me? I deserve nothing. It's all my fault". My attack on myself has a quality of that which is possessed to it. It comes with immense strength and wants to destroy everything, all hope and forgiveness and it also wants to destroy me completely.

I do manage to pull it off and throw it away eventually, but this creates even more fear within me. I am afraid it will come back with increased force and venom. I am afraid of the animal and its potential. At the same time, I am afraid of my own potential strength. In a way I'm afraid of standing up for myself, loving and valuing myself, because these are so 'wrong', there will be repercussions, there will be punishment. I fear the punishment that is yet to come, that may or may not materialise, more than anything else. That is how sure I am that throwing that animal, that vicious being that attacked me and caused me so much pain was bad.

I awake within a dream, gain some level of consciousness and can look at what has happened through awakened eyes, from above, but the fear, horror and pain are still there and overwhelming.

The guilt I feel about everything I do is always attacking me. As a child I was made to feel guilty about existing. I was guilty of everything, blamed for everything by my parents and those accusations remain alive within me and attack me whenever they can, which is very often.

My parents' guilt, which they attached to me has taken hold of me and won't let go no matter how much I struggle and try to get rid of it, it digs in deep. It takes tremendous force to be able to throw it away from me. But this force, the capacity to be able to throw it away from me is petrifying for me as well. That guilt is all I've known. Who am I without that guilt, that force that beats me up, accuses me, hates me. How dare I even think about standing up to my parents, defending myself.

I have a fear of pushing the animal away. I'm so afraid that I will increase its anger and it will return with a vengeance, much stronger, more evil, more destructive and the pain will be even worse. I was afraid of my father too. I could not speak back or defend myself against him, in case he punished me with even more anger, in case the punishment I received became even worse.

But I do wake up within the dream! And that's important. I don't remain completely unconcious in the dream, I gain some level of consciousness. I can see what's happening. I can see that the animal was demonic, not in its right mind and destructive. I can see it needs to be done away with. Yet this little animal, this cute, cuddly animal that causes so much pain in the end is my parents' gift to me and so hard to throw away. But it will hurt, destroy and eventually kill if I don't. It is right to throw it away, not wrong. I need to do it.

I need to keep that animal away from me and heal my wounds through learning self love, compassion and forgiveness towards myself. The negative voices, the accusations, the emotional abuse are all coming from demonic forces. They are evil, they harm. It's time to throw them away from myself. The pain and damage they cause are too much, I have seen this. I have also seen that they do not belong with me, they don't even belong in this universe, they come from some force, some shadow element, some complex, suffering or pain that lies with my parents.

The wound will always be there. What changes, and is already shifting, is my response to it. First comes understanding, becoming aware of the unhappiness caused by the complex and the split in the psyche caused by my parents. Then gradually the feeling itself will change.

24 January 13

I'm working at a hospital. It's time for my break and I go outside and sit on a low wall in the garden. A huge, white, hairy dog runs up to me and bites my right hand. Then, still with my hand in its mouth it rolls onto its back. His paws are up in the air, he's clenching onto my hand with his teeth and he starts peeing upwards into my face. Once he's done, he lets go of my hand and rolls back onto all fours.

I start crying. My hand's hurting and I'm stunned. I ask him "Why?" He says "There's a signal on your GPS which attracts dogs. It is ordering dogs to run up to you, bite your hand and pee on you."

When the dog says this, I remember that this has happened to me before.

I look down at my hand and realise that the tops of my middle and ring fingers have been bitten clean off. I ask the dog if he's eaten them. He says "no". I start searching in the grass for my fingers. The dog joins me in my search. We search for ages and look all around. Eventually we find the two half fingers. I want to take them with me into the hospital and have them sewn back on.

I feel that there's something wrong with my toes as well.

But then I look at my hand again and find that my fingers have grown back on, but they are crooked and misshaped. They are odd lengths and have bite marks on them. I realise that what I have found in the grass are not the ends of my fingers, but the ends of my toes.

I go to the clinic, where I work and tell the staff there I need to go into hospital. There are some ladies lying around on wheelie beds talking to each other. They have relapsed. I ask a member of staff where my boss is. I'm told she's not in. They tell me I need to contact the night staff manager, although she's not due in until 5pm.

I wake up feeling distressed and anxious. There's pain in my navel and chest. My chest feels very very heavy and my fingers are aching.

Fingers help a person articulate, manipulate, and arrange things the way they need to be. We use them to eat, to write, to hold, pick up, move things, we even use them to articulate what we're saying when we're talking. There is not much we could do in this world without any fingers. Without toes we can't move forwards, walking becomes impossible. I have lost and damaged the parts of my body that I need to be able to articulate and move forwards in life. They have been attacked and bitten off. But somehow I have invited the attack. There is something in me that instinctually attacks me and keeps me from moving forward, from articulating. Something in me that holds me back, damages me. There is a voice within me that tells me "you are the problem" and it freezes me in the world. I cannot function properly with that voice impeding me, stopping me, preventing me.

What is this GPS system that I have in me that invites people to pee on me, mistreat me, abuse me?

I have had some problems at work recently. One of my colleagues, someone who has been overly nice and considerate towards me ever since I've joined, which was just over four months ago, has started to make inappropriate comments and has been sending me inappropriate, sexual messages. I know he fancies me. He has asked me out. I told him I'm not interested, I was very clear. I even told him that not only am I still married, I also have a boyfriend, but he keeps persisting.

He started off lightly. He complimented me on my looks, clothes, compassion, how good I am with patients. He pointed out some of my positive character traits. He was not overbearing. He was sweet and nice. We had a good time chatting, laughing together. I could feel he was interested in me as more than a colleague or friend, but I thought his infatuation would pass. I made sure not to give him any hope in any way. I thanked him for his compliments, but didn't return them. I was clear about not being interested in a relationship from the start. I kept the relationship professional from my side. I was able to manage the situation by remaining friendly and nice towards him, while still making it clear that I'm not interested in him in any other way than purely as a friend. However, he got less and less subtle and started to cross my boundaries and invade my personal, private, protected space. He has been making me feel increasingly uncomfortable. His compliments have become overt and personal.

The more he has been coming on to me, the more strongly I have had to defend myself and he has not taken rejection well at all. He is emotionally unstable. Not only is he living with his girlfriend, but she has just had a miscarriage and in spite of this, his energy and interest are focused on me. Instead of getting my message of 'nothing but friendship, or even just simple professionalism' and continuing professionally, decently, he has now started to undermine me behind my back. He has been telling people I'm useless and don't do anything worthwhile at work and that I shouldn't be employed at the clinic in the first place. He sends out group emails to all the staff about the day at the clinic, adding in comments that make me look unnecessary. It's all done semi-subtly. He is supposedly being nice and considerate, but at the same time sending out questionable, negative messages about me. He lacks awareness to such a degree, that he doesn't even realise while he's doing this and sending out these messages, he himself is looking odd. People are wondering what the hell is going on and especially what's going on with him. I feel I'm being put on the back foot. I have to defend my role at the clinic and what I do. I'm fighting against lies, which are not obvious enough to be proved wrong easily. No direct accusations have been made which I can defend myself against, it's all cloaked and fluffed up and paying them attention would work against me.

Working with him has become impossible. It has become a constant source of stress and unpleasantness for me. Either I'm batting off his advances, as decently as I can, causing the least amount of problem for everyone around; or I'm worrying and stressing about the things he's doing and saying behind my back. I feel my colleagues are taking a more negative view of me. They, I am sure, are wondering what I'm doing to invite the advances and the bullying. That upsets me too, as I really like my colleagues.

Although I know that he has problems and the way he is behaving is immature and unstable, as well as most of the time immoral, I still can't help wondering whether I did or said something to lead him on, acted in a way that gave him hope, and made me feel he had a right to treat me the way he does. I am questioning whether I really do have a GPS system that is inviting him to pee on me, as Miles did long ago.

But I've remained strong. I have looked over the messages he sent me and my responses, and I cannot see how I could have possibly led him on. I have so clearly stated that I am not interested in him. I have remained respectful of him and acted professionally throughout. Yet he continues to persist.

The straw that broke the camel's back came the other day. He pinched my bum and I was furious with him. I was so angry and stunned, I could not say anything at first. Then I told him that was utterly unacceptable behaviour. He apologised profusely, but then sent me a text message saying that he would like to pinch my bum again anyway. I was left speechless and couldn't respond. After all the apologies, after leading me to think that he had realised he had acted out of order and was sorry about his behaviour, it turned out he still couldn't see he was acting inappropriately.

I work with him alone on Sundays and Sundays have become unbearable for me. The situation with him is getting worse, I see no resolution. He is on the one hand coming on to me whenever he can, on the other hand he is turning into a bitter, resentful enemy, in active war against me, but the war is happening behind my back in a cowardly, dishonest way. He is doing his best to get me fired. He spoke to the top boss telling him I never did any work and he couldn't understand why I was employed there. He has been spreading nasty comments about me, yet to my face he is still sweet as pie.

I feel bad for him. I feel he is emotionally unstable and vulnerable. I don't want to harm him in any way. I don't want to be a reason or excuse for a relapse for him, he has not been in recovery for very long. I have been protecting him by not telling others just how bad the situation is. I have kept the extent of his messages and comments to myself. In a way I am carrying his burden. I am also taking on and carrying my manager's burden. I don't want to add to my manager's work load with my problems. But yet again, I am taking on a burden that is not mine to carry. He is the one behaving badly, unprofessionally and immorally. It is my manager's duty to know about this and deal with it in an appropriate manner. I am acting the martyr, but for no good cause. There is also my own side to add to this. It's hard for me to talk about this, tell people what he has been doing, because in myself I am not free, I am carrying part of the burden, still wondering if I did something wrong, if it's somehow my fault, if I've invited it.

I am so willing to take on the blame and the guilt. Did I say something to lead him on? Are my actions causing this problem? And yet, this guy so obviously needs help and is not fit to be helping or advising vulnerable people, which is his role at the clinic. He's a trainee therapist already treating and advising addicts, people who are in rehab because they have reached rock-bottom, are at their most vulnerable and are desperate for help. I wonder whether by not speaking up I'm placing patients at risk. It isn't my fault that he is harassing me. I have done all I can, politely but clearly telling him he is acting inappropriately and making me feel uncomfortable. I have given him no hope. And at the end of it all, pinching a colleague's bum is unacceptable whichever way you look at it.

I take on the burden so readily. I'm trying to carry it for my manager, by protecting her from knowing what is going on with this guy. I don't value myself enough, so I don't stand up for myself. I say "I will carry this for you", the shadow, the blame, the guilt. I have been immobilised by this willingness to take on all the negative throughout my life.

I'm being attacked from within. I'm being asked to be the scapegoat by my colleagues. Two of them, two people I respect and care about, said that he is damaged and needs help. They told me I should try to resolve the problem myself and not let it escalate higher up, in case the situation proved too much for him to handle. But no matter what I've done, I've not been able to shake him off me. I've done my best not to escalate the problem or pass it on to my manager, but he won't let up.

I won't be the scapegoat any longer. He needs help, he needs intervention. I can't carry his misbehaviour. It doesn't belong to me. I won't carry the responsibility of his actions. I won't suffer in silence so that people at work can continue as if nothing has happened. I can't continue to work this way. I will have to leave if something doesn't change. Why should I have to leave for someone else's wrong behaviour?

I feel anxious and unsettled. The whole thing is disconcerting. On the one hand I cannot see what more I could do to resolve the problem, what I could have done differently. On the other hand, there is a voice inside of me telling me "you must have done something to ask for this, something that sent him the message that he could treat you this way". The GPS system I worry I carry in me.

I've checked the employee's guidebook and according to that his actions fall clearly under harassment, at times sexual harassment and bullying. He is in the wrong, yet that questioning voice won't go away.

I feel alienated at work. I feel uncomfortable in the environment. Everyone has become suspicious and uncomfortable and a part of me blames myself for it.

But he has done wrong and I won't pay his price. I'm going to have to file an official report. The advice I have been given is that this is the only thing I can do and I should do it. I will do it.

In the dream, at least I'm trying. I look for my fingers, that turn out to be my toes and am going to the hospital. Why has the dog bitten off my fingers supposedly, yet I find my toes in the grass? He's bitten my fingers, they are damaged, hurt, misshapen. I can still use them, but not very well. I think they have gone, but they haven't. The dog that attacked me is helping me look for them. He is not a bad dog, he is kind, he simply obeyed the orders coming from my own GPS system. And yet he has somehow immobilised me. I have lost my toes and am hindered in my efforts to move forwards.

I am even hindered in my desire to go to hospital. Neither of the people I need to speak to are there.

My inner dog is not only attacking me, but also helping me. He is not evil, simply misguided.

26 January 13

I go to a yoga class with Arthur. It's the class I went to for years, the one that got me interested in yoga in the first place. I used to never miss it, no matter what. I went every week without fail and loved it. I'd plan my day and social life around it, even what I ate or drank the night before. I eventually assisted my teacher in that class and even ended up teaching the class for a while after my training. The teacher is Blair, who is a fantastic teacher and who also became a close friend for a while. She's great as a teacher, but I realised after some time that as a friend she is a taker. She takes and takes until she sucks you dry. She has no awareness or consciousness of herself and the effect of her actions on others.

The class is in the studio on the first floor. When we turn up and reach the bottom of the stairs we come across Blair, who doesn't recognise me. There's some confusion. Arthur asks Blair where the changing rooms are. Blair starts to direct him to the changing rooms, which are downstairs, but I tell her I'll take him. I take him upstairs to the toilets.

The class is to take place in a tiny studio. The mats have been set out already. They are lined up in rows. They are so close to each other, they're nearly touching.

I see Emily as soon as I walk into the studio, who also taught that class for a while and who is still a very close friend, someone I love, respect and trust. We are very happy to see each other and hug warmly. Then I look around to find a space where I will be able to place our two mats.

I'm bringing the person I am involved with intimately into spirituality. Yoga is union, bringing together mind, body and soul. A relationship is or should be part of the healing process, part of coming closer to and relating to the Divine. In an intimate relationship we hold a mirror to each other, in the reflection of which we can better understand ourselves, in the most intimate context, see ourselves more clearly. Through this, growth, healing and learning can take place. Together we learn to drop the ego, see the other, care for the other and through that also see ourselves. It is a relationship where our feelings are laid bare, we become vulnerable and these feelings can be exchanged, understood, cherished. Our vulnerable, private, heartfelt parts come to light.

Toilets are where you release stuff, get rid of unnecessary elements, express yourself.

A small room can bring about increased awareness, an increased intensity of experience.

Blair, who has no sense of boundaries, didn't recognise me. I don't engage with her. She has a toxic personality and I am no longer recognised by her.

Arthur is an internal figure as well as an outer figure. He is part of my spiritual questioning. He's there with me. He's there taking part in the healing of my spirit, psyche and body.

Emily, whom I love, respect and cherish, is happy to see me. She is a positive influence in my life, a source of compassion, friendship, sharing and trust. We embrace warmly. Her happiness in seeing me is positive, as it shows my focus is on positive elements in my life, these are what I'm taking in, accepting and being seen by.

I have a dark cloud hanging over me. I'm convinced that no one can possibly love me, not if they get to know me well. Arthur, my partner of twelve years proposed to me after ten years together. That year was the happiest year of my life. We got married the same year. It was magical. And yet that relationship is now over. And not only is it over, Arthur told me that he had "settled" for me and that he had never really loved me in the first place. He had settled for me because of the way I felt for him. Since our separation he has felt relief, while I have felt loss and pain.

Arthur knew me inside out. He knew everything about me. He saw me at my weakest, as well as when I was good and strong. He is the only person who has ever known me that intimately, and yet even he has now told me that he didn't really love me. Well then, who possibly can?

I'm stuck in darkness and despair. I see no hope. I feel unloveable, unworthy, lost.

I'm a tree, already dead inside, but I'm still standing. It will take years before I'm toppled over, maybe by lightning. I am standing, but dead, rotten inside.

And yet the dream is positive. It brings to light the positives, the learning, growth, spirituality, the intimate relationship and a positive person, Emily and her love and warmth towards me.

Searching for the depths

Hot lava, damp earth, darkness
I'm going down
Guided by my own darkness
Buried deep inside my heart
Navigating through the precipices
Finding my way through instinct

I'm going down
Because that's where the truth is hidden
I'm not shying away
From the darkness and my fear
Because the truth I must find
The truth, my treasure

So I'm going down
Each step burning and freezing at the same time
Muscles weak, heart beating fast
Hard to breathe,
But the truth I must search and find

There's a guiding voice
That comes to my aid
And a belief in life and truth that helps me
Through the worst the earth sends my way
There's some love in my life
To warm my heart
Prevent it from freezing

232

From falling apart
Thank you for the voice my Lord
Thank you for the love
Thank you for my heart my Lord
You sent me to this earth with little,
But a strong heart is worth much
Thank you my Lord
For not letting me flee
Fleeing is death for eternity
I may die down here,
But my voice tells me
I'll be reborn once in the depths
The darkest, hottest, coldest depths
Reborn into my true nature,
My truth, my soul awakened

In spite of everything there was something in me that was valuable to other people. I had friends although I had no self value. My expectation and acceptance of abuse attracted Miles' abuse. Yet I survived it. It wasn't my fault!!! I carried the guilt of his actions all my life, I still do to some extent, but it wasn't my fault.

My father's hatred of me wasn't my fault either. It wasn't there because of who I was, but because of who he was. His hatred within himself got projected onto me. Maybe I triggered something in him he could not take in. I was like him in some ways and received his self-hatred.

My mother's narcissism had no space for love. I had to be destroyed. I was a threat. My father's attention could not be divided. My father might have instinctually felt my mother's resentment, so he felt he couldn't love me, it was too risky, it would have caused too great a rift between him and my mother.

I feel I have forgiven my father in a way, I feel sorry for him, but I can't help hating my mother still and I feel guilty about that. I was betrayed by my own mother, she withheld the most fundamental thing we are all born to and need more than anything else, she withheld motherly, unconditional love and care.

11 February 13

*I dream of a mother losing her daughter. There's death all around. I see coffins
and dark, endless tunnels. There are evil ghosts and spirits roaming around, they're
everywhere. Agony builds up in my throat and also sheer fear and panic. I start
screaming, screaming madly with everything I've got within me, all possible
strength I can muster. I wake up screaming, but no sound is leaving my throat. I
start panicking, because the pain and the scream are stuck. They are clogging up
my throat and I can't breathe at all, or swallow. I feel despondent, desperate fear.
I can't breathe. My God, I can't breathe. That scream clogging up my throat, it's
huge and won't let anything pass.*

*I feel broken and despondent. I feel that there is nothing left for me in life,
there's no point in continuing. I can't stand it anymore. I can't carry on.*

Something, some feeling wants to come out, but it's stuck in my
throat. There is a sense of violation that I experienced as a child and
have been re-experiencing recently, due partly to letting these
emotions out at last and also as a result of reading my diaries from
when I was a teenager. This feeling of violation, the pain, the anger
need to come out, they have been stuck in me for so long, they are
huge, but they won't yet come out.

*I imagine what that scream would be. I allow my body to have that scream in
some form, waiting for the form to naturally appear. The scream is a shattering,
burning, breaking sensation in my throat and chest. It comes with a
tremendous amount of fear. There is a sense of death attached to it.*

Something in me is trying to die, it needs to die. Perhaps beliefs imposed
on me, the accusation of my badness, core evilness, worthlessness.
The 'knowledge' that I'm damaged goods, that it was all my fault, that
existing is a sin for me, I never should have been born, that I have no
right to share in the air of this earth, I have no right to be here.

The dream is connected to my mother. She is there with the evil spirits. She is these with her withholding, her lack of love, her voice. They are evil spirits that live on within me. They are stuck, the fear of complete annihilation is stuck, the inability to express and let go rules.

As a child, when we scream and cry and no one hears, when a mother rejects, threatens, punishes, we feel threatened, our life is threatened. A baby cannot differentiate between threats, abandonment for a baby means death, because it cannot yet fend for itself. This rejection, abandonment and the fear and panic that come with it are stuck in my body. They want to be released, but they are stuck.

13 February 13

I go into a shop to buy diet coke. I can't find any. I ask the shop keepers. They give me a small bottle of pepsi max instead and a sandwich which has been partly nibbled, saying I nibbled at it while I was looking around. I say I had wanted two large bottles of diet coke, not a small pepsi max and had never touched the sandwich and I walk out without paying. I'm angry. I have no recollection of touching it, but inwardly wonder whether I did nibble on it unconsciously and forgot.

I go into the next shop, which is rather bare. I walk all the way to the end of the shop looking around for diet coke and then I turn back towards the entrance. The shop is shaped like a long hallway. While I'm still looking for diet coke the girl from the first shop walks in, opens up a freezer and starts digging up bottles of coke and diet coke. I walk over to the freezers. The bottles are tucked away amongst frozen chicken and bits of meat. She's sticking her hands in them and bits of meat are coming out in her hands. I try to do the same to get a bottle of diet coke out, but it's so disgusting, I throw up.

I go into the next shop, which is a grocery as well as a Turkish bakery. I see a cake that looks like chestnut cake and ask the shopkeeper what it is. He confirms it is chestnut cake, so I ask for two slices of it, there are only two slices left, and I pay for them. I hear a couple behind me, the female is saying "she wants it" and the male is saying "but I asked for the last two slices". The shopkeeper asks someone else whether there are any more.

I look at the savoury pastries, but don't see any I like.

In each place, except for perhaps the third one, I am unable to get what I need to be nurtured. But what I'm searching for is not good for me. I'm not receiving any gratification, but I'm looking for nurturing in the wrong place anyway. This might be an attitude, or a way I try to deal with things. I'm trying to get nurturing from something that is actually destructive. Perhaps my self destructive impulse. There is no nourishment in it. I may be going after something with the wrong attitude or intention, trying to be nurtured with the wrong idea or purpose.

Maybe mistaking something that gives me gratification for something that would be nurturing for me is what's wrong. I can't accept nurturing if I believe I don't deserve it, that I am not worth it.

Desperation leads to self destruction.

I need to learn to be with myself in a different way. It's a huge change and it will take time.

Even having the cake I want creates guilt in me. The couple in the background are making me feel guilty about taking the last two slices. I can't enjoy even the cake. And even the cake, although it might be nice, is not healthy.

In the first shop, I know I didn't touch the sandwich, yet because I'm accused of nibbling it, I start to wonder whether I did. I have no faith in my own knowledge. I am so ready to take on blame. I must have done something wrong, that is my default position in every circumstance.

In the second shop I do find diet coke, but it's stored in an unhygienic way. I don't eat meat and haven't for twenty years, so digging my hand into frozen pieces of meat is even more disgusting for me. I do try anyway, but what I want ends up causing me distress and results in me throwing up.

Chestnut desserts are my favourite, although I hardly ever have any. In the last shop I manage to get something I like, all be it not especially healthy, and yet I feel guilty even about that.

Alone

Betrayed, abandoned, alone
Alone after trusting
Having believed
Alone after having opened up
And let in as best I can
Alone in spite of faith and hope
Back to when I was fifteen
All crush, burn, hurt, stone me

237

I keep believing
Until I close up
I let you in
And you betrayed me
Alone, alone, in spite of me
In spite of all I knew
Closing down now
For good, forever
I won't let false hope in
Doors are closed for always

I'm awake, but not completely conscious. I am acting as one possessed. I feel anguish all over my body and I am scratching myself frantically all over, every inch of my body, as if I want to tear my skin off, get rid of it. I can't stop or pause. I just can't scratch enough. I start scratching more and more vigorously. I'm tossing, turning, scratching and crying out in anguish. I am awake, but completely out of control. The anguish is too unbearable, it has taken control of me. I think I might die of it, I'm practically sure I will die of it, if not the scratching, from the pure agony I feel. I feel overwhelmed by a desperate need to get away, to get rid of my skin, to stop the itching, even if that means tearing all my skin off. Inside I am begging, begging for the itching to stop. My mind is screaming "Please stop" so loudly, I cannot hear anything else.

I feel tortured inside, as if I am being roasted on a camp fire. The pain is gradually increasing and I know there is no way out. I know I am being tortured to death and that the pain will continue to increase until I can bare it no longer, until I can no longer stay alive with it.

All I feel is itching.

I feel confused about the experience. I am awake, yet not in control, not fully conscious, just aware of what is going on. The itching is real, but has no physical basis.

Yesterday I told Kendra I would no longer work Sundays. She asked me why and I had to tell her about my colleagues' advances, his unprofessional behaviour. I kept it short and took on a lot of responsibility myself, without giving her the full degree of his unprofessionalism and inappropriateness. I told her he fancied me, was coming on to me and that made me feel uncomfortable. I said that I had made it clear to him that I wasn't interested, but he wasn't getting the message, so I needed distance from him and not be in on Sundays, when it was just the two of us in as staff. I stood up for myself and took a step towards putting down someone else's burden, a burden I was carrying that did not belong to me. And yet I didn't go all the way, I kept a lot to myself, I didn't tell her the extent of his actions.

Like a snake shedding its old skin, I'm trying to rip off my old skin, so it can be replaced by new, healthy skin. I feel more secure in my heart. I'm taking steps to resolve old issues with Miles that somehow combine into new issues with this guy at work. Miles abused me because he knew he could. It was a power play for him, a conquest, with no consideration of the damage he was inflicting on me. I was left feeling hurt, betrayed, sad, but I was unable to feel anger. I saw it as my fault, how could I be angry with him? I was angry with myself. I felt damaged, dirty, I carried the dirt of his sins, all of it taken upon myself.

I feel like I'm in a chrysalis, I'm withdrawing into myself, gathering my energy. But on the other hand, I feel as though I'm stuck. There's something toxic I need to get rid of and that's why I'm scratching, trying to peel my skin off.

Instead of attacking the Demon, I'm attacking myself. The Demon shouts "you have no rights. You have no right to exist, no right to receive respect. You're worthless and evil because you exist"

When we were children my sister used to lie too. She would blame me for things I hadn't done and I would be punished. I couldn't stand up for myself. When I tried, I was accused of lying and punished more severely. I learned to shut down, shut up and put up. I learned that no one would believe me and it was always my fault. This guy at work is doing the same thing. He is lying about me behind my back, damaging me and the way people view me and I am frozen. I can't defend myself. I wonder if it is all my fault.

But this time I have spoken up, I have defended myself, even though only partially. My manager is not convinced of my innocence yet, but I am fighting my side and that feels freeing. Speaking up felt freeing.

I have inner strength and belief this time and am not letting people walk all over me. I feel stronger within myself.

4 March 13

Mick's trying to hurt me, he's suffocating me. He's harsh and forceful. He's aggressive and he's forcing himself on me whilst I'm asleep, I keep my eyes closed when I wake up. I'm afraid. I don't know what I will do and how I will protect myself. But when I awake, there is no force, he's not hurting me at all, instead he's gentle and tender.

I'm re-living the old trauma. I'm sure in my heart that whomever I'm intimate with will hurt me, force themselves on me, betray me, assault me, rape me. I'm hyper-alert when in a place of vulnerability, even with someone as gentle as Mick, who would never hurt me in that way.

In my mind, in my soul, I feel him hurting me, I live it, yet when I wake up I see that he is being nothing but gentle and kind.

The dream is putting me on alert, making me less trustful of myself, giving me the feeling that I can't rely on myself, on my instincts. There is something immature about my own animus. Mick, who represents some part within me is not ready to be in an intimate relationship. Or I am not ready to recieve gentle kindness from someone. Instead I project an aggressor on them.

I'm left scared in the world, of the world. I'm left alone in the dessert.

When I was fifteen years old, I had been promising myself for years that I would no longer cry, ever ever again. Crying was weakness. Emotions were weak. They needed to be buried, forcefully thrown away, deadened. At the age of fifteen I succeeded. I promised myself that was it, I had had enough pain and suffering, I would cry no longer. I didn't cry again until I was in my thirties. At that stage of my life, I had been practising yoga regularly and intensely for a few years and my emotions were unblocked, they released from my body and I cried. I have been

241

crying on and off ever since. I no longer see crying as weakness. I'm not embarrassed by it. I cherish my feelings, even when they may seem to others as weakness. They are proof I am alive.

When I was fifteen, what eventually shut me down was my father's lecture to me, the one he calmly tells me how evil and horrible I am and how sorry he is to have me as a daughter, someone he would not want to know if he hadn't been burdened by the responsibility of parenthood. His pure hatred of me rushing out at me, overpowering me, breaking me, I can still feel it.

And then there was Miles. Supposedly my best friend, someone I cared about deeply and trusted, someone who sexually abused me when he got the opportunity, knowing that I was afraid, that I was defenceless. He would call me his best friend, then treat me like dirt for a few days, then treat me like a princess again. My friends warned me against him, but I didn't listen. I thought I knew him better than they did and that I saw his inner true self, which was beautiful and the outer side they saw was only there as a show of strength, machismo. I was very wrong.

Miles and I were suited to each other in a way. He needed to abuse, hurt, treat badly and I was a willing recipient. Being treated badly was all I had known and the only treatment I could understand and digest. Those I depended on and loved, my own parents abused me, so I looked for it in others, I needed to be abused to feel I was someone for them.

Then there was an event with three girls from my year at school. They took me to one side one day and calmly told me that they didn't want me to hang out with them anymore. They simply didn't like me. I was devastated. And yet I wasn't destroyed by their bullying. I was brave. My bravery softened them. I didn't cry, I simply asked why. I was innocent and sensitive. They wanted to hurt me and they did. And yet they didn't have the victory they had sought. They were confronted with a confused, sensitive, hurt girl and they no longer felt like hurting me after that. I did not break.

And dear old Arthur, my life, my rock, my sun, my love. He was there for so long and then he was gone and as he left he shot me "I never loved you, I settled"

242

And there is Mick. Gentle, soft, sensitive, yet a part of me is expecting his harshness, his abuse, the damage he will cause. I get confused, because it doesn't come.

I'm trying to scratch off the toxicity in my body, the abuse of a lifetime. It brings with it pain and a fear of death. And yet moving through that fear barrier is the only way I can shed old skin, allowing for new skin to grow.

8 March 13

I'm once again semi-awake and semi-unconscious. I wake up feeling ill. I am sure I have had food poisoning. I feel sick in my stomach. I am going over in my mind what I've eaten that day, trying to figure out what has caused the poisoning. I realise there is no chance I have food poisoning.

In spite of knowing I could not have food poisoning, the sensations are so real, I get up and go to the toilet to throw up, all the while telling myself that I can't possibly have food poisoning, but also thinking 'my body knows, there's something wrong'. I'm only half conscious throughout all of this.

Nothing comes out. I go back to bed and fall asleep. I am still feeling ill. I have an inner sensation of decay and death, as if there is something bad in me, something poisonous. I feel decay and gradual loss of functionality.

I wake up excruciatingly tired, as if I haven't had a single moment's sleep all night.

These semi-conscious, semi-unconscious experiences over the past month are perplexing me. I'm half awake while experiencing them and they feel so real, I can't be sure whether they are dreams at all. I wonder if they are not actual reality.

This feeling of poisoning could be the result of opening up old wounds and actually feeling them consciously this time. I swallowed all the bad treatment I received throughout my life and it was toxic, now it wants to come out. And yet when I try, nothing comes out. I feel ill. I find no logical explanation, no physical cause for the symptoms, yet I'm unwell and eventually overwhelmingly tired.

244

Arthur is with Gillian. He also had a fling with another girl. I am there with the two of them. I feel absolute pain. Gillian looks at me with compassion, she is gentle with me, but at the same time her look says "but I have him now".

I feel unemotional.

Gillian's an inner part of me. The dream makes me feel guilty about losing Arthur, about letting him go. Gillian respects me and my place there and she keeps her distance from me, not rubbing her new relationship with Arthur in my face. Part of my own psyche is giving me space and respect for who I am no matter what has happened and what I've done. She is honouring my presence, my value, my worth. She's not trying to diminish me. I need to own more of the Gillian within me.

But I'm also full of guilt and feeling sorry for myself.

The whole point of life is to learn to live more consciously. This cannot happen without making mistakes we can learn from. Yet I punish myself for my mistakes, sometimes even for non-mistakes so harshly. I beat myself up until I'm lying bleeding on the ground, near death. And Gillian is there, with Arthur, yet kind and respectful, not rejecting or attacking, but accepting.

I have lost touch with my emotions. I feel dissociated. I see them together and feel nothing, except guilt and blame for losing Arthur.

I come across a note I wrote down when I was fifteen years old. I had a dream and woke up from it crying "What? What? No! But mummy, what if that star froze? Do you think! Good night" and fell asleep again.

The star has to do with the individual personality, our uniqueness. It represents our unique destiny, the path through which we become what we are meant to be. It is not dictated by the collective, it is personal.

The star also represents the immortal soul.

At the time I saw the dream I wasn't sure whether it had been born from my mother's actions or from Miles'. Only a few days before the dream my friends had told me that Miles said behind my back I was there to be used. This had hurt me immensely, incredibly, in fact I can't even find the words to describe just how much it had hurt me to hear that. My best friend says this? What does he think of me? Who am I in his eyes? I thought of him as a close friend and someone who valued me. I chose not to believe them. I placed my trust in him. I thought it was a macho, I don't really care kind of comment, masking the fact that he really did care. And then of course, three years later came the sexual violation. I should have known better. I was so stupid. I was shown the truth. Yet I chose to trust and believe in him in spite of everything. Why? And in comes the self blame...

At the time I thought the star represented my dreams and they were being frozen. I was afraid of that, of having my dreams frozen. But perhaps the star was me myself and not my dreams. The pain and hurt, the betrayal I suffered froze me, my heart, my hope, part of my life force, my joy and energy, part of connection and trust, trust towards others, but also towards myself. It froze my feelings, because the pain and hurt were unbearable.

Through the abuse I received as a child, from my parents, from Miles, my birthright was stolen from me. They froze my soul, it could no longer move or grow. The ability to know, understand my needs, to express these needs and have them met were frozen. The belief that I deserve to have my needs met was frozen. The belief that I have a right to be happy, that I deserve good things, that I can give and receive love, that I am worthy were frozen. To some extent my ability to live was frozen. To feel. How could I feel the good? Good feelings can only be felt to the extent we are capable of also feeling the bad. The bad was unbearable, so I shut down to the bad and in the process also to the good.

When something is frozen, no life force flows through it. It needs to be thawed to be able to flow again.

15 March 13

A small group of animals are fenced in. They're in a small enclosure. There's an elephant, a tiger and a crocodile. They are chasing me. I manage to get away from the elephant and the tiger and climb the fence. But the crocodile climbs after me. As he does so, the fence door swings open away from me. My mother smashes the crocodile's head with a wooden stick.

I then find myself walking up a busy road. The road stretches as far ahead as I can see. Many cars are driving up and down it. It's very straight. I watch myself walk on, I'm not in me, I'm watching myself from behind. My hair is cut in the style I had when I was at high school.

An elephant, the animal of size and strength, an animal of stability and one that "never forgets". A tiger, my favourite animal, one of strength again, one that is fast and hunts, one that is beautiful and has intense, deep eyes. Although the lion is commonly referred to as the king of the jungle, for me the king is and always has been the tiger. I love its speed and agility. It's also big and it kills to survive, without regret. It is a natural born killer. It is aggressive when it needs to be and no animal can be a threat to him, except for a human being, but only when equipped with a gun.

The crocodile, fierce and yet another killer. I know nothing about crocodiles, except that in my imagination they float around in moats around castles, protecting the castles from intruders.

They are all chasing me, these strong, wild animals. These big, confident animals that act intuitively, driven by their survival instinct. They kill with no regrets, blame or guilt.

I manage to outrun them somehow. I climb a fence, which in theory should render me safe, but the fence works against me, the door swings open and it is my mother, my tormentor and enemy who saves me.

I'm watching myself from behind, me as a teenager, walking

along a road, one that stretches beyond eyesight. A road that helps people and cars travel from place to place. Cars, moving much faster than I am, are getting on with their journey. And I'm watching this teenage girl, my old self, walk on into the distance.

I'm disconnected from her somehow. I can see her and watch her, but I am not her, she is not me, we are separated, although we should be one.

How is it that it is my mother who saves me? What am I supposed to see that is linked to me being a teenager and my mother that shows me the way, sets me on my path? I have no idea at this point. I know I need to look. These animals that want to kill me, I can outrun them and my mother, my inner mother maybe, can help me escape somehow.

25 March 13

I walk into my flat and realise that the bathroom ceiling is leaking. There is water pouring down from the ceiling. My heart sinks. It's such a hassle to try to get work done in the flat and the damage is huge. Then I walk into the living room and see that there is water pouring down where the ceiling meets the walls in there too. The same thing is happening in the kitchen as well.

I panic. I try to call the leaseholders, so that they can send someone over to sort the problem out. I'm having problems getting through on the phone. Eventually I get someone on the other line. I try to communicate the urgency of the situation to him. While I'm on the phone I notice large damp patches forming in the hallway. The hallway is also about to leak.

I forget all about the dream. As I pass the tube station on my way to work I see the contractor who is usually sent to our flats for building problems standing in front of the supermarket. I start walking up to him to tell him about the water leaking through all the ceilings in my flat. Just as I'm a couple of steps away from him I remember that water was leaking in my dream and not in reality.

I get so confused. I hadn't even remembered the dream when I woke up, yet it was so real, I nearly tried to get the problem fixed in real life and the dream suddenly becomes vivid.

I'm alone at the clinic. I'm feeling depressed. I have the urge to throw up, but I don't. Then I get a call from my private student. He asks me if I can teach him at home straight away. I agree and go and teach him and his wife. Although he's meant to be my private student I've been teaching for many years, he somehow isn't him. I enjoy teaching the class, but I'm worried I'll get in trouble at the clinic for leaving it unstaffed for a few hours.

I go back to the clinic after the class, but it has changed. It's now in a big house. The lounge is dark and depressing, but the rest of the building gets more light and is more cheery. We have two old patients there. They want some food.

I go to see Emily, my friend. She's settling into a doorway, where she's going to collect money for charity. It's cold and I jokingly say "You're not really going to sit there, are you?"

She says "Certainly I am". She is glowing and vibrant. She's full of energy and she's bursting with happiness. She's a friend I admire, respect and trust.

I go back to work. Everyone there is happy now, even my colleagues. The television has vanished from the lounge. There are bits of leftover food lying around.

Two other friends appear, although I don't recognise them. We start talking. I tell them I need one more yoga class to be able to leave the clinic as full time staff and go down to four days a week. That way I can volunteer one day a week, working, doing something more worthwhile, like at a charity or a school.

The mood at the clinic has changed. From a depressing, negative place, it has become much more positive. There's lots of sunlight. People are happy. The mood is light and vibrant.

There is leakage in my flat, in my personal space, in my sanctuary, my home, where I come to heal, where I feel safe, secure, where I can be alone in comfort. There is so much water coming through that the whole place is dripping with leakage. It's destructive. It will make the flat uninhabitable. I feel helpless, powerless.

But there are positive, warm, radiant energies shining through.

Another yoga class, sharing my passion and joy, sharing the experience of awareness and union, will make things better. My personal experience, joy, passion, love will join with the collective. All I need is more of that and then I will have more to offer too. Instead of burning myself out at the clinic, I will then be able to use a day a week working for a good cause, sharing my energy with those who need it and appreciate it.

The clinic is at first a dark, depressing place, but Emily's positive energy, her joy in sitting on a doorstep in the cold to collect money for charity, for the good of other people, penetrates into the clinic. It becomes a positive, light space. There are friends there that I can communicate with. The whole energy of the dream shifts. The darkness is taken over by light and warmth.

But there is leftover food lying around. It needs to be disposed of.

Such a mixture of elements: violation of my private, personal space, my safe haven and the confusion around this violation being real or not. Then my sharing my passion with my student, knowing I need more and the change of energy in the clinic through positive sources from the outside.

Once more my connection with Emily has come up and once more it is positive. She is a positive outer source in my real life, but she is also an inner character. She is passion for what I love, teaching yoga, she is selflessness and charity, she is brightness, happiness, joy and life and she is within me too.

The dream is like a sign of the violation I am experiencing and the way out, connecting to my passion, my friends, my inner resources of love, compassion, giving, sharing and a joy for life.

25 March 13

There was strength there for a while. I was getting through somehow, sure of myself, but the strength I felt over the past few days seems to have left me. All I feel at the moment is deep deep pain, loneliness, hopelessness, heartache and despair.

I'm surviving though. I'm getting on with my life, going to the gym, working hard and filling my time. I can't stand not having anything to do at the moment. I can't stand being left alone with my thoughts and feelings. My head and heart are swimming with the usual destructive thoughts: I messed it up, I ruin everything worthwhile and valuable. These thoughts, these voices hang over me like dark clouds and follow me around wherever I go. I have to fight them every single second of the day. I keep telling myself I have so much, that I have given a lot to people, that I have a lot to offer, that I am capable, but the self pity, the self blame are louder. A trumpet in my ear: Bad, bad, evil, worthless, useless, unloveable, bad, wrong, bad.

And the tremendous pain, the pain in my heart, throbbing. The knives in my navel that keep turning.

I forgave Miles so readily, I still do, I carried the blame myself. I still feel no anger towards him, but I'm at least forgiving myself. It wasn't my fault. I know it and feel it.

How can I let go of all these familiar thoughts, feelings, accusations? What will remain of me? Are they not who I am? Are they not what hold me together? What's left when they go? Nothing. Nothing.

But they need to be torn down. I, the I I have been and have known, needs to be annihilated. And then from the ashes a new I can rise, but only when the old one is dead, terminated.

Arthur helped hold me together. I was new with him. He is no more. And the foundations were not there. This time I will rebuild from the foundations up. The foundations will be strong, solid, they will be based on me, made of me, mine. I know these foundations need to be based on emotional discovery, on finding my soul and my heart, finding my true self.

I went on a school trip soon after those three girls told me they didn't like me and didn't want to have anything to do with me. We were on the trip together, practically our entire school was. My diaries are full of how nice they were towards me, and all kinds of other things I don't remember, like a guy dancing half naked in our room. An odd incident considering none of us had had a boyfriend so far, three of us were sharing a room with a girl we didn't know and he was there with her. There's also mention of a dance with Miles, ice skating with those three girls and all kinds of other things I have absolutely no recollection of, even after reading my diaries. But reading my diaries triggered memories in me that aren't even in there. One of those three girls applied make-up to me and did my hair, first time ever for me, I was against make-up, I thought it fake. I got a lot of compliments though and I was grateful to her.

And even more importantly, I have pages and pages, in fact notebook after notebook about Miles. I'm confused by what I've read. Okay, I understand I was rejected and abused by my parents. My diaries cry of neediness, lack of confidence, hurt, sensitivity, an intense desire to be accepted and loved. But I still was open to trusting, loving, giving my all. I keep going on and on in my diaries about how much I trust Miles. I'd trust him with my life. I trust him above everyone and all else. There are incidents where I'm warned against him, told things he's said about me, but I always side with him. As traumatic as my experience with my parents might have been, which then possibly or maybe even certainly led to my relationship with Miles, could he have been the final breakdown? The complete shut down? I still don't quite understand what happened. I need an objective view. Did he finally break me, close me down? Once

I came round to remembering and accepting what he did, I forgave him, pretty much instantly. What happened at work helped me give up my guilt and blame of myself. But the rejection and hurt? I trusted him. Above all else. I trusted him above my parents and all other friends who had not wronged me.

Then again, I feel I invited him in because of my childhood trauma. I could only give this trust and love to someone who did and would abuse me, who was not available, who could not reciprocate. I was searching for my trauma, wanting to re-activate it, relive it, I was drawn back in towards it, I had to have it, because that was all I knew of love, that was my only experience, I needed it. So I trusted and loved someone who was not available, who treated me badly, was harsh at times and eventually abused me in a way that was beyond healing, violating me, my being, my un-blossomed femininity, my soul and life. It had to be him, because I could not accept genuine, non-abusive love. It had to be twisted. I had to relive my trauma.

As many as my complexes and problems may be, is the key ultimately in Miles and not my parents? They and their treatment might have driven me to him, but was he the one that pressed the trigger that exploded the bomb? No, the answer lies in the driver, not the results. I need to dig deeper. I followed his beckoning because of a deep drive in me and that is what I need to understand.

I look for rejection. I'm sure I ask for it, because I don't know any better, any other. So how is it that Arthur, the person who never did abuse me, who still, in spite of everything I've done, has stood by me and supported me, how come he has been the one person who has met my rejection? Where's the fairness in that? Where's the logic? And yet has he not rejected above and beyond all others? He was not available to me emotionally, he did not cherish me and once the relationship ended, he told me he never had really loved me. Is that not the ultimate rejection? Is that not emotional abuse?

I can't appreciate love myself, yet when mine is rejected I'm surprised and hurt? What utter bullshit.

Who am I? A hypocrite or simply mad?

2 April 13

I'm not real. I'm not alive. I'm completely detached from my body, my emotions, my life. I'm wondering through my life, above it, watching.... It's a frightful feeling. No connection to the world, myself, sensations, life, others. Nothing. Complete dissociation. As if life is not real. I'm not real. I'm not living. As if I might wake up any moment and realise it was all a dream, the past two, three years were nothing but a nightmare.

I feel deep down into my core, my navel. There's so much pain there. An overwhelming sense of loss, regret, utter, pure self-hatred. Hatred is overpowering. I hate my mother, but I hate myself so much more.

I'm rocking, cradling myself, trying to rock myself to ease, to calm, like a lullaby, like a mother rocking her baby for comfort, with love, but there is no love. The rocking makes it worse. The pain in my abdomen is increasing. I sense contradictions, a war, a battle between myself and myself.

What a waste of life, what a tragedy. Hatred towards mother getting stronger. How could she. How dare she.

My core, my sense of identity, my entire existence, it's in pain, it's crumbling down, it's in ruins and I'm buried underneath the destruction.

My entire body's in pain, the pain's stemming from my navel, my core. There's a gnawing sensation, my insides are getting scraped out with a serrated knife, with a blunt axe.

I want to butcher my navel, cut my insides out, get rid of the pain. I want to annihilate it, annihilate myself. I want to scrape myself out. I was hated for existing, so I hate myself for existing.

I'm feeling nauseous.

I'm tired, fatigued, worn out, done, finished.

Like a candle that flickers out

My soul has flickered out

It's stopped burning

Gone cold, dead

The room is dark

There is no more dread
Just emptiness, a huge blank
The end
Or maybe the beginning?

3 April 13

Love versus fear.

 I want to embody love, to feel love and let that feeling spread all over me and move me. I can't. I feel nothing. I try to think of and feel places, people that would awaken the feeling of love within me. I think of Arthur, I feel pain. I think of strolling through the red woods, I feel a sense of loss, loss of the way I used to be able to feel and cannot anymore. I used to feel alive there, whole, happy and content. I cannot anymore. I think of my teacher, and I feel a sense of regret, I let him down, I feel ashamed.

 I try to bring up the feelings I had for Arthur yesterday, the love I felt for him, although I felt loss and regret as well. But suddenly the pain takes over and overwhelms all else, then fear kicks in, anxiety and ultimately panic.

 I simply can not connect to my heart. It's gone, buried, unreachable.

 I keep trying, until eventually I have no strength left and I start to cry. I want to scream, run away. I cry "I cannot feel love. I feel nothing".

 I drop to my knees. I can't scream. I want to, but nothing comes out.

 I cry. First from my throat, then my whole chest, then my entire body. I am not crying for anything in particular. I do not feel anything. There are no words, no description. I just cry. My crying increases in intensity. I start to choke. I can't breathe. My throat is blocked. I can't breathe. I know I am about to die. Then I think "You're safe. If you pass out from lack of air, Saraswati will bring you round". I can choke, I will not die.

 I cry and cry and cry. I can't breathe. I choke on myself. The sheer force of my choking brings my crying to an end. I stop. I sit in stillness, frozen, immobile.

 And then out of nowhere a pink-white lotus appears in my heart. I can feel it want to open. I am amazed. It simply appeared from nowhere, out of nothing. And suddenly I feel love. The warmth of love appears in my heart and blossoms. It starts to spread all over my body.

 The warmth and energy from the lotus spreads downwards into my navel. The knife stops its scraping. My navel is healing. My own heart, the beautiful lotus in my heart, my own heart is healing my own pain, the pain that had always been there, that was always there.

The warmth continues to spread, it spreads all over my body, all the way into my toes, my fingertips, to the crown of my head.

I feel happy. I let the love spread and I surround myself with the energy of my own love for protection.

It turns out love was not to be found outside. Neither the man I love most in the world, Arthur, nor the person I respect and admire most, my teacher, nor the location I love most, where I find tranquillity, serenity and happiness, the red woods, could provide me with the feeling of love. It came from within, from my own heart. I had it in me all along and I have spent a life time looking for it outside.

Love is me. Only my own love, my own loving energy can heal my wounds, not anybody else's. I searched everywhere except within and all the while it was buried there in my own body, in my heart.

We all, every single one of us, rapist to murderer, thief to hypocrite, we all have that essence, that beautiful lotus flower within us. Yet how deeply it can be buried sometimes.

I realised what I had been hating all my life. I had been hating this pure being, the body and soul that holds this beautiful lotus flower, this flower that is full of loving power, of pure life force, this connection to the Divine, the spiritual. I have hated it, disregarded it and abused it all my life.

That lotus is anything but unloveable. I am not unloveable. I'm beautiful and worth loving. My essence is pure and worth cherishing. It is sacred and precious.

Fear is the opposite of love. They cannot co-exist. Love mitigates fear. Remember the lotus when you feel afraid. Connect to that beautiful source. It is your essence.

The navel, where all my pain sits, my poor navel, the centre of the ego, where my feelings of loss, regret and fear lie, where I feel the pain of abandonment and betrayal. I can heal my navel by connecting to my heart. The heart is self-less, ego-less, it is our connection to something greater than ourselves, the universe, the Divine, all others. It is about connection and love. It is about dropping the ego.

I have been taught about the Divine within us. I have meditated on my heart, and yet I have never felt it blossom. I have imagined it, but I have never known it, really felt it. And suddenly, at my breaking point, at the point of death and destruction, in amongst the intensity of fear and hopelessness, it appeared. It was there all along and suddenly, when I let go, when I gave up, when I stopped searching for it, when I surrendered, it appeared, opened up and spread outwards. So warm, so full of life, so real and present, such a source of joy and healing, spreading out from my own heart, throughout my entire being.

4 April 13

I've bought an amazing new flat. It's on the top floor of a building, which means it gets loads of light. It's spacious and large. It has long corridors and many rooms. It feels very luxurious. It must be an expensive flat in a good location. It has been done up with high quality material and with simple, luxurious taste. It has been furnished in a minimalist, modern style, making it feel even more luxurious and spacious. Lots of wood and mirrors have been used in decorating it. There is nothing unnecessary, cheap or bad quality in sight.

Martin, Sam and Jackal drop by. I haven't moved into the flat yet, so it's empty except for the basics, fitted kitchen and bathrooms, some wardrobes and beds and bedside tables. No other furnishings, no books or anything else that might be personal.

I'm opening and closing drawers and cupboards, investigating the flat. I notice that the corner cupboards have been built in to maximise usage of space by inserting a rotating hanging device inside. I point it out to the guys and remark "I don't usually like things my parents do, they have cupboards like this in their flat and I like them, so efficient and functional. The builders have done a good job with this one". My friends are surprised that I am seeing these things for the first time and haven't had a good look around the flat before.

We all go into my bedroom and play a board game. I have music on in the background. Sam starts dancing with me. Jackal gets angry and says "Don't do that. You know it was a problem before, don't make it a problem again". I shout at him. I tell him it is none of his business whom I dance with, he has no right to make any comments or express any wishes about my life and he's not even welcome in my flat in the first place. I tell him I had let him in because he arrived with my friends, I didn't want to cause a problem or any negativity by turning him away, but he's not welcome.

They leave. I'm staring at Jackal with absolute fury as they walk out.

Persephone walks in. She doesn't look like herself, physically she looks like me, although her face is different. She is renting a room from me in this flat. Her room is located right by the main entrance, to the left of it as you enter the flat.

She points to the entrance door and says "That's the new bar". We walk out the doors and into the bar. The bar is super posh. Crystal lights, glass tables, leather armchairs, also very spacious and luxurious. It's a long room. I say to Persephone "It looks very fancy". I think in my mind "Thank God she took the room nearest the door. The bar might be noisy, but I won't hear the noise, because I'm at the other end of the flat".

She tells me she couldn't have the two drinks she wanted the other night, because they didn't have any whiskey. She says it jokingly and loud enough for the barman to hear. She's being jovial.

I leave her at the bar and walk back into my flat. There are twenty people walking down my corridor away from the entrance. Most of them are young. They are people I don't know. They are part of a dance group.

I'm furious. What are they doing in my flat? I haven't let them in and they did not ask for my permission. One of them says they needed to use the toilet. I shout at them "How dare you? This is my flat. It's my private property, not a public toilet facility"

Three of them, two women and a man, all in their thirties, are defending the group. The rest of the group is much younger. One woman starts threatening me. I shout back, then hold her by her neck right underneath her chin and push her over a flat, shining surface. I push her down, so that she's half lying on it. I say much more calmly, but in a threatening tone of voice "You're in my flat. If I killed you right now, it wouldn't be considered a crime, as you are in my private property and I have a right to defend it. I'm not going to, but don't you dare threaten me again".

I let her go, but they continue to shout at me. I call the police.

Martin and Sam are supportive characters for me in the real world and they're there in my psyche. They do bring Jackal, although they know I would not want him there, but they leave with him when I get angry. Jackal is part of the old structure, the voice that says I'm to blame for everything, I'm bad, worthless. But the important thing is I stand up to him and throw him out of my space.

The whole thing takes place in a new flat, spacious, luxurious, good, because I'm worth it, a new psyche. A brand new beginning, as yet untouched or soiled.

Parents, my inner parents, in this place are supportive,

something they have is useful to me and I can appreciate it. I don't shun it just because they have the same thing.

Persephone, an image of me, is a buffer between me and the outside, noisy, disruptive world. She is light-hearted and jokes about the lack of whiskey. She's not taking life too seriously. She's not expecting an outcome and forcing for one. I should cultivate her within myself. I should allow for a more light-hearted approach to life, this approach will protect me from outside influences that can have negative effects on me.

A dance group, the strangers that come in to use my toilet, the collective psyche, or my dreams and expectations and desires of life and myself. They are invading my space. They feel they have a right to enter. They are loud and threatening. But I'm forceful and strong against them. I defend myself and my space. I stand up to them and fight for my rights. I am strong. And even when all else fails, I still don't give in, but call for the police. They are there to protect after all and I feel I have a right to call them. I know these people don't have a right to be there. I don't cave in to their threats and demands.

Control versus letting go

The outcome doesn't matter. But I'm trying so hard to get an outcome. I'm trying so damned hard to let go. I want to trust. To trust and let go, but I'm trying too hard to trust and too hard to let go.

I want to let go of taking myself so seriously, my life, my role in life, my decisions. Everything is so serious for me, everything becomes a matter of life or death. And I'm trying to let go. But I'm trying too hard, I'm taking even the task of letting go too seriously. I'm tensing under the strain. While letting go involves relaxing, I'm gripping and stressing.

I fail. I can't let go. So I give up. I give up trying to let go and let myself feel and move in any way that comes to me. Suddenly I take a deep breath in and out, I shake my body like a dog just come out of the sea, I jump up and down and notice that I have let go. As soon as I stopped trying to let go, I let go naturally and life flowed freely.

I feel release. I feel free.

I tried so hard to follow my body while letting go, tracking it, forcing it to let go and I couldn't. I was white-knuckle driving. But as soon as I gave up, as soon as I admitted I had failed and it didn't matter anymore, my body naturally got rid of its tension. It released and I let go.

Trying is controlling. Even when we're trying not to control. The act of trying in itself is an attempt at control.

If we're constantly striving for an outcome, we're tense, life becomes a struggle. But life doesn't matter really. Nothing really matters. Life flows and we can flow with it if we stop struggling so much, trying too hard, fighting, trying to control, trying so hard to understand.

The Persephone in me, the one that takes life lightly, can laugh at her life and is happy. I want to access her. I have spent decades striving, trying to be better in every way, as a person, professionally at work, in society, for my parents. It's so tiring. Letting go is so freeing. My body feels light, I feel happy, as if I could fly. It's the same life, I have the same things and lack the same things as I did when I was trying, yet I'm freer and lighter, I'm happier. As a result I can move and live freely and with more joy and energy.

5 April 13

I feel fragile. Fragile, but somehow not weak. I want to be held. I want to feel warmth, I want to feel somebody's loving touch on me.

Instead of suppressing these feelings, ignoring them, casting them aside as weakness, I hear them. I hear Saraswati's voice telling me it's okay to have my needs met.

I go into a foetal position, lying on blankets and completely surrounded by bolsters, cushions and blankets. Surrounded, cushioned, comforted and supported. I'm buried in these comfortable layers, in darkness and warmth. I close my eyes and lie there. I allow whatever wants to come up to come up.

I feel the comfort of the cushions supporting my back. They're feeding my heart. It feels amazing. It's so nurturing. I realise the importance of touch, of feeling warmth and support from another.

I lose consciousness.

When I eventually, suddenly come back into consciousness, I'm aware of an image of my father. It's not clear, but I know I've been dreaming of him.

As I come out of my little protective space, my cocoon, I feel nurtured, fed. I feel alive and fulfilled. I felt a need, I expressed it, it was met and that felt wonderful. I feel whole somehow, full.

I no longer feel needy or weak.

I remember as a child I always wanted my back stroked or massaged. My mother never gave me any affection, never held or cuddled me. I suppose massage was the only way I could receive safe touch and warmth, physical connection.

I realise how hungry I am at the moment for human touch, a need and desire I have disregarded. I'm hungry for human warmth. I never thought these were important at all, but I realise my body and soul yearn for them.

This was a turning point for me. I have always considered needs to be embarrassing, signs of weakness. Each person should be able to fulfill his or her own needs or know how to live without them being fulfilled. But it was okay for me to have a need, to ask for it to be met and to have that need fulfilled. It felt good.

I now am able to express my needs and wants, my preferences and desires and dislikes. I do not feel vulnerable doing this, whether I get what I want or not. It's just an expression. I do not feel weak expressing them. I used to want people, especially my partner, to read my mind. I would feel hurt if my needs were not met, although I never asked for them openly, because I could not. If I asked and was refused, I would feel rejected and hurt. Asking in itself was admitting weakness, which I could never show. But I always felt disappointed. Nobody can read minds.

Now I ask and I don't feel disappointed if my requests are not met. There is strength in knowing and acknowledging my needs and being able to express them. I don't 'need' them to be fulfilled any longer. If I'm given, I can receive and if my need is not met, it still feels okay, I have at least asked. I have found though, that when I ask, I am usually given what I ask for.

11 April 13

I'm sitting in a large, very crowded cafe. All the seats are taken, but no one has to stand. I'm there with Martin. A lot of the people in the cafe are people I know from high school. Martin and I are having an intimate conversation and suddenly I notice that Jackal is sitting at our table. He has snuck in quietly and taken a seat. He hasn't said a word so far, but is listening carefully. I finish my sentence and turn to Jackal and ask him if he's just going to sit there. He says "yes". I firmly tell him to leave.

Jackal is upset and leaves. As soon as Jackal leaves Martin makes a flimsy excuse about having to rush home to see his son. He leaves before our conversation is over. I know he's rushing after Jackal, to be with him and make sure he's okay. He feels Jackal has been wronged and wants to be there for his friend to support him.

I get up to pay. There's a whole crowd in front of the till waiting to pay. They haven't formed a proper queue. I join the back of the crowd.

I come across Leo, who comments to me that he has no idea why Jackal won't leave me alone. He says they have all told him it's hopeless, but he still keeps on pursuing me and wanting me, even though I've been with so many people. He mentions I was seeing other men even while I was going out with him. He lists a number of names of men I have supposedly been with, but they're people I've never even heard of before.

I tell Leo that the stories are all lies, I have not been with "so many people", I've only been in three relationships all my life, one of which lasted twelve years. Leo stares off into the distance. Suddenly it's as if a light bulb comes on in his mind. He realises they have all been mistaken about me, that they have been wrongly accusing me. They had judged me wrongly.

I leave the cafe to call Martin. I want to make sure he hasn't fallen for these lies as well and clear things up with him.

I am being wrongly accused and judged by a whole group of animus figures, but I stand up for myself. I clear the record and make further moves to clear the false stories with my close friend Martin as well. Martin is a friend I admire, care about and respect, his opinion is very important to me. We have been close for decades and he matters to me. Leo is a gentle, sweet person. Someone who would never harm a fly, a person who comes across as sensitive and thoughtful, as well as emotionally mature.

Jackal has been harassing me ever since he found out I had separated from Arthur. He has been bombarding me with phone calls, emails, text messages. I have responded a few times, explaining clearly, yet nicely, that I have no interest in having a relationship with him, in any way, even as a friend. I have told him that I do not hold the same feelings for him that he does for me. But he still continues to harass me. I have stopped responding at all. It seems that even a negative response from me invites further communication bombardment from him.

I do not feel comfortable discussing Jackal with Martin or Sam. Even though they are close friends of mine, they are very close friends of his too. I don't know how I would explain myself and worry that they would side with him and judge me. So I have been avoiding them.

But in the dream I stand up for myself. I refuse to let myself be misperceived, I clear the wrong judgements made by people. I am also strong towards Jackal, I tell him to leave. He has no right to seat himself at my table and listen to a personal conversation I am having. I am ready to defend myself and clear the air with Martin too.

All animus figures within a woman can condemn her and make her feel inferior. They can simultaneously, or instead, help a woman integrate positive masculine energy within herself, which can manifest as her being able to follow her dreams, make changes, stand up for herself, speak out, act from the heart with truth and genuinety, move on in life and achieve.

I take upon myself the responsibility of creating a more positive inner atmosphere within myself about who I am. This is still in the process of happening.

I am clear about my truth and state it with confidence. I am who I am. I stand up for myself and am at peace with myself. I don't get crushed by the lies and opinions of others, no matter how important they are to me and no matter how many of them share these views. I know my truth and am willing to stand up for it.

The dream has strength in it, an inner strength that helps me act, that keeps me whole and intact and that will eventually change others' views of me and their relationships with me.

I have been shivering for hours. I feel that hole within me, the painful emptiness, the overwhelming loneliness. I feel so cold. I stay open to the sensations. I stay with them, aware of changes, of what is going on in my body. I pray for guidance, help and support.

I'm feeling myself shut down. The pain is too much for me. I am still aware, but numbness takes over. I'm closing down, disassociating. It's more comfortable this way. It becomes bearable.

I fall asleep.

When sensations in our body or feelings become too unbearable, too threatening to our existence, we shut down to survive. I stay with the painful sensations for as long as I can, but our bodies have their own intelligence. Eventually my body decides it is too much and goes numb. I sleep. Healing happens during that rest. I am aware of the shutting down process, which most often happens unconsciously. I stay with it, but then allow my body to complete its own process.

20 April 13

In spite of what my colleague at work, the one I like and respect, said about my decisions and actions regarding Stan, the colleague who has been harassing me and bullying me at work, I didn't doubt myself, or feel bad. I felt okay. I knew I did what I had to do and it was the right thing to do. I was calm, confident, serene and comfortable.

I have found my heart. I can actually feel it, not just imagine it, I feel it. It's alive.

The first organ to come alive in us as a foetus is the heart. The rest of our being evolves from it. If we can maintain contact with the heart centre, we become grounded, centred, whole and in tune with the rest of life. We can also then connect to our emotions, positive or negative, love or hate, compassion or anger. They are all part of us, they need to be accepted without judgement, felt and allowed to be. Trying to suppress emotions only leads to damage and shut down. Even though we would all prefer not to feel anger or hatred, these emotions are also part of us, they are usually justified, they also need to be recognised and accepted. This does not mean acting them out unconsciously, but it does mean not rejecting them.

I filed a bullying, harassment and sexual harassment report at work. My manager had to manage the situation. She took in all the evidence and conducted witnessed and recorded interviews. I was questioned harshly. Every single kind word or action of mine towards Stan was questioned. I felt I was on the guilty stand and was being blamed and made to walk over nails and burning hot coals. But I stood my ground. I answered all the questions honestly and from my truth. My report was fourteen pages of copied and pasted messages and emails, every single one of them would be enough proof for harassment. The sheer amount of them was astounding. Even I was stunned when I finished it. There was so much from him, with no response from me, nothing to lead him on. And for so long I had been wondering whether I might have done something to lead him on. The report itself proved to me beyond any doubt that there was nothing I had done wrong. The interview was harrowing, it was horrendous and I will never put myself through something like that again, I hope, but at the end of it, I felt strong. I wasn't to blame. It wasn't I who was damaged.

Stan ended up getting a written final warning for his behaviour. Unfortunately this meant he put all his energy into making my life hell at the clinic. The atmosphere has been horrible and colleagues blame me for speaking up. Why couldn't I stay quiet and just deal with it myself? They wanted to ignore what was going on and continue as if nothing had happened. The negative atmosphere at work affected everyone and they, at least partially, blamed me for it. But I did all I could.

I even confronted my colleagues eventually. I told them the extent of what had been happening and what I had done to deal with the situation without escalating it. I explained there was nothing further I could have done. Whether they believed me completely or not I don't know, but their attitude towards me did change for the positive. At least they were able to see that whether I had dealt with the situation well or not, I had done my utmost best and I had acted truthfully, honestly and from my heart throughout. I could not have taken a different route. I was true to myself. My relationship with them once again became warm and close, as it had been before all the drama.

Confronting them was practically a bigger step for me than even going through the complaint procedure. To face them and stand up for myself, truthfully, rather than wondering if I had been wrong after all, was an incredible step for me. In the past I would have shut down, felt hurt, blamed myself and probably eventually left.

Not only did I feel release from the whole Stan situation, I also felt released from Miles. I could not tell people what he had done to me, because I thought they would blame me. But I told my manager what Stan did and she did not blame me, he was punished after a process that involved reports, interviews and witnesses. I was not to blame, I had done nothing wrong. And perhaps, I had done

272

nothing wrong with Miles either. Perhaps he was damaged, controlled by who knows what complexes, by hormones, God knows. But it was his stuff and not mine. I had done nothing to deserve it. Something in me lifted. Something in my body that had been there for two decades. The shift was palpable.

I was astonished to realise just how much guilt and blame I had been carrying for the Miles situation. I hadn't realised how much I did. Yet there it all was, huge, bigger than any other emotion, bigger than hurt, violation, certainly bigger than anger, which I still don't feel. I carried it for so long. Me, the bad one, evil, damaged, wrong, it's all my fault. I didn't even realise I was carrying all this. I was astonished and relieved.

My GPS system attracts bad treatment from others only when I don't value myself, not because I invite them in. I was the dog that peed on me. I accused myself, blamed myself and punished myself for everything. But no longer. I feel strong. I will not let others harass or mistreat me. I have the strength, courage, self-confidence and belief in myself to stand up for myself now.

24 April 13

I'm having a party at my place. My house is huge. It has a big garden. Persephone is there. So are Martin and Sam. It's crowded. Persephone comes up to me and says she needs to leave but will be back shortly.

Natalie's husband also came and then left saying he would return.

I've prepared lots of good food for the party.

The party goes well. The morning after I ask everyone whether they found a comfortable place to lie down and if they had slept well. They all say yes, especially Ant, who is very pleased with everything.

I need to take the rubbish out, there are bags of it. I start chatting to Blossom, a beautiful person. She has a beautiful soul, but has not been dealt a good hand in life. She is alone, single, she has never had a boyfriend and experienced emotional and physical intimacy, because her parents were overly protective of her. She still lives with her parents and is not happy. She is not content with her life and would do anything to find a suitable partner. She isn't looking for passion, or exceptional love, just a partner to share her life with. I like her a lot and am quite close to her in a way. She is deeply sensitive. She feels another's pain, hurt and love, even if she might never have experienced these herself directly, she empathises in a way that is very special. Not many people have that degree of sensitivity and empathy. She makes beautiful jewellery and has attempted to open up her own jewellery business to become independent. Unfortunately, what with the financial crisis and all, the business failed, so she is back to living with her parents. She's very dainty, thin, sensitive, emotionally mature and kind.

I am shocked to see her the way she is there. She has totally ballooned. She looks pregnant, but isn't. She tells me she has become like a stone. She says she cries when she tries to fit into her little black dress.

She's wearing a black dress, but she's trying to hide her huge size under an extra large, baggy jumper.

I wonder how it's even physically possible for her to have put on so much weight so quickly. I feel her pain in my body. I feel so sorry for her. I can feel her loneliness and hopelessness, so much so that it hurts me deeply.

I am providing enjoyment, nourishment and a place to sleep for a great many people. There seems to be more psychic space within me. But there is also some part of me, some deep pain that still needs to be seen more clearly.

A little black dress is simple and perfect. It helps the wearer look trim and neat and everything's in the right place. It is the classical wear for all times, never out of fashion and appropriate to wear pretty much anywhere and to any occasion.

Yet here the perfection is worn over imperfection and they are both being hidden by a baggy jumper, an item of comfort clothing. Ballooning in that way could be caused by not being able to release emotions, having to keep them in, emotions that won't integrate, they balloon out. Her feelings are of loneliness and hopelessness, feelings I am familiar with. Sometimes I feel completely alone in this huge, wild, hostile world and I try to grasp on to moments of hope, but they're so fleeting.

This beautiful, sensitive, dainty woman, unsatisfied, emotionally starving lady has everything trapped within. She can no longer wear the perfect little black dress, because the outer garment no longer fits the inner. There is a lot of desperate loss and dissatisfaction that has not been addressed and the weight of what she needs and wants and cannot receive is huge, weighing on her, making her feel like a stone.

And I empathises with her deeply. There is a part of me that is not content, dissatisfied. A part of my needs are not being met fully. My outer persona, the one that is trim and fits in, no longer fits me, because there is so much turmoil inside. There is a huge part of me that seeks and wants that perfection and a part of me that is rebelling against it, refusing it, not wanting it. There is turmoil and a mismatch, a clash.

I am feeding, housing friends, and yet I can no longer accept the little black dress. I feel loneliness and pain.

I'm seeing things in a different light. I have more clarity within me. I stood up for myself in the Stan situation and went through the entire process. He no longer determines my actions or my life at work. I cleared the air with others and feel much better in myself, at work, in my life.

At times I feel tremendous inner freedom. I feel more grounded and the ground is solid, I can trust it.

There is still Arthur and our relationship. I don't know what's going on on his side at all! It's still unclear and unresolved. I still don't know. But this has always been the pattern in our relationship. I open my heart to him, I offer him my heart, but never know what he feels, what he really feels. He'll give me a yes or no, he's pragmatic, he makes decisions, but I never know what he feels. I never have known his true feelings. Did he love me? Did he settle for me? Does he care? Does he miss me? Is he hurting, questioning, wondering, missing, feeling loss? Or has he moved on completely and is just simply being kind to me by staying in touch and being supportive? Does his kindness come from a place of love or responsibility? I have never been able to work through these questions and contradictions in the past. My actions have been determined by the strength of my feelings, my wants. I have not known his. I have hoped he feels the same way, but never received that feeling from him, never really, fully felt it. I have never been able to decipher his side of the story. I have hoped, analysed, decided it might be, but never known in my heart that he loves me. I have known I love him, but his side has always been grey, even now after our separation, I still don't know. I don't know whether he's being the contained, strong man who shows no emotion, who in fact possibly does not even know the emotions are there. Or is he truly feeling nothing but relief, he's moved on, but his feelings of responsibility keep him caring for me in some outer way.

I can't ask him, because I'm too afraid to hear his answer. The risk of him saying something I don't want to hear is too great. But the alternative is to continue feeling confused, to not know, to not have any clear path or route, to lie to myself, to question every word he utters, trying to understand what lies beneath it. So much stress, burden. So much energy wasted.

I owe it to myself, I need to be true to myself. Only small steps, nothing drastic, step by step, I can decide how much to disclose. I can be honest about my confusion, wanting to see things more clearly, understand the whole picture. I can hunt down and track the truth of my own heart.

Incredibly I am learning how to find the courage and strength within myself to stay true to myself and have confidence in my own truth. It does not have to be everyone's truth, in fact it does not need to be anyone else's truth at all, but it is my truth and it is what it is. It is the only truth I have, it is who I am and I feel confident and strong with it. I feel comfortable within myself as long as I stay true to myself.

The path is not to try to achieve an outcome beyond finding a way to relate in the most forthright and honest way possible in the moment. The honest communication will free me and no further outcome is necessary. What others think, whether they'll judge, leave, get angry, doesn't matter. The only thing that does matter is tracking what's going on from my own heart and expressing that.

Something is trying to come forward, into consciousness, into the light and at the moment the only thing important to me is to stay true to this one thing, to be honest, to communicate from my heart, even when I think it might be scary or silly,...

2 June 13

I'm living on a farm in the country. We are all awaiting for an impending natural disaster. We have been warned and informed, and now we are waiting. We have been told that we need to vacate the area. I'm looking over all my belongings and trying to decide what is absolutely essential for my survival, what I simply can't leave behind. I can only take one rucksack with me and I have to decide what I will put in it.

I start gathering items, my old diaries, keepsakes, mementos, things that are really important to me. One of the things I pack is a poem my granddad wrote to me when I was only one. I still have it hanging by my bed. It has been with me everywhere I've lived, always hanging in my bedroom. It's very valuable to me.

I've gathered too many items. They don't fit in my bag. I look at them again and think "none of these are essential. In fact I don't care about any of them". I decide to leave every single item behind. They are only 'things', they don't really matter anyway. I remember the Buddhist poem about material things being worth nothing in the greater scheme of things, because when we die, we take nothing with us. I leave everything out except for my granddad's poem. Only the poem is worth taking with me.

Suddenly the news changes. We won't have to evacuate after all, but we will be imprisoned in our homes for an indefinite amount of time. I feel a surge of relief and go out to the shops to get some supplies.

My granddad's poem:

Thanksgiving

When to the sweet soft sounds of distant Sophia's voice
I listen with enraptured parent ear
Though seas divide, I still rejoice,
For Sophia's lovely picture and her voice are here.

278

O Sophia, loveliest of all the flowers of spring.
Our hearts with thankfulness to God o'erflow;
What presents can we ever bring to Him,
To cancel out this wondrous debt we owe?
There is not anything that we can give,
This miracle of life to stand beside;
Only if we give ourselves and live
As He has taught us, all self denied.
O Sophia, what is your secret power
That makes us dote on you from hour to hour?
F.E.W.

"Only if we give ourselves and live". That is the only thing that matters. That is the only thing worth taking with me. There is nothing we can do or be that truly matters in the bigger scheme of things. The only thing important, the only thing worthwhile is to live fully, with our whole being.

My granddad, the person who loved me absolutely and unconditionally as I was, for who I was, with no judgement or criticism. All he wanted of me was for me to be happy. He shared his passion for literature, his love of parks and ball games, his love of poetry and his time with me. He read a book if I recommended it and talked to me about it. He listened to my problems, went on walks with me, made his home mine. He loved me without expectation, without judgement, he loved me pure and simple. And as lost as I might feel right now, my dream is telling me that the path is set right here, clear and obvious, "give yourself and live", that is the only way. Not to live half-heartedly, bitter, afraid, feeling damaged, hiding, but to live full-heartedly, as myself, with my whole being. To live, no matter what life throws at me, what suffering and pain may come my way. The challenges, they are all there to be lived, fully, to be experienced, to be learned from and to be grateful for. Pain and hurt are emotions, they are part of the human fabric and need to be experienced fully, consciously. They show us we have hearts, that we are not ghosts roaming the world, but human beings, alive.

No point shying away from what life throws at me or shutting down to it, ignoring it. Even if I survived that way, it would be a shadow of a life, a half-life, only half-experienced. The only way is to live fully, stay with the emotions, be alive to feelings; whether pain and hurt, or beauty, joy, warmth and love.

Real value in life is not in material things, it is to be found in the emotional, spiritual. It's not about what we have, what we do, it is about how we live, how we respond to what life throws at us. It's about finding joy and gratitude in everything, in the small and large, the good, the hard. It is about embracing life, like a butterfly flying from flower to flower, like a flower blossoming to the sun, like the morning dew, fresh and vibrant.

It is not focusing on the suffering, the depth and intensity of it, but how we learn and grow from that suffering and open our buds to it. It can be found in our connection to our heart and finding the warmth and love in it, even when it cries with pain. Life plays in music, in feeling music and dancing to its rhythm. It radiates out to us when we can see and let in the beauty inherent in all things and we embrace that beauty. It's in being able to receive all through the eyes of the shining beauty contained within our inner world. Life is "giving ourselves and living" fully, with all our being, open to life's currents, with acceptance and with the ability to flow with them, finding joy in them, gaining strength from them.

It is about having an open heart and choosing life, choosing to live, to be alive, to feel.

The more we are afraid, the more we defend and protect, the more we hold back, the less we live, the less joy we feel, we close up, we are not alive. To live fully we must learn to let go, to let go of our fears, our inhibitions, our protective walls. Fear of pain is also fear of life. Fear freezes us and prevents us from living. Fear of pain and life is fear of being happy, to feeling fully, to embracing life with all that is has to offer.

Being happy for me is at some very deep, cellular level disobeying my parents, going against their will. I'm challenging their belief that I don't deserve to be happy, I'm challenging the way they taught me to live and be. I am challenging their voices. They made me feel I had no right to be here in this world and I learned to withdraw from life, touch around its edges instead of plunging into its deep waters.

I'm afraid to be happy, because I'm so sure it will be taken away from me. As a child when I was happy, always something was said or done to crush me. I have learned to block the feeling of complete happiness, because the pain is sure to follow and it will be all the more crushing for having experienced the warmth of joy just a moment before. I dare not believe that I deserve it and that it might be here to stay. For me, happiness brings fear. Getting something I want petrifies me, I'm so sure it will be taken away from me, if I depend on it, trust it, like it. So I try not to feel, not to hope, not to have. But a life lived like that is so constrained and limited, so poor. I closed myself to survive as a child, but I am stronger now and don't need to shut down anymore. I can live fully and flow with the pain. Otherwise life becomes survival, hanging on, not living.

The answer to the question "What can I do? How can I get out of this? How do I live my life?" is contained in the poem. "Only if we give ourselves and live". My grandfather is telling me how to live, the only way to really live.

I can bring his unconditional, complete love, devoid of any judgement, any pretences or expectations into my heart and let that experience fill my physical and mental consciousness.

I can't remember his funeral, even now, it must have been too traumatic for me to be able to experience it fully. I can remember his love, there for me always, as I was, without any burdens placed on it, without a price attached to it.

I'm staying contained at the moment. I'm holding my place, and that feels like there's no movement at all, as if I'm stuck, frozen. The seed has been planted. It's underground, dark, waiting for spring. It takes time.

My mother is so all-consuming, the only way I could survive her onslaught was by staying separate. She would have otherwise usurped me for her own life. She wants to rob me of myself somehow, she's envious in some way. She's either trying to muffle me or steal any happiness, energy, fulfilment I have.

Any contact with her and I feel her trying to take over me,

drown me. I need to forgive myself for wanting to stay away from her, at least for now.

I need to open myself to life, to real life, feeling alive in my cells, accepting pain, anger and even hatred, as I want to accept joy, love and happiness.

The thought of my granddad is comforting. He loved me for who I was. He accepted me and gave me unconditional love. He gave me time, tenderness and discipline, in a genuine, heartfelt way. He was kind and strict. He was warm and loving. His time was mine if I wanted it. I cherish what he gave me, deeply. Someone did love me, knew me and loved me, I cherish that. And his words resonate "Only if we give ourselves and live". Live Sophia, spread your wings and fly…

I'm travelling on buses in Malaysia. Darcy and Nile, very close friends of mine from university, are there with me. The bus drivers are being total jerks. None of them will let me get on their bus. I go from driver to driver, but they all refuse me, rudely. They keep me waiting for an answer when I ask them a question and are nasty and aggressive towards me.

I'm meant to be returning somewhere, I've tried all the buses in the area and still no one has let me on. I'm the only one left without a bus to travel on.

The situation reminds me of my school days when after school we would all gather at the square where all the school buses for our school were parked and find our bus. We had to be on time. I didn't feel I belonged on my bus. I didn't have any friends on it. All my friends travelled on different buses. I felt excluded then too. But here I'm excluded completely, as I'm not allowed on any of the buses.

There are so many buses, but none are available to me.

The whole image is one of a group of buses and lots of people travelling on them, the collective, moving together in groups. But I'm excluded. I've never felt part of the collective, I've never made choices that fit in with what society deems to be the 'proper', usual choices, somehow I've never completely fitted in. But do I even want to get on a bus? I'm trying very hard to, so at some level it seems that I do. But I'm not allowed on, because I don't fit in, even when I try to.

What is core to me? Where does my heart lead me? It doesn't really lead me into the collective. It never has. The collective told me to act in certain ways, for example continue in investment banking, a career recognised and approved by many, one that earns good wages and provides a decent lifestyle, but I chose to leave that path and become a yoga teacher, an occupation seen as fringe, more fun than work and one that means constant financial struggle. I spent most of my adult life together with the man I love, although we didn't fit into norms, we didn't get married or have children, we had a very independent yet supportive relationship. I am accepting and non-judgemental of people or behaviours that are shunned by society.

In spite of these life choices, a part of me does get influenced by the collective. I care about what they think. I try to fit in in various ways and be accepted.

I eventually do manage to get on a bus, but I'm the only one on it. I spend so long running around trying to join one of the buses there, so many of them full with groups of people, but eventually the one that I do manage to get on, has only me on it. I am going to be travelling alone on my own journey. My journey is not one of the common, popular journeys, it does not bring me into the collective, join me with them, but I feel comfortable and satisfied being on my own on the bus. It feels right.

Nile and Darcy are positive figures for me. They are close friends, whom I can depend on, whom I trust. They are beautiful, warm people and I love them and know they love me. They are there to support me at the start of my journey. Their support, presence and energy are there for me as positive resources, but I have to travel the distance alone.

The baby cries. She is left there. It's meant for her own good. She is meant to learn to fall asleep. In time she will no longer cry when put to bed, that is the hope. It is called positive discipline, teaching the baby not to cry. But that is not what she learns, what she learns is that she can't depend on others, her screams aren't heard, her needs will not be met. She cries until despair and fatigue take over and she falls asleep. She has been abandoned. There is no hope, only despair. The terror, the loneliness, the pain of abandonment is too much for her to take in, to experience, so she freezes, shuts down.

The child grows up. She's resented by her parents. She's punished, because she's inherently bad. She's told she's bad. It's all her fault. She is hated because she is who she is, because she exists. She learns to hate herself. How can the all-knowing, powerful parents be mistaken? She is bad, evil, she is to blame because she is alive. She knows this to be true. It cannot be any other way.

Parents' actions, knowledge and words are never questioned by a baby or a small child. They are to the child as a God. Their non-existence would mean death to the baby and survival instincts mean that the baby must learn to cope, appease, be quiet.

Parents don't necessarily mean to harm their child. Most of the time they are doing their best, acting in ways they think are right, in ways they were brought up by their own parents. They are also guided and driven by their own characters, impulses, shadow material and complexes. They do their best in their own way. And yet the damage can be so tremendously significant. In fact the way a baby and small child is treated by its parents defines the rest of its life, unless it goes deep down into the shadows, into the dark recesses of its phsyche and heals the wounds created. That path is dark, painful and long, but ultimately it frees us from our shackles to our parents' shadows. We can then continue our lives free and light, guided by our own inner soul, our own heart, rather than our parents' sword.

26 June 13

I feel completely numb all over. I notice no emotions at all, nothing except for a dull aching pain in my heart. I feel shut off from life. Something's wrong with my body. There is so much tension gathered in it, it feels like it will explode. The tension's crashing down on me. I can't sleep at all, I've never had a sleeping problem, but I can't now. I am extremely tired all of the time. My eyes are stinging and constantly watering, they hurt. I had a coughing fit last night, although I'm not ill and don't have a cough. I feel like I'm breaking down. My body can't take it any longer, it can't take any more of the pain, the awareness, the uncertainty. And yet I don't know why all this is happening, I don't understand. All I want to do is sleep. Close my eyes and sleep, peacefully, for a very very long time.

I feel like I'm sitting outside of my life, watching, disinterested, not engaged with what I'm seeing in any way. I'm watching alone. I feel alone, but that doesn't cause me distress. In my mind, I'm terrified of being alone, yet in my body being alone isn't a problem. I feel cold. My heart has been replaced by an aching ice cube. I feel isolated. So much in the background, yet in the foreground it's just me, watching, not feeling and alone.

I want to be able to love, but there's a casket of steel around my heart, locking it in. The casket is shut so tight, nothing leaves the heart and nothing enters, no warmth, no sunlight. I cannot love, my heart is cold, it is incapable of warmth and love. I'm trapped, locked in. I can't breathe.

I want to die, more than anything in the world, I want to die, but I'm afraid of failing and having to live out the rest of my life in pain. I don't have the courage to act on my desire.

I want to be held, loved, told "It's okay. I love you as you are, I love all that you are. It's going to be okay", but I would not be able to return that love, so I don't want it. When it's there, I kill it. I've thrown away the key to the casket that guards and protects my heart. The key's lost, my heart is gone and I'm lost.

I want to hide under covers and cry, but there are no tears, I'm dry. I'm left emotionless, cold and dry. Am I alive?

Could someone please, please, please break that casket so I can feel once again? I'm powerless. There's nothing I can do. I do not understand. I'm this tiny little figure, alone, in a huge desert, sand as far as the eyes can see in all directions. I'm tiny and the world is a big, hostile place. I want to hide. The world is too much for me.

I feel like I'm rotting, as if I need cleaning. I feel disgust undirected, but landing on myself. Shit is being stirred with a propeller, my shit, decayed matter, me. Instead of sinking to the bottom, the murky matter is getting stirred into awareness.

I feel into my heart. It hurts somehow. I feel the steel gates. They're locked. I can't get in. I don't feel my heart. It's not beating. I give up.

I feel into the steel gates. I become the steel gates. The gate has cold, steel, gnarled poles. The poles want to lock out life, they want to squash all life, hope and joy. They want to dig their roots into life and as they enter, life turns to ice. It freezes over and is no longer. They have only one aim, one desire, they are there to kill.

It's dark all around. Dark, damp and cold. I can smell damp and decay. The whole place reeks of death.

I become the steel gates. I feel like them, wanting to kill, only to kill and cause suffering. I realise, the gates have always been there, they have always enclosed my heart. I ask them how they got there around my heart in the first place, who placed them there? An image of my father's mother appears.

I try to understand, it doesn't make any sense at all. My grandmother was always good to me. I was her favourite, being her first grandchild. My grandmother always had favourites and made sure everyone knew who they were. She was a bitter, bitter, evil woman. She felt no happiness and allowed for no joy in life. Her entire life was built around making those closest to her suffer. She lived a life of unhappiness and complaints. My aunt was her carer for the last fifteen years of her life and she made my aunt's life hell, often for no reason at all other than wanting to make her suffer, the only person around that would take it, whom she could make suffer, whom she had power over. She was unhappy, so everyone else had to be unhappy too.

I didn't like her. I hated her for the way she treated people, for the way she favouritised me over my sister and made that felt by my sister acutely, by the way she used and abused my aunt.

I focus on the gates. I know, my body knows, they are there to destroy joy and life, to kill and punish. I wonder why. I feel their hatred of life, their resentment of happiness, their desire to destroy. I feel their overwhelming desire for revenge and infinite hatred. I can feel their hate spread throughout my body, into every single cell of my body. It tastes bitter, it is pure poison. I'm suffocating. The hate is too overwhelming, it's too much, it is drowning me in its poison.

And suddenly I see, feel and know. I know it in my heart and soul, I really know, not just understand, figure out, think, but know within me that it is true. Those steel gates have their roots in my grandmother. My dad's abuse was caused by those gates, by his mother's nastiness and bitterness, her subconscious drive for revenge, her pure evil emanating out.

My grandmother did not shout or punish, she was manipulative subtly. She hated life, she had been unhappy all her life and she could not bear to see happiness in others. She was selfish. If she couldn't be the centre of the universe through love, she would get what she wanted by manipulation and emotional blackmail.

My dad could not accept his mother as evil. He couldn't see the poison in her. His mother was untouchable. He couldn't face the gates himself, so he passed the gates on to me. All that was evil that came from his mother was placed by him on to me. She was incapable of love, so in his mind he made me incapable of love. She was evil, so he thought of me as evil. All the shadow he could not see in his mother, or carry for himself, he placed on me. He hated me for being alive, just as she hated life and he didn't even know why he felt or acted the way he did. He could not hold the gates, so he planted them in me. He felt the poison within him, the hatred and anger, the bitterness, the death of joy, but he couldn't own them or face them, so he placed them on my shoulders to carry and to own.

My father could not accept my grandmother's shadow, her evil, poisonous side. Even the mere thought of thinking bad of his own mother is too outrageously wrong, unacceptable. A mother must be respected and cherished. Any faults in his mother were impossible, unbearable for him to consider. His trauma shifted on to me. I was innocent, he could turn on to me what he couldn't onto his own mother. She had outrage in her, a hatred towards life, she wanted to destroy, the power of the evil she felt was fierce. She's the one who's cruel, disgusting, who kills life, not me.

My father's suffering, his unexpressed emotions, the abuse he received when he was vulnerable were mirrored on to me. At the same time he could not understand why he treated me so badly, what drove him to abuse me, so instead of looking at himself, he placed the blame of his abuse on me as well. I must be a terrible person to induce treatment like that from him, because he couldn't possibly be in the wrong, he couldn't be bad or even fallible. The only way he could accept the way he treated me was if he believed that I deserved it. I must be inherently evil and bad. He couldn't love me, but he thought of himself as a good, moral, loving person, so it must be I who could not be loved, not he who could not love. What could he do? He provided for me, fed me, sent me to school and hated me, wondering what he had done to be given such a bad child. After all, he was doing all he could to discipline me, to make me a better person, but nothing I ever did was good enough, he always saw darkness in my person, my being, my actions and words. All this darkness I have carried as my burden, and all the while it belonged elsewhere.

Seconds after the understanding I feel my heart release, as if the steel gates are melting away. I can breathe again. There is light. Warmth spreads out from my body. I feel complete love and compassion towards my father. I feel total forgiveness towards him. I can love him without pain or anger, without resentment or hurt. Pure love.

People's unresolved bitterness, anger and resentment, if not faced, owned and addressed get placed on someone else, usually the child. My father carried my grandmother's shadow and passed it on to me intact, without understanding it or realising what he was doing. He could not face it himself. But I understand now that the shadow doesn't belong to me. It is not I who am unloveable or evil or bad, it is someone else's baggage.

I have been talking about and working on these issues for a while now, yet 'knowing', feeling, understanding something in your body, in your heart is completely different to understanding it analytically. With that image, a deep understanding, a knowledge somewhere deep within appeared and with that knowledge came release and freedom, the ability to really forgive from my heart and to love genuinely.

I feel love emerge from my heart, a huge surge of pure, untainted love and empathy towards my father. I feel his suffering and forgive him naturally and easily. I love him and I forgive him, with all my heart.

My chest feels light now. The tension has lifted and out of all that darkness, contraction, bog and locked gates pure love has emerged.

She wanted to kill life. But life has emerged after all...

I can feel that things are shifting. I feel stronger within. I have connected to my heart and I know it's there, available to me as a source of life and love. Life hasn't suddenly become easy, quite the opposite, life continues to throw shit at me, but I feel more whole within myself and can face life standing erect, rooted and tall.

I had a moment of clarity the other day. I realised I have always searched for happiness outside. If I do this, move there, work here, see these people, live in such a place, at such a location, have this,... then I'll be happy. Just as I have always searched for love from the outside. I needed someone to love me, I was not able to give love to myself, I needed to see it in another for the hole within me to be at least in part filled. I had little self-worth, so my worth depended on others' thoughts and feelings of me. But there's always something we don't have or that we want. Getting all of them would still not make us happy, if we don't have the source within us. And if we do have it within ourselves, then having none of the outside elements will not be able to make us unhappy.

We are constantly struggling in life. There's always a difficulty, some event that hurts us, sets us back. There is always something we are less than satisfied about. But life cannot be perfect. Having everything right will not give us satisfaction either, even if we did get to that place. A year ago I had everything in my life I had ever wanted and was crushed by the realisation I still did not feel happy. I couldn't understand why. And so started my descent.

The solution is not changing our environment, living in a better house, finding a more fulfilling job, a new lover, although these changes might be necessary. The ultimate solution lies within ourselves. We can be happy having nothing. Happiness doesn't come from outside sources, it lies in our hearts, and if we allow it to, if we break down all the barricades surrounding it, it will explode and spread throughout our body.

Connection to the heart and meditation, I find peace and satisfaction in the now, in things as they are.

I have spent my life trying to fill holes, complete missing pieces. That search has no ending and there's no point to it, no satisfaction to be received from it...

Things have shifted for me. I have stood my ground at work, set and defended my boundaries, I spoke my mind and heart to Arthur, opened my heart, made myself vulnerable without fear of how he would respond or what he would think and I felt good about all of this, I felt comfortable inside and confident. I stand taller now, stronger, I face life with confidence and awareness.

A patient at the clinic wanted a private yoga lesson every day and practising with him every day has shifted my recent lack of inclination to practise. Physical yoga has entered my life once again and once again I feel it's power to transform.

Old patterns and tensions have been releasing from my body, leaving me, letting go of their hold and in their place space and light, life and joy are appearing. I'm alive, my cells are alive and I am aware of their subtle vibrations, I feel content, comfortable and confident. I am happy!

4 July 13

I walk into my room. It's bare. There's not a single item of furniture in it. It is a poor dwelling. It looks old and decrepit. There's a seal in it. What's a seal doing in my room? Suddenly, perhaps surprised by my entrance, it leaps up and is standing upside down on the ceiling, looking at me. I'm wondering what's going on. Not a single emotion comes up for me, no fear or concern. I feel indifferent and just think it's odd.

I switch the light on. The light startles the seal. It moves with incredible speed and leaps out of sight. It moves so fast, I don't even see the movement. How can a seal move so fast? How the hell did it manage to stand on my ceiling anyway? And what in the world was it doing in my room in the first place?

The seal has left deep indentations and dents in the ceiling. The ceiling is severely damaged from its movements.

A seal's natural element is water. But the seal's out of place, it's not only on dry land, but it's in a flat, where you don't see seals and it's walking upside down on the ceiling, which is physically impossible, as is the speed of its movement when the light comes on.

Water represents the unconscious. But the seal is for some reason not able to be in the unconscious, the deep psyche, where it belongs, instead it is in an arid space, moving in the realm of ideation rather than embodiment, it's in the head, on the ceiling, where it can only move upside down. Similar to how I respond when I see the seal. I feel nothing, not even surprise or fear. I only think and wonder. Emotions are cut off for me at the moment; the unconscious is not within my awareness. I am only in touch with logic and thoughts.

The unconscious, the deep psyche, the home of emotions and sensations are misplaced within me. I've moved them into my head, when they should stem from my heart. I'm trying to understand and analyse. I'm thinking rather than feeling. But that's all upside down and not the way it should be. I need to connect with the unconscious, with feeling. I need to allow myself to actually feel what comes up and live it, let it be felt and seen, rather than trying to analyse and think my way through it.

When I walk in, I can see that the seal is out of its element, but there is a lack of emotional connection there. I don't feel anything. I do switch the light on though, to see better.

For some reason I am not connecting to the feeling level, everything is moving up into my head, into thinking, even when it's feelings that I need to engage with. The indentations and destruction caused by this movement are quite severe.

The room is bare, there's a feeling of poverty in my home. It is not welcoming in an emotional way. The feeling of homeliness has not been created. It is completely bare, there is nothing in it to receive someone, to welcome them or to make me feel comfortable in there. It is barren. There are no personal touches. It is an old room, a room of old habits and patterns.

Like magic, the seal, the unconscious and realm of feelings, jumps into my head. There is within me a tendency to always rationalise, use thought and cognition and try to analyse my way out of difficult emotions. It's the most familiar, comfortable way for me. It is the old way. But it causes destruction and the seal vanishes without creating emotion. It has not served its purpose. It remains unfelt, in a way unseen.

I like my independence, I can't be tied down. I try to analyse why, whether that's my nature or a way of self-defence. I think of my mother. I feel strong anger towards her. She was there in body for me, but in no other way, she was too consumed with herself to be able to love, care or share with another. She withheld everything. I feel a deep, deep betrayal by my mother and I hate her for it.

I try not to, I fight the feeling, it seems so wrong, but it's hard for me to feel compassion after such huge betrayal and abandonment. In fact at the moment it is impossible, although I am fighting my resentment and hatred, because they are 'wrong', one cannot hate her own mother, that is bad in some way.

I try to think my way out of it, analyse my feelings so that I can understand why and how and stop hating. But I can't. These days, even the sound of her voice gives me goose pimples all over and a feeling of disgust rises in my throat.

Maybe I should accept the way I feel, let it be, let it live out its life. Things do transform and a deeper, feeling and sensation led forgiveness, understanding and compassion might yet come. In fact, recognising how I feel, accepting the emotions, letting them surface might be the only way of releasing them, causing the least amount of harm, both towards her and myself.

Letting go of trying to control and change, just letting be, being with what comes up, whatever emotions I feel, whatever sensations arise, just being with them, accepting them would be the seal's way. Forcing, analysing, refusing to accept, labelling as wrong is turning it all upside down, on its head, in an unnatural, impossible habitat and only creates damage.

6 July 13

I feel hurt and betrayed. I feel let down. My navel is screaming. God, so much pain, I can't possibly survive it. My whole body hurts, but the pain in my navel is excruciating. I feel knives thrusting in and twisting, thrusting away into my navel, in, twist, out, in, twist, out. So much pain. I think I will die. I will die of the pain, just the pure intensity of the pain, it's so fierce.

I know, I know within me, the pain was there anyway, it had always been there. It had been triggered by recent events, not created by them. The events were not what caused the pain, they touched an old wound and made it bleed again.

I stay with the pain, with the sensations. No thoughts at all, no analysis. I simply watch. I feel my mother in there, somehow she is part of the deep, old wound, and my father and Miles. But I don't follow these thoughts or try to analyse what is going on or what I am feeling. I stay with the sensations in my navel. They are excruciating. At times I can't breathe. I feel the knives. I feel my abdomen bleeding.

I stay there, in these sensations, with them, gently crying, holding myself as I feel. After three hours I can take it no longer. I think "I give up". I go to bed and let my mind wonder to walks, travel destinations I've been to, work, unrelated things, pleasant things. I allow my mind to drift.

Suddenly I start shaking uncontrollably. My whole body is shaking, my teeth chattering. I feel freezing cold. I'm shivering. I curl up under the covers, drawing them in around me and lie there shaking. I let the shivering, shaking take over. No thoughts, just the shaking.

I fall asleep.

I wake up feeling refreshed, healed somehow, whole. I feel within me that hurt, betrayal, heart break, abandonment will no longer hurt me in my navel when it comes, not in the old way. The old wound has released its grip. My body has re-adjusted and let go of the tension held there for decades.

I had not analysed or understood the pain or tried to track it down to its roots. I had just let it be and felt it, allowed it expression and release. I had simply stayed with it and watched it. With that simple action of accepting and being, somehow it had been expressed and released, it was no longer buried under analysis, covered in layers of logic or frozen out and ignored or brushed aside, it had not been forced away from my conscious experience. It had not been squashed back down deeper into my being. It had had a chance to live, express and release.

I feel this is another turning point for me. The fear of emotional pain, betrayal, being let down, abandoned have always triggered this pain in me in the past. I have suppressed it with force, carried on with my life, distracted myself through doing and reacted by changing the circumstance that had led to the re-triggering of the pain, mistakenly believing that new circumstance to be the cause of it. In truth all those incidents were only triggers. The real cause, the source lies far back in time. Just allowing the pain to be, letting it rise to consciousness and accepting it have melted the wound's hold on me. Also the realisation that staying with it didn't kill me, I survived and in fact felt better afterwards. The pain and the fear of annihilation it brings with it have lost their hold on me. I know that pain won't resurface, not in the same way. The wound has been acknowledged. An event will no longer have a greater effect on me than its due, the pain won't be exaggerated or misplaced. I can now respond appropriately without the clouding over created by the re-bleeding of an ancient wound.

9 July 13

Arthur is over. I want to talk to him. He asks about Mick. I tell him we broke up a long time ago. We go to a restaurant.

He says he needs to go to the toilet. I walk into the courtyard and call Mick, we haven't broken up. I go inside after the call and Arthur is waiting for me there with that look upon his face, that look that says "you liar, so out comes the truth", a look of accusation as well as resignation. I say "You heard me, didn't you" But I feel relieved he's found out. I have nothing to lose now. I can be completely honest with him about everything.

He asks me about internet connection at my place and tells me he needs to do some work. Then he says my connection might not be sufficient for what he needs. He starts to leave. I call after him "But you're still going to listen to me, aren't you?"

I realise that with all the lies I've told, I've lost my chance of having an open, honest communication with him, but I feel relieved at the same time. With everything out in the open, I have nothing to lose and so no need to hold back in any way. He's angry and he no longer trusts or believes me. To him I'm just a liar. I realise any honest conversation between us is going to be difficult to have.

Any situation based on false pretences will try to come out to the surface and be resolved truthfully. When not seen and squashed down, they can explode and create havoc. Honesty and open communication is the basis, the foundation of having a free, genuine life. I have nothing to lose. I might as well be honest. There is strength in real truth that comes from the heart, even though we might think we're leaving ourselves vulnerable and bare by opening ourselves up.

It will be a difficult conversation. I know that, because I feel guilty and at the same time vulnerable. I will have to open my heart, which leads to me feeling vulnerable, but there is strength in being able to accept and be with our vulnerability and allowing another to see it, because although we fear they have more access to us and can hurt us more deeply, we have been ourselves as we are and huge strength emanates from that.

The 'outer' internet connection might not be strong enough, but I still want him to listen to me, to my direct voice, my personal communication. Our relationship and communication at an outer level may not be functioning properly, it might not seem strong enough, but I still have my voice and he his ears, I still want him to listen and I want to be heard. As difficult as doing this might be for me, it is what I want to do and am capable of doing.

At work a colleague told me today that I made his day and that our conversations fill him with a positive feeling. I was surprised and happy to hear that. It had never occurred to me that I may, just by my presence, be a positive influence on anyone, or the way their day is going. I couldn't imagine that someone might simply like me for who I am and enjoy my company. I find some people inspirational. Time with them, their presence make me feel happy and energised. But I have never thought I could have that effect on someone myself.

While speaking to him, our conversation led to a realisation within me. We were talking about not being able to fit into society and conform to their norms. The image of those buses I had tried so hard to get on came up for me. The buses full of people and I wasn't allowed on any, until I found a bus just for me. At school I wanted to be 'part of' a group, have a best friend, be the same as other girls in my year, but I never really felt part of any group, not fully and I never did have a best friend, although I had many close friends. That felt like a problem for me at the time.

I no longer have that desire. I no longer want to be part of a group, or 'belong' somewhere. I no longer want to get on one of those buses. I'm happy to ride on my own and choose my own route. The thought doesn't make me feel alone either. It feels good. I'm comfortable with it. Friends, real friends, support each other on their individual journeys and I am truly lucky to have people in my life I can call true friends. Moving on my own individual path, with the support and warmth of my friends, who are on their own, separate paths feels good.

I also realise that although I didn't have a 'best' friend, I have always had so many close friends, ones I can count on, ones I care about and who care about me. The 'best' friend idea is just another label imposed on us, especially teenagers, by society. So many people don't even like their best friends. There can often be resentment and competition between them, sometimes outright animosity. And yet I'm happy with my close friends. We cherish each other and our friendships without the need for labels. The realisation comforts and warms me.

I feel within me and an image appears, forming gradually. I realise that if we are truly aware of our true selves and connected to it and if we can be confident in ourselves, in who we are, what we want and our connections, then we can all be individuals, not outcasts but individuals, all on their own separate paths, but there for each other, to support each other, learn from one another. We can be individuals, yet connected to other people and groups of people by thin spider web strings, leading out from our being and connecting to all the others.

I see a stick man, made of embroidered strings. He's running and laughing. He's happy and full of life and energy. His strings are leading out from his heart and connecting to many, many others, all beings with their own separate identities, running joyfully and connected to many others in turn. Many webs and strings connecting many happy stick men. It's beautiful. The image fills me with joy.

I got on my own bus, alone, on my own way, shunned by all other buses there, but I felt Nile and Darcy's presence. They weren't on the bus with me, but they were with me in spirit, supporting me on my individual journey as real friends do.

I feel comfortable and happy within myself. I am not caged in by the constraints, labels and judgements that come with being part of a fixed group, I am bound to no society or person or gathering, I lead my own life and make my own decisions. I have chosen jobs that don't fit in with the way we see success in the West. Even though I have the education, training and experience for well paying jobs, I have chosen severely underpaid careers. I recently started a training that wasn't the one my manager wanted me to do, but it was the one I wanted to do, so I went for it anyway.

I take the difficult path if my heart calls for me to, even when I know how hard it will be for me. I have always followed my understanding of my heart's guidance. I have never gone for the easy option, I've gone for what feels right and the beauty of this moment is, suddenly, instead of questioning it, I feel comfortable with all of this. I am happy with my choices and decisions. I have no regrets.

18 July 13

Arthur' eyes are so swollen, they're almost shut. His eyelids are swollen, I can't see his eyes.

Arthur can't see or perceive what the situation is and hence his lack of any response to my communication. He isn't able to connect to his own feelings and therefore cannot respond to mine. It's like an emotional blindness.

I liked who I was with Arthur. In relationships we hold each other, somehow provide a solid ground from which each can stand tall and grow. There's a sense of protection, safety. He brought out the best in me. But he is no longer with me. It hurts, I feel the loss, but I also understand that he needs to clear his eyes and see me, see himself as well, his feeling side, for us to move forward together. I cannot compromise on this point any longer. I need his eyes to heal.

He was like a mirror that projected me and my life the way I wanted to see them. I no longer need that projection. As much as I miss him, I want and need a deeper, more emotional connection between us and that will and can only happen if he opens his eyes.

Arthur comes to stay with me in Zwich on Langstrasse. He says he wants to buy a few things from Uniqlo and Fopp before his flight. I say I'll go with him, but I need to pee first.

I end up taking a long time. I have to go outside of the flat and into the public corridor. The toilets stink of male piss. The one that's free is disgustingly dirty, small and cramped. The same toilets are also being used by the restaurants downstairs. The hallways are noisy, there are a lot of people buzzing around.

I decide to also change my top. I want to wear something nicer to make a good impression on him. I take off the top I'm wearing and put on a sleeveless one instead, but I'm not satisfied, it doesn't look good enough, so I decide to go and buy one that's better, perhaps sexier.

I leave the building. I realise I don't have keys with me to get back in. I start wandering the streets and I run into Jim, a good friend of mine, walking his dog with a friend. I'm in a hurry, but I don't want to be rude, so I have a short chat with them.

Then I continue walking through the streets. I don't see any clothes shops and don't find anything I can buy. At some point I realise that I've walked quite a distance and am now far away from the flat. I don't know what time Arthur's flight is and I suddenly panic that he might have already left. I'm overwhelmed with sheer panic and anxiety that I might miss him.

I find myself standing on a freeway, lots of motorways weaving above, under, through each other, cars driving by fast.

I try to grab a taxi, although I know I can't afford it, I guess it will cost about twenty francs. I have no Swiss money on me, but I do have my credit cards.

I manage to hail a cab, but another woman comes up to it as well. She tells me she's going to take the cab. She's in a wheelchair. I'm already giving my address to the taxi driver when she comes up to the cab. When I see her wheelchair I automatically take a step back to let her through. She smiles in a

victorious, derogatory way. I tell her I'm really in a hurry, my partner's about
to leave to catch a flight.

She cuts me short and says "yeah, yeah, yeah" sarcastically, as if I'm
making it all up. She leans over towards the driver to give him her address. It
angers me that she feels she has a right to the cab just because she is in a
wheelchair. Her derogatory, nasty smile is infuriating too.

I say "fuck off", I give my address to the cab driver and get in.

I'm terrified Arthur will already be gone.

I wake up feeling utterly numb.

I run off from Arthur following my own selfish desires, missing what's really important at that moment, which is what he wants to do in his limited time there. I run to find a t-shirt that will help me look better, but what does that matter if he's not there to see it when I return? I don't do the things he wants to do, I'm so preoccupied with my own stuff, lost in my own selfish world.

If only he could hear my heart.

I tell the woman in the wheelchair to fuck off. She's trying to use emotional blackmail to get what she wants, but I stand up to her. She's taking it for granted I'll step aside, but although I do at first, I realise that I have a right to that cab and my need is urgent, so eventually I take it. She's a persona within me, one that is derogatory towards me, although limited in her movement. She can get her way by using her disability as an excuse to make me feel guilty and bad about myself. I'm saying no to the quality in me that uses emotional blackmail and pity to get its own way.

I'm trying to connect with Arthur, also an inner figure within me, perhaps someone firm, independent and standing strong. I'm trying hard to overcome obstacles I encounter along the way, some created by myself, some out of my control. I'm trying to reach him, although I walk away from him to start off with, not realising his importance. I've lost track of the inner Arthur through distractions. I'm lost in my selfish needs and desires. But I awaken to this and put in all the energy and power that I have to reconnect with him. The desire to buy a t-shirt, look good, go off and do my own thing and the woman in the wheelchair are what are trying to keep me away from Arthur. These are material, worldly distractions and the inner figure that uses emotional blackmail.

Clothes are symbolic of what we show to the world, how we are seen by it. I want to look a certain way and am distracted by this endeavour. How I want to be seen in the world is distracting me from connecting to the more evolved, developed, whole sense of my standing in the world that comes from within.

Restaurant and the public toilets are the collective. They are noisy, they stink and I want to express and relieve myself there in a dirty, uncomfortable, public environment. This seems inappropriate.

The freeway, all those motorways, are the collective getting places fast. It is unnatural, dehumanised. They are driving around at high speed, disconnected from nature, from each other. They are using machines and highways, motorways, man built, unnatural structures. The whole setting has a sense of anxiety, stress and hurry associated with it.

Langstrasse is the centre for addictive behaviours; sex, bars, drugs. Addiction is a way to avoid suffering. It keeps us from feeling, from connecting to our strong inner self. It creates a distraction that takes over a person's life, so that they are no longer connected to their feelings, to themselves. That is where I am, with Arthur, before I set off. I am disconnected to feeling, to what is important to me, to a connection with Arthur. I wake up feeling numb. The terror of losing Arthur is so overwhelming, I can't stay with that feeling for long and I go numb, I disconnect to protect myself. I am already disconnected when I wake up. I am probably at some level disconnected in my everyday life, distracting myself in various ways.

There is a hole within me, a deep, dark void that I am having difficulty filling or staying with at a sensational level. The void is there because I don't feel connected to what Arthur represents. And there is huge anxiety and fear around the possibility that I might not be able to, ever again, with him now gone from my life. But I go for it with all I've got; the little money I have, all my energy and strength.

The emotional blackmailer within me is the one who uses disability as an excuse to take from me, perhaps the voices that tell me I am not capable, I'm not good enough, I don't have the resources or ability within me, that I'm not worthy, that I don't deserve anything better. If I want to move on, I need to tell these voices to fuck off. They disable me, hinder my movement, create self-pity. And here I do, in spite of the outer, negative picture it portrays, I stand up for myself, I am strong and I move on.

Those background voices are always there. They're there without me even being aware of them. They disable me in their own way and keep me from moving on, from connecting to what is important to me. They know what they are doing, her victorious, derogatory smile tells me that. They want to impede me, harm me and are confident that they will be able to. I don't let them win.

My attitude at work is tainted by these voices. I assume that as I'm not a qualified therapist, it's my place to have to do all the shitty jobs, that's all I have to offer them. But half the staff are trainee therapists and I have just as much to offer as they do, if not more, due to my experiences and background. And yet I undermine myself, I undersell my abilities and my worth and do work that does not fulfil me.

Even with people I know socially I let the voices through. I think it's a favour for them to see me. I find it hard to imagine that they might like me and enjoy my company because of who I am. I feel I have to keep doing things for them to feel worthwhile. I am never completely sure of their love and affection, even though there have been so many signs to prove otherwise. I easily pick up on the negative and strongly ignore the positive.

22 August 13

I'm thrusting a serrated knife into Arthur's heart. I stick it in with force, then turn it around and then again and again. I draw it out and stick it in through another point in his chest and again and again I turn it around. While thrusting the knife into him and moving it around to cause maximum pain, I'm screaming "Does that hurt, you fucker? Does that hurt you? Can you feel anything at all?" He remains indifferent to my thrusts, to the visible wounds the knife is creating. He is above it all, separate from any pain I may be inflicting. He can't hear my screams.

I'm feeling anger towards Arthur at last. In fact I'm raging. He has hurt me deeply and I'm able to recognise that. I feel anger towards his lack of feelings for me, his lack of response, his shut down heart.

So far I've taken on all the blame for our break-up. I've felt all the emotions, the pain, loss and hurt. I've been grieving. My anger has been turned inwards towards myself and at last, for the first time, I am feeling absolute fury towards him. He also played a part in our separation, it was not all my fault. He didn't, couldn't have carried all the good, while I was responsible for all the bad.

His lack of any emotion, his lack of response have so far not angered me, although they have hurt me. But I deserve more, I deserve better. We were married after all, we were together for a very, very long time. I have every right to be angry, even furious with him for not caring, for not responding to my attempts at open, honest, heart-felt communication and connection. He has rejected me and as well as pain, it also creates anger and at last I am feeling that, I am accepting it and letting it surface rather than directing it all towards myself.

I'm away on a business trip. My small stone, which I picked up on my hike during the second day of my backpacking trip around Brazil and carried in my pocket throughout the trip, holding it whenever I felt vulnerable or sad, is

threatening me. But it is no longer my small stone, it is a big rock. I shout at
it and fight back to protect myself.

There's music playing in the background and lots of shouting.

The chef at the clinic has used my credit cards for the client's shopping
instead of the company one by mistake. I'm shouting and swearing at him.

A drugged up, fake-blonde girl is causing problems. I speak to her softly
and gently, but don't give her what she is demanding. She calms down.

The background music becomes very loud. My speakers are in the band's
room. I go to fetch them, but they're broken.

I used my stone as a source of comfort and protection while I was
travelling on my own. I was emotionally fed and consoled by
feeling it's presence in my hand. It was a token of strength, of the
earth, of my free-spirited trip of being with myself and allowing
myself time and space to explore, feel, be. But it turns into
aggression and is used as a weapon against me. If I don't set my
boundaries and protect those boundaries well, something small and
meant to be there for comfort and protection can turn into a
negative, threatening force.

Yet when I deal with things calmly, as I do when I speak to the
blonde, the aggressive, boundary-breaking, attacking, violating
energy, it calms down. The problem is resolved, although I have not
had to sacrifice or cave in in any way. The music is too loud, the
chef has broken my boundaries by using my private credit card for
company shopping, there is a lot of shouting, distress, activation and
aggression. By being there, listening to the girl, seeing her, I manage
to calm the situation without even giving the blonde what she is
demanding and the energy settles.

This links into what's going on at work for me at this time. My
manager had been mistreating me, nothing very obvious, but in the
form of subtle negative remarks here and there, undermining my
work, making me feel bad or insufficient. I dealt with the situation
by approaching her gently, instead of facing her with animosity,
which would have made her defensive. I asked her if I had done
something wrong to offend her, not in a meek, on the back-foot
kind of way, but from a place from my heart, with interest, wanting

to know and understand. She responded to me with warmth and the problems were solved.

I feel rejected by Arthur. I have received nothing back from him in return for opening my heart to him, and for my honesty regarding the way I feel about him and our relationship. I feel rejected and deeply wounded. I also feel outraged. I'm angry. I need clarity and closure to enable me to move on. He won't let me go, but he won't take me in either.

I feel stuck. He is giving me no closure, yet he is also not responding to my actions and words. I have felt this way with him before, many times, perhaps in the background it has always been the case in our relationship. An ambiguity in our relationship, leading to me having to make a decision, make a change, say or do something. I have never been absolutely sure of his feelings and where he stands with regards to our relationship. But life went on, other things took over and we continued.

It is the same now. I have no idea what he is thinking or feeling. Does he miss me? Does he really feel nothing but relief? Is there some doubt in his mind? Is he sure? What does he feel? What does he want? I don't know and can't even venture to make a guess. So I can't move on, because I'm not sure it's over. Yet he's not responding, so I feel rejected and hurt. It hurts in all directions and I'm frozen somewhere in the middle, feeling the hurt or drawing inwards and going numb.

27 August 13

Certain events at work brought to light to me just how much I discount myself and all I have to offer. I do my best, work hard and yet don't feel appreciated. I have so much I can give, I have my training and personal experience, my compassion and earnestness, yet none of these are valued by my manager. She keeps giving me menial jobs and discounts me constantly. But somehow I am allowing her to do this. I tell myself I'm not a therapist, so I should be doing the menial jobs so that the 'real' therapists can focus on their work. But my role is valuable too. Patients connect to me. I offer them some insight and support, I offer them a way of connecting to their body, which is so fundamental in dealing with addiction. And yet none of this is recognised by her.

How familiar to my home environment when growing up all this is. I could never do good by my parents. Nothing I ever did was good enough for them. Nothing I did had any worth. They taught me to feel that I myself could have no worth, could not be good enough.

But I'm finding my worth at work. I can see what I bring to the place and what I bring is good and valuable. I am finding my own self-worth and confidence. Others at work value me, my manager's inability to do so stems from her own insecurities, her own shadow material and lack of consciousness. Standing up for myself, owning my positive sides, valuing myself, this is new territory and I find myself in these new pastures. I am welcome here and I welcome the beauty surrounding me.

Everything in our life happens for a reason, although most of the time we cannot see the reason when things are actually happening. There is a pattern and sense to our suffering. As I move deeper and deeper into the caves, following the path of my descent, I encounter people, experiences, places that help me see the layers

I'm exploring. They appear at the right time, when I'm ready to see them, recognise them, learn from them, as long as I keep my eyes and heart open. They are there to help me, shine a light into those deep, dark caves, bring to attention things that are so deeply buried and yet need to be seen and recognised.

As I go through the various layers, bringing to light different memories of abuse, patterns from childhood, issues with parents, I find that my current life, my work, colleagues and patients, my personal relationships, odd occurrences and situations that take place now and then, everything around me is helping me on my journey. Sometimes I am forced to stop where I don't want to, so that I experience that layer more fully. Sometimes I'm pushed from behind, so that I fall to the ground and notice the texture of the earth in that certain place or see a carving in the wall, or smell a different smell. Sometimes I lose my grip on the rocks, sometimes the steps disappear and I slide, hurt myself and have to wait and be for a while. Each time the experience is painful and undesired, but when I look back, each and every one of them turns out to be necessary and valuable and I am grateful for each one of them from my heart.

6 September 13

Lea is crying, saying she is incapable of loving anyone. She's talking about her boyfriend and asking me for advice. I can totally understand her, I know exactly how she feels. I tell her I am the last person to be able to help her, because I have no idea how to love or make a relationship work either. I tell her to leave him if she can't be with him. She keeps repeating how good he is for her, how well he treats her and what a wonderful relationship they have together. She wants to make it work, but can't seem to be able to. So in the end I say "then put everything you've got into the relationship. And I mean EVERYTHING! No half way stuff"

Lea was my best friend when I was very young. She is a very confident person and very social. She has a wonderful, strong mother, one older, fragile sister and a father, who had a mental breakdown when we were young. He had worked in a war-zone for many years. Her mother took care of the whole family, both financially and emotionally. She was a container for all of them.

Arthur is staying over. I'm dealing with things that need to be done, nothing important or urgent, just stuff. He buys fanta, 7-up and water. I question all the fizzy drinks. He says they may be good as cocktail mixers.

I lean against him, stroking him. He says very gently "whenever you're ready, Sophia" meaning whenever I'm ready to get back together with him, I should kiss him. I smile. I understand. In my heart I know I'm ready.

I'm telling Lea to put everything she has into finding a resolution within her relationship. I need to do this myself. I have nothing to lose. I want to be able to love, but feel incapable at the moment. I feel stuck.

I need to put everything into being able to relate to another. Being able to put everything into a relationship, any relationship, is an inner attitude and condition. It involves honesty, humility, vulnerability, speaking from the heart and not the mind.

Lea's expressing where I feel I am right now in terms of my relationship with Arthur. I feel stuck, unable to move forward and confused. I tell Lea to put everything, absolutely everything, into finding a resolution with her boyfriend and relating to him. I feel I need to follow this advice myself.

Arthur tells me he's ready. I know and feel I am too. It's time to take the plunge. I feel strong enough to, at last. The strong, stable, grounded Arthur within me is ready to take a risk.

I've been feeling so much gratitude recently. I've realised the importance of feeling genuine, heart-felt gratitude. It can be cultivated even when not properly felt at first, it gradually blossoms. It feels beautiful and spreads throughout my body with warmth, triggering a feeling of joy and excitement for life, bringing happiness and energy with it.

23 September 13

I wake up crying, sobbing bitterly. I don't know why. I'm thinking or feeling nothing in particular, my mind is blank, but I'm crying.

A patient at the clinic has brought up very strong emotions in me. He triggers feelings I have not allowed myself to feel towards my mother. These feelings are being misplaced and directed towards him. He disgusts me. Sometimes I hate him. All of these emotions are misplaced, I know, I hardly know this guy and it makes no sense I would have such strong negative emotions towards him. But he is an extreme case of a severely narcissistic being, even more so than my mother. My feelings belong towards my mother and have been misplaced on him. A part of me hates my mother for the way she is and the suffering and trauma she has caused. But I have never allowed myself to feel hatred towards her. I can't help feeling that hating my own mother would be immoral, wrong. The feelings are there though, buried, trapped, denied and they have surfaced against this guy.

The experience of my feelings towards him has helped me see the dynamic between my mother and myself more clearly. It is so much easier to see, everything is so much clearer when watching someone else's drama, life and behaviour. I am aware of how subjective my feelings towards him are.

He is embroiled in his family drama. Yet everything is always about him, he must, absolutely must be the centre of the world, the centre of all attention, they don't matter other than how they serve him. He is harming his family through selfish, destructive behaviours and he doesn't give them a seconds thought. He doesn't care about the turmoil he's putting them through, in fact he is unaware of it. He attracts attention to himself through his alcoholism, through needing help, through moaning constantly

"Why me? My life is unbearable", through playing the victim. He doesn't care one iota about his children's happiness and how his behaviour might be affecting them. He demands full attention and compassion from everyone all the time.

He has no core. He survives on other people's energy and he drains all who come near him. He drains the blood out of them, as my mother does. He is an energetic vampire. Inside he is empty, he has no self, no real identity, his need to be nurtured, filled is huge, he cannot be satiated. Even when one of his children needs his support, he focuses on himself and how those needs may affect him.

He reminds me of my parents, the way they were at my wedding. Luckily I was surrounded by people who love me and had a wonderful husband by my side, so they weren't able to dent my happiness. It never really occurred to them that the day was about their daughter and they should be making an effort to make it a beautiful day for her, being there for her in the way that she wants. They did all they could to ruin the day, because I had planned it the way I wanted it and not the way they would have liked to have it. They acted out their drama, were angry that they were not getting their way and took their anger out on me. They can't be happy for their own daughter. They resent her happiness, it cannot be allowed, it asks for punishment.

My wedding was beautiful in every way. It was magical. Every one of my friends gathered there and put in their energy and love to make it perfect for me and they succeeded. My parents did turn up, but I felt like asking them why they had bothered afterwards. They were nasty to me, my dad was able to find two separate excuses to shout at me, both times unnecessary. My mother refused to keep my dress in her room or help me prepare. She did not even lend me a piece of jewellery for the occasion. I was arranging tables and making sure everything was ready in the dining room two hours before the wedding, with my hair already made up. I received no support from them.

Mum was wonderful though. She took care of my dress and helped me get ready. She lent me her diamond ring, a gift from her daughter, to wear as something borrowed. My American sister did my make-up. They and my friends were there with me to celebrate the preparations, make the whole occasion special and fun and to help. I was surrounded by so much love, my heart was full and I was happy.

The wedding was the last straw for me in terms of my relationship with and expectations of my parents. Somehow, in spite of everything, I had still been waiting, expecting a shift in their attitude towards me. I thought on such a wonderful occasion they would be happy with me and be there for me, but they weren't able to. I let go that day of any expectation from them. It was a release in a way. But I do know that the worse thing a parent can do is not to not turn up, it's to turn up lacking love, goodwill and acceptance and to try to poison something that is beautiful. To let their daughter down and deny her even a small piece of warmth and love. To make the day about what they want and don't have. To resent the fact that for one day they are not the centre of attention.

I'm still struggling to let go of Arthur. I miss him, I've told him so. I've opened my heart to him and received no response. Yet he's there in a way. We talk, we see each other, but I don't feel him. He's disconnected somehow. It hurts me to feel this. It hurts me deeply. But at least I am feeling. I'm connected to the pain. He is not.

27 September 13

No knives, no, I got rid of them
No cramps, no anguish
I said goodbye, put them away
But a deeper pain
A knowledge I'm a lost soul
A knowing that I have no home
A feeling that I'm scrambling
A sensation that I'm drowning
Sinking, blinking, searching
And I know
I've been here before
And at last I also know
It's time to give up.

In the deep darkness
I still hoped
I thought
If only I can locate the light switch
If only I find a crack
The irony is that I did
I'm back in the sunlight
But inside I'm still dark
I need to choose
Do I live or die

I scavenge in the dark,
I die
Not a slow death
I'm close
Salvation? There is none

But peace in black darkness
Pitch black
Unknowing, unfeeling...
That's bliss

Or I choose to live
I turn my back on the dark
I walk away from my searching
I disown my earth goddess
I close the door
Only then can I live
Only if I build a wall
Between consciousness
And the unconscious
Because the unconscious
It is not ending
It's too deep
And I wasn't taught to swim
God gave me the feeling
He forgot to give me the compass,
The strength and understanding
God forgot to remind me to believe
God left me, then found me
But only gave me shavings off His food
The crust, the leaf
The poisonous bits
The inedible
The parts that have moulded
The parts that are dead
God kept me alive, only just
But held back the breath of life

Well my search for you
My ever vanishing God
Is over
You have not given me enough

I am stuck, so stuck
There's no life in me
I can't move on
I can't go back
I find no joy
No relief, no peace
No gap, no respite
I say to You God
You gave me more than I could handle
If You mean well
You hide it well
Take your lessons away
Because I am done
Life, my life, is not worth living
I turn my back on you all
Goodbye

I go to visit Arthur. He's living in a huge, beautiful mansion. It's spacious and obviously expensive, decorated with high quality furniture. The mansion is full of people who are his friends. They're happy. They're all enjoying themselves. There is a warm atmosphere there. Arthur is with his girlfriend. He's content.

She's polite and kind to me. I can sense she feels threatened by me, but she is full of compassion towards me and treats me with respect. She has deep, sad eyes. They see my pain and understand it. She respects my place as Arthur's ex and her eyes show sadness and warmth towards me. She has dark, curly long hair and a very fair complexion. She's thin, but not overly so. Her eyes are full of compassion. I can feel the depth of her soul.

I'm nice to her, but inwardly I want to kill her. I want to extinguish her. He's mine, with me, he cannot have another woman in his life.

Arthur makes love to us both simultaneously. I hate making love to him with her there, sharing his affections and attention, but I do it without showing how I feel about it, because I want to be with him more than anything else. I swallow my pain and my pride and let him make love to both of us. I feel anger and hurt, but I comply. I do not dare say no or express how I feel in fear

319

of alienating him, losing him. I want him, even if he is willing to give me only half of his self. I would pay any price to be with him, to feel him again, to have him back in my life. I would accept any form he offered his presence to me in. Anything.

I worry that he might have caught a disease from her, but I dare not ask him to use a condom. I comply quietly.

I have bought tickets to a concert for the two of us. A band he loves are going to be performing. I was always the one who made arrangements when we were together, I bought tickets to plays or concerts, booked our holidays, organised get-togethers with friends. He used to deal with the more day-to-day stuff, like communicating with builders and sorting out problems with bills. I felt that was something I added to his life, something I brought in that made his life richer. I want to remind him of that, remind him of my value, bring something back into his life I shared with him when we were together. But when I mention the tickets, he tells me "no". It turns out that very band live next door to him. He knows the members well and goes to their concerts for free often.

I feel despair. I have nothing, absolutely nothing, to offer him. There is nothing I can give him that he either doesn't already have, or cannot get better elsewhere. He has no need for me, there is no reason for him to want me in his life. I add nothing to his life at all, nothing. I'm no longer part of his life. I'm nobody.

I wake up, but the girl is haunting me. Those deep, sad eyes and her look of compassion and yet she's the one with the prize. I seem to be carrying her with me, in me, on me. She's like a cloud attached to my being. She's covering me, she's in the air I breathe. I feel so much pain and despair, I fear I will break. I'm so sad, so deeply sad.

The whole dream centres around Arthur. How much he has, how fantastic he is, how wonderful his life is, everything good's projected onto Arthur and I have nothing to offer him. He has everything and I have nothing to give him. There is no way I can make his life richer.

This is the very important and real dynamic that has always existed between us in our lives and our relationship. He was perfect, I was not. He gave me so much, I can't imagine what I gave him. I was faulty and damaged and had to fight for him. He just simply was Arthur and I loved him as he was.

This is a picture of what I do. I'm always to blame, at fault somehow. If something goes wrong, I must have caused the problem. Arthur emerges as a spectacular, pure and clean piece. He is perfect. I am nothing, nobody. I am damaged, soiled, at fault.

The other woman could be his wounded anima, the wounded inner woman. That woman lives in him. He has not been able to access her, which is why he cannot respond to me. She's in his life. He might acknowledge her, but he's not dealt with her. He needs to claim her. Otherwise I become the one who's emotionally distraught, because he hasn't dealt with emotions himself. I carry all the emotions, including his, for him. I take part in his love making with her. I become the shadow in the relationship. I carry his shadow and merge with him by accepting and taking on his shadow, although I don't want to. It sticks to me like a cloud that follows me everywhere all the time. I breathe it. It fills me with pain and sorrow, with deep, calm sadness and resignation.

Perhaps he's relieved by our separation, because he no longer has to see or deal with that whole area of life, the murky, emotional side of our being. She's so sad and wounded, yet there is no recognition of her feelings. As far as Arthur's concerned, everything's fine. He's happy, he has everything, yet there is this wounded woman he is with and me, with all my pain. He attached his wound to me in the past rather than facing it and I became the problem. I was the emotional one who would cause fights, who would cry. I was the one who needed to pull myself together. He doesn't even notice the depth of sadness in his inner woman. He's not touched by it.

In a real, practical way he did everything I wanted. In the dream, in the emotional life, I do everything he wants. I feel I have no value in relation to him, so I am willing to do what he wants to be able to keep him at some level. I did that when he broke up with me before and I know I would still do it again if he wanted me now.

321

I'm willing to crush my needs, my need for a deep emotional connection and understanding, my need to feel loved and valued, just to be with him. I would forget it all for him. But how can I be happy like that?

He can't love or let anyone in fully until he claims this unconscious woman, his wounded anima. Part of it is because he can't let in a deep emotional touch, he can't allow himself to be vulnerable. Going there is terrifying to him, so it never breaks the surface. He's certain he has no needs. He does not need anything from anyone, so he also withholds. He won't allow himself to be touched, so he can't touch. There is nothing he wants, no desires, no emotional needs, asking for these would require seeing the need. He would need to get in touch with his unconscious, he would need to allow himself to feel. To feel is too terrifying for him.

How do I find closure? Do I accept that in some form it will hurt for the rest of my life, the pain and missing him won't vanish, they will remain a part of me? Can I let go and move on?

I hereby stand to claim my own worth. I will not make love to another woman for him, I will ask for a condom if I like. I have a right to my needs and wants. I will not brush them off me like bread crumbs to be with him. They are a part of who I am and I have a right to them. He will need to see me. He will need to face the other woman. The alternative brings too much sadness and pain.

5 October 13

Wise words from Saraswati: "We do gravitate to what we know and what we are used to, that's right. So when we haven't felt loved, we gravitate to those who have a difficult time expressing love, or feeling it. It's what we do to try and learn. We repeat the situation until we have learned enough. If we are fortunate, we can work this through with the person we are moved toward….if they, too, want to learn to be more whole. Otherwise, we must be ever vigilant in seeing the patterns we fall into, choosing people who fulfil these harmful patterns. We can learn. And that's what it's all about; learning more and more about how we keep ourselves from feeling deeply connected, to ourselves, to life, to wholeness, to the divine."

"The anger has been a long time coming. Just allowing yourself to feel anger about your childhood, about abuse, from your parents and others we've spoken of has already been a huge step. There is so much you are experiencing yet to come"

I know, yes. All the negative feelings I feel towards my mother surfacing and me seeing them, accepting them must be the first step. First all the dirt from the bottom of the sea needs to be lifted, the water looks dirtier and murkier and only then can the dirt be cleared... that was one of the first things I was taught about meditation: it gets worse before it gets better.

My obsession around Arthur is keeping my heart closed to the outside world, it's like a buffer, as long as it's there, no one else can come in, which keeps me safe from harm. It's my new wall, my barrier to loving, receiving, connecting deeply and risking rejection, hurt, pain or abandonment, patterns all too familiar for me.

323

10 October 13

I feel hate. It's poisonous. It spreads inwardly. I'm not sure where it starts, possibly in my heart and it feels like a poisonous drink I have swallowed. First it enters my organs and then my bloodstream. It then gets carried into every single cell of my body, taking its bitterness and darkness with it everywhere. I know it also involves caring. You can't hate someone you don't care about.

Anger is a purer form of hatred. It is a real feeling, quite often, possibly always justified, if the root cause of it is understood. It is a perfectly acceptable feeling to have. And yet we're conditioned to believing it's wrong, immoral, bad. We squash it, force it down. If not accepted and released anger turns inwards. It becomes the poison of hate. It spreads throughout our being and takes over. And often it is still squashed and denied. It lies inside waiting, ready to pounce or explode. Then we wonder why we have suddenly, for no obvious reason snapped at someone, or made a sly remark to hurt them, or withheld from them that which we were meant to give.

Anger is just another emotion, like love or sadness or joy. We don't label colours as good and bad, no one argues that navy blue is a bad colour while red is a good one. And yet we label emotions as good or bad, acceptable or out of order. And yet emotions are natural energetic expressions. They are what they are. They only cause harm if ignored or suppressed. If accepted, seen, recognised, they simply are and can be released in a healthy, constructive way. They can lead to understanding, bonding and connection.

Unexpressed and denied emotions become forces within us. They can explode, cause illness or depression. We lose understanding of our actions and thoughts. They end up running our lives and we don't even know what's happening. Becoming aware of our emotions, accepting them without judgement, whatever they may be, leads to understanding, compassion and genuine connections with ourselves and others.

I feel my hatred turn towards my mother. Even the thought of her arouses feelings of disgust in me. I feel threatened by her, in danger and my hatred is a form of self-protection. Anything that comes from her is bad for me. I think she would kill me if she could in her own way, not physically but psychically. The hole within her, the darkness in her pelvis, the lack of connection to her true self means that she needs to take from the outside. She is like a hunger that cannot be satiated. She sucks the life and blood of those around her, trying to fill herself, but remains unsatisfied, because her hole can only be filled from the inside, by herself.

My negative mother, both outer and inner, needs to be defended against by not letting her in, by not being the sacrifice, by not being devoured. I need to keep my distance from it to survive. One way to do that is by building an armour of hatred.

Anger towards my mother, myself and life get tangled into a tight knot. A knot that blocks my life force. Anger turns to hatred poisoning my blood. My protective shield becomes my killer.

But I can't seem to find a way to forgiveness. I want to so badly, but my body refuses. And further anger is turned towards me. How dare I hate my own mother, what kind of an evil person am I?

The circle is compounded and I go round and round. But at least now I am aware of it. My feelings are not unconscious and suppressed. They are there, at times overwhelming, but there to be seen, felt and heard. The only way healing and transformation can take place is if what needs to be transformed is first recognised. I recognise what is going on. I can't change it, yet, but I'm allowing the feelings. I'm telling myself it's okay to feel this way, although as yet I don't believe that is so in my heart.

I spoke to Arthur on the phone today. It felt to me as if he was clenching when he called. There was tension and holding back. He has locked me out and that hurts tremendously. I am standing outside his castle walls and there is no way in unless he himself opens the gates. I feel rejected and abandoned. I miss him and his blockade hurts me. I know there is a treasure of deep emotion and sensitivity within him, but he has shut me out. I can't reach it or touch it. And he refuses to touch my soul. We are broken, our connection is superficial, something deep has been blocked, there is no flow.

Is he protecting himself? If I opened myself up completely would he respond? Would he see me, hear me, feel me and open his gates?

There's an opening within me, if he could open to that, we would create a very different dynamic in our relationship. One that connects soul to soul, where the soul is left bare and honest, it is vulnerable for the other to touch. But we both have our protective shields around us. I'm opening mine for him to reach out and respond to. So far he has not reciprocated. Our relationship was functional and guarded. I want to move to a deeper place with him. Will he follow?

I paint a picture of the emotions my mother brings up in me. The painting is of a sun mostly covered by heavy, dark grey clouds formed of drops of purple poison. Purple, her favourite colour. The poison droplets are forming groups, they are surrounded by darkness, they bring darkness with them. The poison and the clouds are trying to immerse the sun, cover it up, usurp it, but the sun is too strong and too bright for them to succeed. There is much darkness, but also much light.

The poison I felt within myself, in my body is not mine, it belongs to my mother. The anger and hatred are forms of her poison, they try to take over my sun. They try to poison and darken it, cover up its light, diminish its warmth, suck out its energy so that it fades, but they haven't been able to so far and the sun is getting stronger by the day. Eventually her poisonous dark clouds will be dispersed and my sun will be able to shine with all its force and energy, bright and warm.

What a blessing to have that painting, to see clearly that the poison does not belong to me, that to feel warmth and light, joy and happiness all I need to do is to focus on the sun and let the clouds drift away.

17 October 13

I'm trapped into anxiety. It feels sharp around the edges, with so many corners. I feel like a rock with a dark black hole in it. My muscles are contracted, my whole body is in contraction. I'm practically in a state of spasm. My movements are sharp and erratic. I feel tired. Every move I make takes so much effort.

I create the opposite movement. My movements become fluid and free, there are no corners or edges, no sharpness to them. They're curvaceous and flowing.

I can only move from the first to the latter by relaxing my muscles, letting go of holding, wanting, hoping, just allowing for whatever wants to happen to come out. I connect to my heart. Fluidity in movement rises from my heart, while the contraction descends on me from the outside.

I let go of all feeling and I start to dance, like an African tribal dancer, with rhythmic movements, grounded, connected to the earth, strong, yet fluid.

The worse thing to do with anxiety is to try to control it, force it out, or try to force it to shift. The only way for it to release its hold on you is if you can let go completely, let go of all expectation of an outcome, let go of wanting fluid movement. Just be. By letting go, our connection, our source of communication moves from the ego to the heart.

I become aware of a complete break at my diaphragm, my heart is cut off from my navel. They are disconnected, my own body, my lower and upper bodies are disconnected. I can't move sensation from one to the other naturally, fluidly, I can't move awareness from one to the other without a break in the flow.

There's a jump that takes place at my diaphragm. I'm in the navel, then woops, up in the heart, no energy flows in between. It strikes me that there never has been an unbroken fluid flow between the two. My main meditation for years was to take my awareness up and down my spine. There was always a jump at that point. I have to force my energy to jump from one half to the other, it won't flow naturally.

Trauma creates a split. The body has to break within to prevent energy from flowing easily. If it didn't, the sensations would be too painful, too much for a body to bear. So I broke off at some point. Circulation is cut, feeling doesn't flow, I live to see another day. My energy cycle is broken, I'm cut off, but I survive. Otherwise the pain would be overwhelming, threatening, possibly deadly. It is a natural defence mechanism for the body. But I am older now, stronger, more mature. I can face the traumas of the past. I can allow myself to feel them. I can learn from them, grow through them. I no longer need to impede the flow of my energy, I want it all, I want to feel it all, I want joy and love to flow throughout my body and this can only happen if I am able to allow distress, pain and sorrow to flow also. I won't leave my lower body buried in darkness. I am strong enough now to bring it to light, to re-connect my two halves, to let it all flow. I can be with whatever comes up.

I try so hard, to create outcomes, to guide my way along the path, even to try and change my surroundings. All I do though is to create spasm, contraction, stagnation.

I take life too seriously. Every little thing matters. Everything I do, what others say, every choice I make is critical, a matter of life and death. But that in itself is ludicrous. Life flows, I should flow with it. Things and events, feelings and thoughts come and go. None of them are a matter of life and death, not the ones I struggle with frequently anyway. Acceptance is key. Rejection leads to stagnation, trying to force change, suppression and as a result the natural flow of life gets blocked. Acceptance means flow, nature, connection.

Those who are happiest in life are people who don't take themselves too seriously. They laugh at their mishaps and see beauty in life everywhere, not the damning, heavy weight of responsibility, where every thought, action and word matters. "Take what you do seriously, but never take yourself seriously". I understand that.

I see my little Buddha statue in my yoga corner at home. His cheeky little face is smiling through a rock. The rock encloses most of his body, but there's an opening in the rock and his face is poking out of it, laughing, so light-hearted and merry.

He is my guide for this moment. Enclosed in cold, hard rock, and out he pokes full of joy and laughter. He's not taking his circumstances seriously. It doesn't matter. The joy and happiness are inside and poke out anyway and the feeling the statue emanates is one of warmth.

I think of Mum. So much energy and passion for life, a source of infinite love and compassion. She has so much within, so much joy and laughter, so much love, she can share it with everyone. She has a kind word, a positive response to give everybody, even a cab driver she talks to for five minutes is affected positively by her light.

She inspires me. I think of her when I'm low. I bring up within me what she spreads from within herself and I'm basking in it. What a wonderful person. How grateful I am to have been touched by her light. She lives, joyfully, with acceptance, warmth and love, every moment. Her joy and warmth spread, they're contagious. She brings joy to those around her, they bask in it, come back for more and reflect it back to her.

She is strong. She knows what she wants. She is who she is, without denial or shame. She is honest and genuine. She lives from her heart and her heart is overflowing with love and joy.

18 October 13

An ocean of tears are swelling up inside of me. They make me feel uncomfortable. I'm full to the brim. They are creating a wave like motion within me, which makes me feel nauseous.

I move to the rhythm my tears are creating. Gradually they start to release. The movement is freeing. They dissipate into the air around. As I move to the rhythm of my tears and my wave-like emotions of grief and loss, they are able to live out their lives and release.

I feel weak. I need grounding, a connection to the earth. I feel tired. I lie down on the floor. But somehow, as tired as I feel, I also feel whole within. I feel a deep sense of peace and contentment.

I let them be. The grief and pain are there and instead of forcing them in one direction or another, trying to control them or change them, I move with them, I let them be, I become them myself through my attention and movement. And I'm taught the same lesson again: don't try to control or suppress what is inside. Don't analyse or try to understand all the time. Just be with the sensations, be with the feelings, let them guide you, move you. Let them be. Flow with them.

The result is release, freedom and peace. They have been seen, heard, recognised and expressed. They can flow freely outwards into the earth and sky. They are not trapped in my poor body any longer.

Our biggest role in life, the best thing we can do for ourselves is to not interfere with our bodies. The body knows, it knows what's happening, it holds the trauma and the pain, it also knows how to heal it, as long as we don't impede it by controlling, forcing, trying too hard. Don't interfere, just watch and let it be.

I'm on the first module of my Somatic Experiencing course, trauma release through bodywork, body awareness, being present and letting the bodily sensations of the trauma manifest and release. I am absolutely hating the twenty minutes to half an hour we spend in our smaller check-in groups first thing in the morning. I hate being there, I feel so uncomfortable, I feel furious, I feel I don't belong and my entire body and soul is resisting being there.

I am having my first personal somatic experiencing session with a therapist. She asks me how the course is going for me so far. I tell her I have been enjoying the lectures. I feel disconnected from the rest of the group, but overall I'm okay, but the morning sessions are very hard for me. I tell her I absolutely hate being in them.

She asks me what would make the morning sessions better for me. I try to imagine what would make the situation in morning groups bearable. I know that they can only become bearable if Alse vanishes. I wonder how I would make him vanish. To my surprise the image of shooting him appears in my mind of its own accord. I reel from the idea. I'm not a violent person, I have never harmed anybody physically, I have never even been in a physical fight and cannot imagine ever hitting anyone, let alone shooting them. But there it is, the image of me shooting him out of existence has appeared and is present. The intensity of my hatred towards him is startling. I'm afraid of sharing this image with the therapist. What will she think? She doesn't know me. She might think I'm capable of such an action, that I'm inherently bad and evil and will harm other people.

I swallow and breathe. This is what the session is there for, to be completely honest. What's the point if I can't tell her the truth? It takes courage and some amount of wilful force, but I tell her. She suggests I do it. I'm surprised. There is no judgement in her voice or expression. She doesn't seem startled or surprised. She hasn't recoiled back from me in horror. Instead she is suggesting I go with what I'm feeling, let my feelings express themselves and see where they take me.

I decide to follow. I close my eyes, hold an imaginary gun up and pull the trigger. He vanishes, vaporises into air. I sigh a deep sigh of relief. The bang has gone off with a loud explosion, a shaking, resonating explosion and I feel lighter.

I start to shiver all over my body, but I'm not cold. I'm shivering uncontrollably. I feel tingling in my pelvis, like millions of butterflies flying around. They must be panicking, in terror for their lives, the tingling is so strong it could only be caused through life threatening panic. The tingling starts to spread down into my legs, all the way to my feet.

Suddenly my whole body feels connected, whole. I can feel energy flow throughout my body without any fences or stumbling blocks, without knots or blockages. I feel alive, although very shakey.

I cry.

I hardly know Alse. My only experience of him is based on one of his comments. And this is where my dislike for him stems from. His presence triggers self-defence in me. I'm not sure what it is about him, but I dislike him. I wonder what the reason for such strong emotions towards someone I don't even know is.

Thinking about it, I notice that his comment stands out for me. It is heavily sexual.

After the session I knew that for whatever reason, somewhere in my body Alse had something to do with Miles for me. He doesn't look or act anything like him, but somehow he triggered my bodily memories of Miles. The release I experienced during the bodywork was immense. An entire blockage broke down, I felt my pelvis and energy was flowing freely throughout my body, connecting my upper body acutely with my legs. Some of the blockage set in with the trauma I experienced with Miles had gone, I could feel that, yet why or how was not completely clear to me yet. When Miles violated me, the trauma and fear must have been so intense, my body shut down, it disconnected in some way. My pelvis remained unfelt and there was no clean flow from my upper body to my lower body. In fact the experience was so traumatising, I didn't even remember it had happened for a while. When following certain experiences I forced myself to remember what I could, the memory only appeared in fragmented photo shots. It does not run through like a video. I have an image here and there, a memory captured in one moment that is disconnected to the next memory I have of the event.

The tingling in my pelvis continued for an hour or two afterwards. I felt free and happy. And then I felt really tired and slightly emotional and extremely vulnerable, so I went home, which brought to light another trait I carry with me, guilt, even when things that have absolutely nothing to do with anyone else are concerned. I felt guilty for leaving early.

The acceptance of my intuitive feeling by the therapist gave me space that allowed my feelings to surface naturally, without judgement or constraints. Acting out the image that came to me in a safe, contained space, in a conscious, aware way released the energy trapped in my body. It is unlikely now that I would act out my hatred in an unconscious, inappropriate manner. In fact the hatred has disappeared.

Guilt came like thousands of bats batting their wings in a constrained space, the space within my navel. I watched them for a while, felt their wings beating manically. They made me feel physically uncomfortable. Then I let them rise up and out of my body. They took flight and flew up into the space around, they became one with the air, they dissipated. And I was left with space, comfort and freedom.

I learned that I need to protect myself from the feeling of guilt I myself place on myself. It is a pattern drawn from decades ago by my parents, yet at this time it is I who repeat it. It is not placed on me by another. I feel guilty even when there is no need to be. I shoulder the blame and feel guilty about everything. That is my way, that is my pattern, that is my rut. But instead I could value myself, my wants and needs. Oughts and shoulds bring guilt with them. We can never fulfil all obligations and expectations. We need to recognise that our first responsibility is towards ourselves. An unhappy, depressed, depleted, forlorn person is no good to others, family or friends and is no use to the world. A happy, fulfilled, content, whole person can spread joy and healing. Such a person has so much to give. With oughts and shoulds we prison ourselves, we set goals we cannot achieve, we force ourselves onto paths that are not natural for us, they are inhabited by enemies and we set off. How about I choose to, I want to, I would like to, I wish to. I do have a right to lead my own life in the best possible way for me! If I do, I will have so much more to share with others as well. If I bind myself down with the oughts and shoulds of this world, I become a prisoner, useless and bitter. I kill myself and harm others who might come anywhere near me.

My tooth falls out. I feel no panic. In fact I'm interested, but disengaged, disassociated, distant. It could have been a feather I watched falling from the sky. It means nothing to me. The event brings me no fear or panic or pain.

I know major changes are happening within me. I need to be nurturing towards myself. So much is going on and all of this takes energy. I'm working 60 hours a week, I can't make ends meet, because my life choices have meant very low paying jobs. I am stressed about my bills, I am over-worked, under-appreciated by my manager, who sucks up anyone's goodwill and gives nothing back. I am not sure I'm succeeding in surviving in this hostile, barren, enormous world. I feel lost. I am sinking. And yet part of me also knows I am following what's right for me and instinctually I feel that if what's right for me sinks me to the bottom of the ocean, or a shit pool, then that is where I need to be.

Teeth falling out in dreams is usually an image of a person loosing their grip on their life, on their reality. Life becomes overwhelming, perhaps too hard and they can no longer bite into it. It's time to pay attention to self-nurturing. In some ways I'm falling apart. So much has been going on inside. So much realisation, confrontation, understanding and growth. But this all takes energy. I am drained. I don't have much energy left to share. I am drained and need some input, even if this is only a kind word, some kind of positive support, a smile, a massage, some time to sleep. I need something, my body and soul are depleted.

Kali is the destroyer of life. She destroys what is old and over so that what is new and has potential and is real can grow and be. Through her destructive force, new life is released. She is the destroyer and yet at the same time the creator.

A caterpillar needs to shut itself up in a cocoon to be

transformed into a butterfly. It needs to spend time in the cocoon for this to happen. And for the butterfly to fly out into the world and live its life, the caterpillar must first die. The caterpillar has already lived out its life, its potential, its calling. It needs to close up, go inwards and transform. And then, only then, can the butterfly fly out.

There is an element, a sense of destroying that which has no more use, which needs to be transformed, so that whatever it is that needs to come out can become reality. Wood burns and turns to ash. Caterpillar dies and flies out as a butterfly. The ugly duckling turns into a swan. The snake sheds its old skin for the new one to appear. We are constantly transforming, changing, renewing. If we hold back, we decay and die with what is old. If we flow with destruction and accept our death, the death and destruction of what we have known, are used to and feel comfortable with, only then can new life, new opportunities and visions, new paths appear.

I cry for Arthur during the lecture. It's the fifth day of my course. I have no idea what triggers the distress, sense of loss, abandonment and grief, but I cry. And I allow myself to cry.

He is so much a part of who I am and what I feel. In some ways he symbolises the pinnacle of rejection and abandonment for me. As a baby I trusted and had to, for my survival, trust my parents and yet they could not give. They rejected and hated me. They resented and abandoned me. And now Arthur, the person I have loved and trusted above everyone else, has turned his back on me and walked away. And I am standing with the pain, loss and grief I feel from his absence, but also the pain and trauma of what was inflicted on me when I was young. The wound has been re-opened. The trauma is re-enacting itself. And I am overwhelmed. Yet I am present. I am there, feeling, hearing, noticing, and as much as possible, hardest of all for me, accepting rather than judging and punishing. This is different. Now is my chance to heal.

3 November 13

I spent half the day going through all the photos I have. Some go back to when I was a baby. There are photos of school years, as well as later ones. I burnt them all. Photos of parents, Miles, Arthur, all of them. I felt I was letting go of my past.

I felt so much emptiness afterwards. I felt depleted, as if I had no energy to move at all. I had to lie down for a while. I have released some of my past in the action of burning. I was watching as each photo burnt, one after the other, leaving me with all its memories, releasing the grip my past, with all its stories and pain has on me.

A hole has opened where this grip once was. The old has left, there is space and freedom, but the new has not yet come in, it is not ready. The soil needs to rest before new crop can grow. My soil has been cleared, perhaps even sown, now the seeds are underground, in darkness and stillness, waiting. They are not ready to shoot out and bud yet. They lie dormant, taking in nutrition from the soil and just waiting.

I feel so still. Still and empty, like there is a vacuum inside of me.

7 November 13

A dog and a girl are dying. I carry them back to their home. The dog's the
gentlest, sweetest thing imaginable. The dog's owner, a man, has already died.
The girl tried so hard to save the man and to heal the dog, to bring them back
to life, but eventually she gave up, she felt she could not keep them alive. Now
the dog's dying. I know I need to save it. I must save the girl and dog somehow.
That the dog and girl are dying makes no logical sense, they are both
perfectly healthy physically, physically there is nothing wrong with them at all.
They look like they have so much potential, so much life still within them.
The girl has a healthy form and look and the dog is fine. But they're dying.

The dog symbolises the instinctual side of life, intuition. Dogs are
driven by natural laws and instincts. They don't analyse or think or
plan. They don't base decisions on their past or hopes of the future.
All their actions are instinctual and rooted in the moment, in the
present. There's beauty in those instincts, animal instincts though
we call them as if they are something to be ashamed of. Dogs can
be gentle and sweet. They don't complicate matters through thought
and analysis, directed by their complexes and past pains. Their main
concerns are to find food and shelter and to love unconditionally
and be loved, and those are the things they find in life. They enjoy
each moment and are content easily. They understand through
smell. Their judgement of the nature of people is quite often
accurate, responding by barking when there is a threat present and
nuzzling up and licking when they feel safe.

The animus figure, the man, has already died. He could no
longer act, be strong, change, control. Somehow the feeling is that
it's okay for him to have died. I feel no sadness around that. My
focus is on the dog. I need to save the dog.

The girl gave up, the young anima, the part of us that is
connected to nature and emotions, the part of us that feels and

338

accepts, the part that has hope and a joy of life within her. She is in danger too. But I don't focus on her. Somehow if I save the dog, the girl will be okay.

The dream ego realises the importance of saving the dog, my instinctual energies. Through the death of the dog, instincts will be left behind, my connection to nature, to what is. I need to save the dog and not resign myself to its death. The young girl has given up, she has lost hope, but I can save them both.

I need to create more space in my life to be able to live in it more freely. At the moment my personal, emotional life, coupled with my work life, which is a huge physical and emotional strain on me, are leaving me no space. Instead of giving up on my inner life, my instincts, the voice of my heart and forcing myself to carry on, I need to listen to my instincts and be guided by my soul.

I need to gather round me things, activities, people that nurture my soul, that keep it alive, healthy and nourished. Walks in nature, flowers, writing, painting, dancing, sitting quietly, connected to my inner being, these nurture me, I know. Instead of running around in the outer world, using all the energy I have for survival within the material world, I need to turn inwards and save my inner dog so that the young girl can live. At this stage the man, the symbol of acting and doing in the outer world, moving on, thinking and analysing, is not essential, I can let him go for now.

14 November 13

I wake up. I can feel Persephone's desire to die. She's had enough. She wants to leave this world. She's made her peace, death does not frighten her, she welcomes it.

I feel immense sadness. I don't want to let her go. I want her to stay here, with me, but that's selfish. I kiss her and bid her farewell. Whichever path she chooses to take, my heart will be with her.

I feel that understanding her desire to die and not trying to keep her from it is in a way being there for her unconditionally. I will no longer fight her wish. I will support her in who she is and whatever path she chooses to take.

I feel all her innocent suffering and pain. My heart goes out to her. I feel her pain and I understand in my own heart, she is welcoming death. But death in one form gives rise to life in another.

Is it just the outer Persephone who is wanting to die? What part of me is ready to die, willing? What does she signify for me, in my inner world? She is the one who has so far not been able to survive in the real, outer, material world. In her own way she has turned her back on society, friendships, work, what we call a normal life. She has withdrawn into a dark inner place, where she is lost. She struggles with her addictions and is controlled by their power. She is powerless herself and lost. Do we not all have a Persephone within us? One that gets thrown this way and that, unable to function at times, one that shuts down and freezes, gets lost in the labyrinth of a dark inner world filled with pain, suffering and trauma?

I have descended to save her, to heal her, but mainly to heal my own wounds, my own shadow, the part of me that has been buried and lost. That part of me is ready to leave now, to let go, stop clinging, stop being thrown around. If I can let go of my wounded part, a new healed me will surface. Letting go of her is somehow connected to letting go of the abused me, the child that was not loved, that was abandoned, betrayed and rejected. As a child these acts were committed to me by others, I was defenceless, but as a grownup I have continued to treat myself in the same way. I abuse myself with my harshness, with my derogatory attitude towards myself. I reject myself by seeing only my faults and not my strengths. I abandon myself at every turn, telling myself that anything bad that happens to me is my own fault, I deserved it, asked for it. I turn my back on myself, I do not nurture myself, I never forgive myself. I betray my inner soul, my heart by overriding it, refusing to follow it, assuring myself that I am wrong and bad.

A whole, healed, happy me cannot come to life unless I let the old abuser, rejecter within me die. Those voices within me that are so strong need to be stilled, turned around. They are harmful and destructive. They destroy life within me, they break my heart and crush my soul. They need to die. The child victim needs to pass away for the adult soul to shine.

18 November 13

My parents, sister and I are in a flower garden in Fenerbahce Park. We used to go there and sometimes and swim off the rocks when I was about five or six years old.

But it's night, so we can't see the flowers or the water, grass or trees. I don't want to go with them, I don't see any point in going to see a flower garden at night, when you can't see anything. But my parents force me and my sister to go with them. My father tells me in his usual way "It's fine if you don't want to go, but if you don't, then you're not part of the family and so will obviously have no dinner with us tonight". So the blame and guilt has been placed on me for not wanting to go. I'm at fault for not wanting what they want. If I don't go, I'm bad, I'm guilty, it's my fault, I exclude myself from the family, I don't belong. Their rejection of what I want is turned into my rejection of them. I am forced to go and I'm annoyed. I feel wounded. I say to my sister "This is stupid. The best part of this place is the flowers. What's the point of coming here at night?" She just shrugs, she couldn't care less.

This is a typical way of responding for my father. If I ask for something that he doesn't think I should have, he will say calmly "that's fine if you want to be so utterly stupid as to want that", or if I want to do something he'll comment that doing what I want to is fine, if I don't consider myself a decent person. Just like here I am told that it is fine not to go, but that only shows that I am not part of the family. He says these things in such a gentle, calm voice, but what he says at the same time carries so much blame, guilt and poison attached to it. He has always had a way of masking his insults and threats with a high-minded attitude, suggesting his insults are my own doing, he's only being kind by showing me the way things really are. His insults carry guilt with them. He takes an attitude of better than though, your want, your fault.

I'm pointing out the obvious, yet I'm disregarded and even my sister pays no attention. I'm insulted and rejected and made to feel guilty. Such a simple, accurate picture of my family life.

There's a group of us there, including Miles, but I have nothing to do with Miles.
My sister calls me.

My father, the punisher, and Miles, the abuser are there in a place where beauty can't be seen. Their presence cuts me off from emotional life, experience and beauty. My father forces me to go against my inner impulses and desires. I feel guilt for not wanting to go. It's my fault, everything is my fault. This feeling prevents me from taking a stance, holding my boundaries.

I manage to remain completely disengaged from Miles. My sister, my shadow, calls me, she is trying to connect after having ignored me previously. There is an opening there. Although I lose the fight against my father, I keep my boundaries intact against Miles.

There is beauty in sadness. Sadness and suffering exist. I need to learn to accept them as they are, rather than trying to avoid them. There's no point searching for untainted happiness, it does not exist in this world. But sadness and suffering come with their poignancy and accepting the suffering, one can still live in a beautiful world, experiencing and feeling the beauty.

I feel sad. I am suffering. I am fighting it. Fighting it is fatiguing. If I could embrace it, accept it, live it and let it be, then I could still feel love and beauty within me, even through the suffering.

23 November 13

I'm staying in Martin's flat. I wake up in his spare room. I can hear sounds coming from the next room. The boys are watching football in there. I get up to investigate. I walk towards the sounds and notice that there is no wall between my bedroom and the living room where they are, there's only a curtain separating us. I realise that they can see my feet from underneath the curtain, it doesn't reach the floor.

I feel obliged to go and join them, although I had no intention or desire to, but I feel that as they know I'm up, it would be rude not to. I'm resistant. I feel resentful that I have been placed in a room that is not separated from the common area and that a whole group of people are socialising in the common area while I sleep. It feels to me like my boundaries have not been respected and my privacy has been invaded.

Straight across from me to the left Ian is sitting with a few other guys. Directly opposite him are Eon and Jackal. Persephone's sitting closer to the curtain and to my right. To my very left, practically out of view behind the corner are Elle and Bea.

I have a conversation with Martin, but suddenly realise he's not in the room physically. He's there as a presence, but not in body. To start a friendly conversation I jokingly say "Last time I was here your team lost, didn't it?"

Jackal says to the room "You still don't get it. She's looking at me while she asks the question and I know nothing about football". But I hadn't looked at him. I was looking at the group as a whole, at everyone, only to be polite. I didn't want to be in there in the first place.

After that I consciously make sure I don't even glance in his direction. He notices my effort, laughs and says "Shot myself in the foot"

I speak to Persephone, she's obviously been using some substance or another. She's not meant to, she's supposed to be in abstinence based recovery. She responds with eyes open, unnaturally wide, uttering some nonsense about it being great here and that there will be some food at home now that I'm in Istanbul.

I notice Elle in the corner and I speak to her, mentioning how long it's been since we last saw each other. She doesn't answer. She's staring at me with unseeing, wide open eyes.

I'm wearing scruffy jeans and a purple sweatshirt, clothes I only wear when I'm home alone. I go back into my enclosure to get changed into something more presentable.

Only once I'm in the enclosure do I feel anger rise within me. I become furious because Martin invited all these people, effectively into my bedroom, without even asking me, or informing me. He also invited Jackal, whom he knows I want to have absolutely nothing to do with.

Jackal has been staring directly at me, unabashed the whole time. He makes me feel very uncomfortable.

Martin, who is a positive male figure in my life, a close, trusted and respected friend of mine, has violated my boundaries. Maybe something that I once trusted within myself, a logical thought, an inner animus, can no longer be trusted. Even what I could trust most in the past has now turned against me. Martin is not physically present in the room, he is present in some other way. His presence is felt and heard, but not seen.

Martin in a way symbolises the logical, analytical voice within me. Logic within me is strong. It has kept me alive, strong and functioning so far, but I can no longer trust its voice, it has turned against me. It is violating my personal space somehow.

Martin has chosen a life of hard work, family and routine, although his inner nature cries out against these. He would like to follow his dreams, connect to nature and not work in an overly stressful job that he despises. But pressure from society and his family, his own morals guided by what is accepted as right, good and valuable in society have directed him onto his current path. He feels he is responsible for his family and his greatest obligation towards them is to provide a good life for them financially. This role he fulfils well, however he has lost touch with simple pleasures of life, with beauty, time off, time for one's self and family and emotional connections.

His logical, society driven mentality is the aspect of me that is invading my boundaries. I am connecting to my heart and emotions and separating myself from what society deems right and valuable. A part of me that still has society and its norms as a guide is trying to break into me. I respond by feeling furious towards it. These voices are not even real any longer, they have no physical presence, they are in the background of my mind.

I don't want to join the group, yet I feel obliged to. I don't want to come across as rude. But joining them means I fit in. They have in a way invaded my bedroom and instead of kicking them out or defending my space, I accept their actions as normal and okay and I join them to fit in.

The two girls in the corner have no facial expression, they stare wide eyed without thought or feeling shining out of their eyes. They are nothing but vacant bodies, as if they have lost their souls. The eyes are the windows to the soul and their eyes look on vacantly. They are the estranged anima figures within, left speechless, thoughtless, mindless. They are disconnected.

I talk to Persephone, but she has been using substances and is also somehow disconnected from me and from life. The male figures are present and make me uncomfortable and eventually angry. They are disrespectful of my boundaries. Jackal stares at me and tries to own centre stage of my attention. I avoid him, but cannot stop him.

I have not been expressing my anger towards my parents concerning how they are dealing with my sister. I feel they are killing her with their decisions and actions and through their selfishness. I try hard to convince them to make different choices, but am left unheard and ignored. They know best and can take no suggestion or advice from anyone else, especially not from me. I don't want to have anything to do with them, but I have to for her sake. I can't just leave her to them for them to destroy, unconsciously led by their own shadow. But I am fighting, disconnected to emotions and instincts. I am fighting with logic, but my logic can no longer be trusted.

I need to express my anger somehow and let it out, not directly at them, but in some way, maybe in meditation, bodywork or imagery.

I need to own my personal space and protect my boundaries.

I'm in a house I don't recognise. I think it's meant to be my workplace. There's lots of money in the safe deposit box. I consider taking it, no one would notice, but I don't. Taking it would be wrong.

I then see my mother's notes and diaries, some are about my sister. I want to take these too and read them. But I don't touch them either. This time it's because I just can't be bothered. Her writing is near impossible to read even at the best of times and I simply can't be bothered trying to read her illegible writing.

Money signifies resource. There are resources available to me, but they don't belong to me, they're not mine and I can't use them. My work has taken all my resources and made them its own. I don't have access to them.

My mother's inaccessible to me as well. Her writing's so illegible, I can't even be bothered to try reading her notes and diaries, even though what she's written concerns a person I love dearly. In some way she is also a resource unavailable to me. The inner mother, the figure that nurtures and loves is not there for me. I cannot connect to her and I don't even want to, at least not enough to put in some effort.

There is no sense of belonging, no love from the mother. The mother is not there, although her writing is, but even her writing is inaccessible and I don't even want to try to read it.

Both these positions are preventing me from setting and keeping my boundaries, from being strong within, from saying no when I need to, from using my resources for things that are important to me and fulfil me, from living in a way that is nurturing and makes me happy.

It is critical for me to set strong boundaries and keep them, especially at work where all my resources are being drained.

It is also important to somehow connect to my inner mother, the aspect of me that accepts me unconditionally, loves me for everything I am and nurtures and protects me.

25 November 13

I want to work on my anger and resentment towards my parents with my Buddha statue as witness. My Buddha statue is a beautiful, serene, simple figure that I feel connected to. I've been trying to find an appropriate offering to my Buddha for this exercise and wasn't able to find anything, until I decided to take out my engagement ring from where I had hidden it, with a vague idea of wearing it. I felt ready, or thought I did. I dug it out from a box and came across the old key to my grandparents house. They had given me a key, because I spent so much time there before my granddad died. I couldn't part from it when he died. It makes me laugh every time I see it; the key is on a key ring which has their address printed on it. They must have been so trusting, or maybe life was different in those days. I suppose the idea is that the finder can return the key if it gets lost. The idea that a thief might find it instead obviously never bothered them. Their house was home to me. I was loved, accepted and welcomed there.

I offered my Buddha the key, which is so valuable to me, it is a connection to my dear grandfather. I then sat and visualised my dad at the end of the hatred fuelled phone call and my mother's letters. I couldn't visualise my mother in person for some reason. I feel anger towards them and hopelessness for my sister. I sit and watch.

Heat rises up my body and suddenly I feel sick. The sensation is coming from my navel, from just above the belly button. I feel so sick, I have to lie down. The internal heat is getting increasingly stronger. I know it's my parent's poison I want to throw up and I need to remind myself that I no longer need to take in their poison. I can refuse their poison.

There is no big outbreak of release, but there is a gentle understanding and tears. Nothing heals, I don't think anything is released, but there is more awareness of and acceptance around the wound.

I go to sleep.

1 December 13

George is talking to me about something, I can't remember what. He's created these parachute like things out of cardboard. He wants to use them to fly off a high building. He speaks to Jenny, with whom he's had an affair and treated badly. Then he speaks to his illegitimate child. Jenny says "no" to something he says.

Then he suddenly jumps off the building holding his two children close to him, taking them down with him. They are falling too fast. They won't survive the fall.

I'm not sure if George thinks the carton parachute would carry them and they'd be okay, or whether he jumps to his death taking his children with him. He's laughing as he leaves.

I have been trying so hard to be light-hearted about Arthur. I have been trying to work things out between us and take an "I cherish our time together, I'm okay" attitude, but the weight and pain of the separation is too much, my cardboard parachute of taking the good, being merry and moving on lightly isn't working, it's not strong enough to hold the weight of my sadness and loss. I'm still grieving.

Arthur treats his soul, his emotions, his feminine side badly. He mistreats the feminine within himself. He disregards her, ignores her, suppresses her.

With my cardboard parachute, I am also mistreating my emotions. I am making light of them, trying to force a positive light on everything and pushing the negative feelings away. What's produced of this is an illegitimate child, a result of lack of honesty about affections and relationships, a child born somewhat inappropriately.

The feminine feels and accepts her feelings as they are, in all their shades. She doesn't cover up, twist, hide or change what is. Instead she acknowledges it and allows it honest expression.

My mourning is not yet over and I need to respect that. Jumping off with an attitude of "I'm fine, with gratitude and love in my heart" is not going to hold the weight of my grief.

On his way to his destruction George is also taking his two innocent children with him. Children are potential, new life, creation. They are dependent on their parents to survive. They are innocent. His attitude is destroying new life and potential.

The feminine, the emotions and feelings, need to be recognised. We cannot brush aside grief, loss and pain and act as if nothing to hurt us ever happened. We need to allow our grief and pain to live out their life, however long that might take. We need to recognise them and allow them to be what they are. Ignoring, avoiding and suppressing them will only cause destruction and death of new life, potential and possibilities.

I do cherish the time I had with Arthur, but I am still mourning the loss of our relationship. My grief is not yet over. Taking on the attitude of 'everything's fine, I'm moving' won't mean I will move on. I might take flight, but my emotions are heavy, while my fake strength and positivity is only made of cardboard, it won't hold.

14 December 13

.

I felt pure outrage and anger the other day. My anger was so strong, it petrified me. I felt that if I allowed it to, my anger would explode and whirl rampant like a tornado. It would destroy everything, including me, it felt like it had the power to. It was not directed at anyone in particular, it moved from person and object to all in general. At times it settled on Arthur, then moved on.

The image of three heavy, lead, dense, rectangular, perfectly formed structures appear within me. They do not have a single imperfection on them. They cannot be digested or broken down. They are lying in my stomach, preventing any movement, I feel incapable somehow, they're too heavy. I want to get rid of them, throw them out. If they were thrown into the ocean, they would sink straight to the bottom. They can't float or swim, they would not disintegrate.

I take on these structures. I become them one by one. First I become the largest structure. I take on its form, the denseness of its being. I realise the structure is abuse. All that abuse whether physical, mental, psychological, or emotional, years of abuse locked into this dense, heavy, perfect form.

I then become the medium sized structure. It turns out to be a sadist. The sadist is laughing at me, saying "that's what you deserve, take it, drown, you deserve to sink and drown" The weight of deserving death and destruction is so incredibly heavy.

I become the smallest one of these structures. It is death. There is no life or soul in it. It is wordless, thoughtless, feeling-less, expressionless. It follows orders, that's all it does. It has no persona of its own. Its soul has died and can no longer differentiate what's right, what path to follow, what it needs, what will nurture it and make it happy. There are no feelings attached to it at all. It might as well be a robot. Nothing matters, it doesn't care. Everything inside has died.

I wonder how I can assimilate these structures somehow or release them. They are too heavy for me to carry. They weigh me down, they prevent life.

I know I can't integrate them, or digest them. I know I can't simply throw them out.

And then suddenly I know, if I allow my anger to explode in them, they will blow up into smithereens. The solution is finding a way of releasing and expressing my anger, in feeling and accepting it and using its energy to break down the abuse I suffered, the underminer of my worth and the death of my soul.

15 December 13

I walk into my flat. The purple plants that normally greet me there at the entrance have all fallen out of the pot that holds them. They're scattered all around the hallway, lying dead on the floor.

There are things lying around or dead everywhere in my flat. Death and decay is everywhere.

The state is one of disorder and death, flowers strewn around, items in disarray. The purpose of flowers is to convey beauty, to bring up beauty within the soul, they symbolise life, joy, colour, but here they are dead and in fact the way they are strewn around on the floor reeks of destruction, perhaps even aggression, like the aftermath of a battle.

A feeling of death and decay reigns all over my flat.

There certainly is a sense of death in my life. An old way of being is dying, the perfect, dense structures exploding, teeth falling out, old ways of thinking and being are falling away, my sense of myself is changing, the way I connect to life is changing.

The image that comes up is a lifeless square picture of before, a mirror of how I'm feeling.

I want to go to bed and sleep, so that I don't feel or think, so that I don't see, so that I am not.

I want to switch off, it's all too much. I'm drained physically and energetically. Animals sleep when they need to heal. I need to heal. I'm deeply wounded by Arthur, old traumas are resurfacing, so many changes are taking place, openings are appearing, old ways are leaving, life is throwing things at me from all directions; challenges, opportunities, joys and pains. The feelings that come up within me are overwhelming, at times too much so. I want to switch off, not feel and sleep. When our emotions are more than we can handle, we disengage. Sleep is a way of disengaging from life, drawing in. I need rest, to draw inwards and heal.

I felt I was worth something when I was with Arthur. I feel worthless now. I'm clinging on to what was, who I was, what I had. I need to let go of all of that. Not only is it in the past and clinging on is unhelpful and destructive, but also that way of being did not serve me, it wasn't right for me, something was missing, something I needed and hence the separation. I needed something different, something more, a deeper connection to feelings, a connection to my heart and soul. And although I am on the right path and being guided towards what I sought, part of me is fighting what is happening. Part of me is battling to stay put, to go back. Part of me is gripping on to what was, but this is preventing me from moving forwards naturally and freely. I end up frozen. I need to let that gripping, warring part of me die, otherwise I carry death and decay within me wherever I go. The only way to be reborn is to allow for death to take place first.

Stillness and rest are needed to allow for rebirth to take place.

It's coming up to the winter solstice, which is a time of death and rebirth. The old way and the old way of being, the one that fights, constricts, battles, rejects, forces, does without feeling, ignores intuitions, cannot accept, must change and do, wants, the one that abuses, undermines, devalues has to die. In its place life, flow, feeling, heart-led movement, letting be, allowing, accepting, spring, and appreciation of myself are coming to life.

It is pointless to fight the fatigue. I might as well accept it, let it be what it is and rest. It would be wonderful to only respond to impulses that arise from my body, and not be driven by the shoulds and oughts that dwell in my mind, throwing orders around. Shoulds and oughts are engrained within me. They carry with them guilt and failure. They are not choices, they don't come from the heart. By their very nature they force, constrict and block. The body fights them even if the mind doesn't. They turn the body into a battle ground. They are tiring and draining.

If they are replaced with heart-led choices, life becomes more joyful, it flows easier and more naturally.

For someone who has spent an entire lifetime aiming, trying, doing, forcing what does not come naturally, abusing when this proves hard, it is difficult to suddenly let go and be. For someone who knows only how to control or if control fails, shut down and become the victim, it is difficult to suddenly simply flow naturally and accept. But life comes from this acceptance. Life is flow. Every forceful action or thought creates a blockage, a constriction. Acceptance releases those constrictions and life is able to flow once more.

25 December 13

My love,
There is beauty in surrender,
In the beating of the heart
Beats the rhythm of drum'n base
And that beat lifts you to the stars
And the stars are dreams
And as you float through the clouds
Leaping from one vision to the other
You are alive

You can take your life in your own hands
Face mortality
Defy God
And think you are laughing in His face

But my beautiful, white marble, perfect sculpture
What then?
You have defied fear and death
You have pointed the third finger to mortality
And then what?
You go home to a cold flat
Boxes unopened
No arms to greet you
No ears to hear of your heroism

You sip your whiskey
and you smile to yourself
'I am above it all,
I showed them all
I need no mortal

I'm free and independent'
And as your whiskey runs low
And the taste is mellow
Many have you had
Without a word or an echo
You decide it's time for bed
No body to warm
No finger on the tip of your arm
You have shared your day with no one
And my love when you wake
And the excitement of the snow covered mountain calls
And you dress and prepare
And you gulp down your coffee or tea
And you set off
And... what?
Was there someone who shared your joy?
Someone who laughed with you at your child like excitement?
Is your coffee waiting for you, ready?

Was your home warm when you returned?
Could you recount your experiences, your adventures to anyone?
And when life got boring, tedious, irritating,
Who did you complain to?
Who's warmth did you feel by your side?
An anchor, a rock, a sound wall,
One that would not crumble
And your joy; the moment you felt glorious
and rode to the stars
The world was yours
You owned it and rode it
Who did you ride with, my love?

And when you were down
Searching for oysters with pearls
and there were none in
the depths of the ocean

and all it offered was darkness and despair
No way out, no fight, no hope
Who did you go to my treasure?

And the banal, tedious day in, day out
Who did you share your burden with?
Who did you complain to by and by?
Where do you go to my love every night?

As each person lulls off to sleep
Are you so locked out of life that you cannot see?
We, none of us, live in isolation
We thrive with each other's energy

My beautiful, perfect, gorgeous,
cold, white as moon marble statue
You are closed and fading
I reach out to you
Hear me
Hear me despairing!
Hear my call!
Feel my grasp
and cling on
we will propel towards the light together...

My last call to him. I will send it out. I will reach out. There is nothing further I can do, but before I give up I must have tried every single possible way of re-connecting, of opening the tiniest hole, the thinnest slither through which I can touch his heart, through which our hearts and souls can connect. I have been writing a book to him, everything, my heart and soul bared, and I will send it when I'm finished. Then it is up to him, whether he responds, whether he's willing to let me in or not. I have one last call to make.

4 January 14

My sister, a guy and I are on the run from the police. We try to exit Angel tube station without being noticed. We are going to walk to Highbury and Islington from there, which is where we want to go. The guy's helping us. My sister's worried about her dog, but he assures her that his friend is taking good care of it.

As soon as we exit the tube station my sister walks straight up to the policeman, who's wearing plain clothes and asks him about her dog. At that stage she's not even sure the dog is hers and anyway she's been assured that it's being taken care of, so there's no need for this. She's trying to attract police attention to us, which is risky and potentially dangerous behaviour.

I shout at her and tell her I want to never have anything to do with her again. I'm angry she's sabotaging our escape. And anyway, we're on the run from the police because of a situation she put us into in the first place. I'm afraid of getting caught by the police and my fear is leading to anger. We start shouting at each other and arguing at the top of our voices.

My sister's accusing me of doing or saying something to harm her behind her back. Apparently my parents have told her I've wanted to harm her. I'm shouting that I would never do such a thing and that I have always stood up for her. I shout I would never ever do anything to harm her and how could she believe this? She has lived with me, I have taken care of her, I have always been there for her and I love her more than anyone else in the world. She must know it's a lie. I tell her that I say "yes, yes" to my parents sometimes, because I don't care about their opinion and just want to get them off my back, even if only temporarily.

I shout that I've put my neck on the line for her so many times and that I've done so much for her, made so many sacrifices, it's insulting that she has taken any notice of what they have been saying. I keep repeating "I would never do that".

She then becomes sad and says she knows I wouldn't and that's why it

360

hurt her so especially much. She doesn't believe that I have done what they have accused me of doing.

During this time the police has come up to us. I start shouting at him to leave me alone. I turn away and storm off. The police grabs my arm. I turn to him and shout "Who the hell do you think you are?" He replies "Police". So I shout once again "Since when has shouting at your own sister become a crime?" I'm indignant. He tells me he's holding me for something else. I say "That has nothing to do with me" and try to wrench my arm away from his grip and walk off again, but he won't let me. He's stronger.

I feel a tremendous amount of guilt, which is also the overwhelming feeling I wake up with. Guilt for not having stood up against my parents and defended my sister.

What stands out is the huge guilt I feel for not standing up for my sister, although there doesn't seem to have been any special need to cause a scene against my parents and my "yes, yes" response towards them is justified, as they never listen to, or hear anything I say anyway, so what I say makes absolutely no difference to any outcome. But still, guilt is the one lasting feeling through and beyond the dream.

My sister's acting the saboteur. I have been unable to stand up to those negative parental voices. I have been betraying myself and a part of me is so hurt, she has to attract attention and sabotage so that the police, the defender of our rights and our protectors in society, can move in. The deeply wounded part of me that is represented by my sister is feeling betrayed and outraged, the part that is thinking of her instincts, the dog, worrying about them, but not even sure she owns them and is incapable of taking care of them, so that she has had to leave them in the care of some other unknown figure.

I have been standing up to my parents recently and drawing boundaries, but obviously more is required, not necessarily with outward actions, this could also be an internal setting of boundaries. In spite of my stronger boundaries against them, I also still give in a lot and at times stay quiet to hold the peace, because the struggle is too fatiguing. But my wounded part demands more. The wounded part will not take any more lying low, being quiet, giving in and she will sabotage me if I do. She won't sabotage just herself, but the whole of me, even if it is at her own cost. She will do this just to be heard and seen. She is afraid and needs to be heard.

The police provide and defend law and order. We all need justice. They are there to deliver it. A part of me demands and needs justice, even if this means a struggle for me and perhaps even punishment. I need to be seen and heard with all my truth, but at the same time I fear this.

My sister's upset because I haven't defended her, although I have stood by her side, this was not enough. There is anger and resentment there. They have wronged her, yes, but it hurts so much more that I did not stand up to them for her, because she trusted me more, had faith in my presence as her protector, defender, carer. So the feeling of having been let down when her expectations were not met was all the more painful. I need to stand up for her and for myself fully, not half-heartedly, but completely, without concern for outcomes and punishment. I need to do this for myself.

I'm ready to teach George. He has made me a pasta dish. I feel obliged to eat it out of politeness, although I would not normally eat anything before a class, especially not something as dense and carb-based as pasta, but he's prepared it for me and I don't want to be rude or reject his gift. While I'm eating it, George goes away and gets changed back into his work clothes. I'm surprised when I see him and ask him "Don't you want a yoga class?" He seems unsure. He tells me he wasn't wearing his own yoga clothes in the first place. He had forgotten his clothes and had borrowed someone else's. But I convince him to get changed so that we can practise yoga. He goes away again to change back into his friend's yoga clothes.

While he's away the meeting room we use for our yoga classes starts to fill up with his employees. Some of them are friendly and speak to me. They are gathering there for a science class.

Eventually George comes back in and we leave the room together to find another, unoccupied space where we can have our class.

Suddenly I'm leaving the ladies' toilets. A girl, one of the employees working for George, appears and says "I'm going to show you something. I think you'll like it" and takes me to a room with artwork hanging around it. She talks me through the artwork on display, sharing with me information on each piece.

I run into two colleagues from work, one male and one female. I think the female one is meant to be Kendra. We go into a fast food joint together. I don't want to eat fast food, so I tell them I won't eat with them and that I'm going to go home. They ask me when I'll next be working. I tell them tomorrow.

My yoga classes are a place where I provide a non-judgemental, non-competitive, accepting, nurturing, spiritual space. I teach from my heart and find myself nourished at the end of a class. George lives and works in the competitive, high-achieving world of finance. He is smart, intelligent, driven and highly successful. I want to take this more material, driven side of me into the accepting, spiritual space, but it's not quite ready to go there. It doesn't want to let go. It doesn't have the necessary clothes to practise in, although it does manage to borrow what is necessary to be able to take part, but then changes its mind. It is undecided, torn between the two spaces, hesitant.

A part of me, in fact a large part of me, is still trying to stay in control and in charge, it won't let things happen organically, it fights and tries to change and direct. It has not yet learnt to be yielding enough.

There is a conflict taking place inside of me, a stress between the accepting, spiritual side of me and the achieving, driven side. I have created the space to accept and be, to feel and allow within me, but part of me is fighting the desire to let go. It wants to control outcomes and is driven by wants, needs, desires, wrongs and rights. It wants to direct what happens. This force prevents things from coming up organically from inside.

The room, the physical space where the two are to come together and find a spiritual wholeness, some unity and understanding, a connection to the Divine, the Higher Force suddenly becomes unavailable. It is taken over by a pragmatic, science course. We leave to find another space.

I go to the toilet, where expression and getting rid of unnecessary stuff occurs. Once that is done, I come into contact with someone who guides me in the world of art. Art is a way of emotional and spiritual expression. It is a form of communicating from the soul and expressing what is hidden in our hearts. An inner female figure acts as a bridge between the emotional, expressive form of art and the more pragmatic, worldly side to it of information.

My work comes in, another place where I can connect to my inner calling, where I can help people in distress and be of some use to them. It is in a way a spiritual job, but my colleagues are going to a fast-food restaurant, where nurturing nutrition is not served. Instead, what they consume is food that is not good for the body. I refuse to take part, but assure them that I will be at work the next day. I keep myself safe and healthy, while still maintaining the contact with work and my colleagues.

I called my parents on Christmas Day and just because I reached out to them in that simple way, my mother decided to grab my semi-open hand and rip my arm off. She sent me an email that created strong emotions of resentment and anger within me. She overstepped every single possible boundary. The entire email was about what she wants and needs, what I can do for her, what she can take from me, what she demands of me. No space is left for me as a person, an individual, a being. She drowns me.

She goes into a whirl-wind of self-centred wants, expressed greedily, starting with wanting to go with me to the park where my granddad's ashes are scattered. She goes on and on about alternatives. Then she details her plans for her trip, she's going to be in the UK for two weeks in July. She demands my time over her first weekend, although I've already told her I will be on a yoga course in the States and won't be returning until that weekend. She has planned the Saturday and Sunday and says she will come to my yoga class on Monday, without even enquiring if that would be okay with me or even if it would be possible at all.

Then of course she asks about the two following weekends after that when she is still here. What will I be doing? How much time can I spend with her? She continues her assault by mentioning her research into my Somatic Experiencing course. She has always done courses or workshops with any of the teachers I've ever done any training with when they have taught in Istanbul. Whatever I do, she wants to do too, whatever I have she wants to take for herself. Even with this new training that I have started, she is already moving in. She wants to do it too. She leaves nothing for me for myself. She informs me that she has noticed they offer workshops, but not during the time she will be here. She asks me to look into workshops for her and order the book written by the founder of the course for her too.

The email evoked absolute fury in me, so much so that I simply could not reply. I felt so invaded, as if by pirates whose only aim is to slaughter, rape, steal and plunder. They take, take, take. They invade the ship to steal its treasures and any humans they encounter are nuisances to be slain with a sword and thrown overboard. I felt completely disrespected as an individual. Not only was she invading and trying to take over every part of me, she was asking me to help her in this endeavour.

It's as if there's something in me that she is constantly grasping at. She wants it and then she wants to destroy it. If she can't have it, she still wants to destroy it. I feel like if I don't protect myself against her, she will kill me, actually kill me. The treasure she sees within me, real or imagined, is all she sees. I as a person, the real me, doesn't even exist for her.

I wondered whether she was reaching out to me in her own way and that I was unable to see her good intentions. My manager talks about demonising the mother and placing our own shadow on her. But my therapist explained that there is a difference between placing our shadow and being over-shadowed.

It is my mothers' shadow that I have been carrying. It is my mother who is placing her shadow on me, not the other way round. It is not my fault! There is that deep dark hole within her and she is grasping at me, to fill it with what I have. In a way that means destroying me, taking everything from me, sucking my blood, my energy, my life. My fury is there for protection. If I let her, she will take all, until there is nothing left. My anger protects me from her and it is well justified. She has not respected or valued me in any way. All she sees is what I have and that she wants it for herself. Who I am, what I might need or want does not even exist for her.

I try a few times to respond to her email in a firm, kind, but protected way. I find I am not capable of this yet. My anger seeps through in some form or another. I can't write a reply that won't hurt or want to hurt her in some way. So I decide not to reply at all. I don't want to hurt her, but any communication from me at the moment cannot be free of some subtle arrow. Time will show me how to respond. The work I am doing on myself, my body work and meditation will guide me in my healing. I just need to give it time. At the moment forgiveness and healing around the wound created by mother is not yet accessible to me. But I know it will come.

10 January 14

I'm talking about Arthur and all the barriers he has put up against me. I cry randomly, sometimes without even knowing why. Thinking of our good times together can trigger my tears, imagining what could have been also triggers them. I feel warmth when I imagine what could have been, but also fear. I fear that I would mess it up again, even if I were given another chance. Ultimately it still wouldn't work out. My heart and body are telling me that I would mess it up. I want him, yet I fear having him. I miss him, yet I fear being with him and still not feeling happy. I fear there is something wrong with me, which prevents me from loving and receiving love and I fear that has not yet changed, so how could I make it work with Arthur? I had everything and threw it away. I went on a journey, a search for some deeper understanding of myself and I feel I have learned much. I want him to join me on my journey, but don't know if he would want to, or if he can. I don't even know if I am capable of sharing such a deep connection and experience with someone fully. Can I trust and open up to that extent? Can I become so absolutely, fully vulnerable?

I talk about my mother's inability to love me and both her and Arthur's rejection of me. Rejection and betrayal seem to be the themes. My body aches from the pain. The pain of all I carry, all that has been added onto this poor body of mine throughout my life.

She placed her hand on my back, just gently, at the level of my heart. Straight away I felt instant warmth where her hand was and it started to spread outwards. This was followed quickly by a tension in my abdomen. I felt rejection within me. I was rejecting the touch, shutting off from it. My abdomen was churning.

I closed my eyes and went inwards, feeling into the sensations in my abdomen. I saw a little, very angry, blue, male cartoon figure holding a hammer up shouting "It's toxic, it's poisonous, scrape it out". I stayed with him, this little angry man. I felt my internal walls in my abdomen being scraped out. It was painful. I felt empty, as if I was hungry. I felt the desire to spread silky soft, warm balm on it to soothe it and cover up the parts that had been scraped out. At the same time, I wanted to throw up.

I realised, I'm at war with myself. I want the silky balm, I want it to heal and nurture me, I trust people and let them in, but at the same time my body rejects the balm and the people I have let in. It fights the trust and the nurturing. It questions any warmth given and is sure it is all poison in sugar coating.

I understand my reactions now. I let people in with hope and love, I get close in my intimate relationship, then through some unconscious energy I end up creating fights and problems, causing havoc, pushing, kicking them away. My mind tells me to trust and love, it refuses to become bitter and questioning, it refuses to be distrustful and at the same time my body reacts and pushes away what I have welcomed consciously.

The little angry man is fighting for my protection. He was born very early on out of the experience that motherly love and nurturing come with poison. He learned to protect me against the sugar coating, but he has gone too far, he no longer serves me, in fact he's now destructive, because he sees all sugar as coating for poison and cannot differentiate poison from sugar.

The little angry man is at war with the side of me that wants to trust and love and I am at war with the little angry man. I want to vaporise him. I want him gone. But he is an essential part of me. There must be a way of reconciling the balm with the little angry man, finding a way for them to work together constructively. Trying to get rid of him will only harm me more.

I place my right hand on my abdomen. Instead of easing the tension, this touch increases it. It feels like there are waves inside, fierce, crushing against rocks. They are shattering the rocks bit by bit, with force. It's an uncomfortable sensation, but somehow feels more natural. The scraping away of the walls was so unnatural and alien in comparison.

As soon as I remove my hand from my abdomen, the tension eases and the waves subside.

I want love, warmth, nourishment, but I can't receive them, my body wages war against them as toxic, poisonous.

My life gets tainted by my inner core sense of being, which is I am worthless. My relationships, my work, my friendships, everywhere I look I can see the trademark of this one parental poison. It influences how I act, react and respond.

I am valuable to my friends and at work. I don't need to serve to have a right to be there and yet this belief leads me to stoop low, assuming that is the only way I will be accepted.

Arthur was a mirror, in whose reflection I liked who I was and what I did. But there are other positive mirrors available to me. I light up when I teach and that is core to my essence, of what I love doing. I have close, loyal friends, who are there for me and always have been. I'm surrounded by people who love me and yet I block the positive reflection they shine on me out, I question good reflections, wondering why they are there and in fact if they really are there. My parents couldn't see any positives in me, how can I dare to?

I am my own enemy, no one else. I block the good that is trying to come through and replace it with insecurities and scepticism.

I paint the little angry man and send my love to him. I feel him in my abdomen and feel gratitude towards him for protecting me. I accept him and my navel pain ceases. My little angry man can work together with the silky balm. They both belong to me, in me and they are both there for my own good. Fighting the little angry man is fighting myself, it is destructive. I welcome him instead and feel at peace within myself.

I've lost my favourite hat. My little grey hat I've had for years. It's warm and comfortable, it's not made of wool so doesn't make my forehead itch. I love it, but I've lost it. I search everywhere, trying to find it. I feel forlorn.

At last I find it in the dirty laundry bag. It's buried under socks and my other hat, the white woollen one, which does make my forehead itch and I don't like half as much.

I bought my grey hat in my favourite sports shop by St Pauls, which is my favourite landmark in London. This is also the place where Arthur proposed to me the second time, once my engagement ring was ready. I waited for him there with my ring. He got down on one knee and asked me to marry him. He placed the ring on my finger. We joined, me and the man I love above all else.

A hat is a way of being, of thinking. We use the term "I have my ... hat on today" quite often. It is the symbol of a persona we take on. My favourite hat's in the laundry bag, it needs to be cleaned. Some way of thinking, perceiving I have needs to be laundered.

My entire life has changed, what I do, where I live, how I live and especially that I'm no longer with Arthur after twelve years together. Everything in my life is completely different now to what it was a couple of years ago. I know myself better. I have connected to and felt my heart. I am aware of my unconscious and my deepest feelings. I live a truer life, one that is guided by my inner heart.

Some aspect of my perspective still needs to be cleaned up though. Perhaps I need to change my perspective on my marriage. Some old way of thinking is no longer viable. The way I saw our relationship needs to be looked at through new eyes.

It could be that I see Arthur as the be all and end all of everything. He is the only man I would want to live my life with. Now that he's gone, I will live the rest of my life alone. This might not be the healthiest way of looking at things.

Also, the fact that Arthur stood on a pedestal for me. He was perfect, I was damaged. Everything good came from him, all that was wrong or bad from me. This perspective also needs to change.

I have a new life now. A fuller life, one that I am living more wholly, with all my being. I am present in the world and to my own feelings, the murmurings and responses of my unconscious. Yet I still have a tendency to blame myself, to beat myself up, punish myself. This needs to change. There is so much that is valuable and worthwhile in my life and in me. There is so much beauty and love around me and I do deserve all the good I'm surrounded with. There is wholeness in my choices and honesty in my actions. All this needs to be valued and appreciated by myself.

20 February 14

I see images of pre-addiction Persephone. I wake up. I know she's dead.

I expect a call all day. I'm waiting for the call that gives the news. The call doesn't come. I call them in the evening. She is alive and well. She's not dead. I'm relieved but perplexed. The awareness of her death was so real. I feel confused.

I wonder what it could have meant. Images I saw of her all belonged to a time before her addictions. Maybe I saw the death of Persephone's soul through addiction. The pre-addiction Persephone has died. She is no longer the same person she was a decade ago, she has not been for a long time. She is disconnected to life and people. She lives in a separate world, consumed by her addictions most of the time, but even when she is going through a period of recovery, somehow she is not there, not quite the person I knew and loved so dearly.

I have been waiting and hoping she will pull through. Waiting for the day I meet her and there she is, the way she was. But it has been too long and that Persephone is gone. If she succeeds in maintaining recovery, she might still be accessible, someone I can connect to, but she will never be the same person.

Or is the dream a warning? Those voices within me that tell me I'm unloveable and worthless, they are killing me, they will kill healthy life within me.

Is it telling me a part of me is dying? Or maybe it's telling me that a part of me, perhaps the unknown shadow within, the one I started my descent to find, is dead.

Who does Persephone symbolise for me? What aspect of me does she personify? The 'I don't care about the world' side? The withdrawn, dissociated side, disobedient, rebellious side? The side that tries to distract from who she really is so that she can avoid living wholly?

I'm in a very large building. The building's like a maze. There are so many entrances, corridors, stairways and doors, you never know where you are or where you're going. The building also houses a large lobby, formed like the entrance to a very large mall. The ceiling is four or five stories above and it is lit super-bright with lamps, lights and chandeliers. It feels spacious, but at the same time industrial somehow, unnatural, fake, too bright, too light, too big, too busy.

There are flats in the upper stories of the building and in all the spaces around the main entrance lobby. There are shops and cafes surrounding the open space in the centre of the lobby. The shops and cafes are spread all around and inhabit the four or five stories up to the ceiling. The centre is empty. The floors are a light coloured, cold stone. There are many mirrors.

I start off in a flat, which in the beginning is meant to be Cara's flat, but ends up being my aunt's. Cara's a lonely woman. She has managed to alienate all those around her, even her own son is fed up with her. She is unhappy. She saps people's energy and there is no joy to be found in spending time with her. I leave her company depleted each time I see her.

I'm helping out in her flat. I have my backpack with me. I'm meant to be with Mick, he's supposed to be my boyfriend. Cara doesn't like him. For some reason we all leave the flat and the whole building.

I do a stunt. I jump off something high. A rope is tied around my waist. I jump off and fall into bags of rubbish. My dad watches. He's meant to do the stunt after me. He has tears in his eyes and refuses to do it. My grandmother is watching and she looks at me with utter hatred. The three of them, my aunt, grandmother and dad walk off.

They don't want to let me back into the flat, now my aunt's flat. I tell them I have to get my backpack which I left in there. They tell me to wait outside and they will throw the keys down from the balcony. I wait and wait. They don't appear.

I have to go and get my backpack. Everything I own is in it. So I enter the building. I don't know which way to go. I see a friend from high school, called Uri. We were never close at school and I've hardly seen him since. I hardly know him.

When I see him I run up to him and ask him to help me find this flat. Persephone's with me now. He agrees and we start going in and out of corridors, up various staircases. They're dingy and need repair badly, they're breaking down. There is a sense of decay all around.

Suddenly Uri also vanishes and I have to find my own way. Persephone's still with me, following a step behind me. The last staircase we go up is really dangerous. It is so decrepid, we need to be very careful not to come crushing down with it, broken stairs and all.

I find the door. It is exactly the same door as Cara's front door.

My aunt won't let me in. I start crying, saying everything I have is in that bag, I need it. I start pushing the door. She's pushing against me. It pains me to push, because I hate using force against my aunt, but eventually I push with all my strength and get in. I'm still crying. "Why you, aunt? Why you?"

Persephone's there in the latter part of my journey, practically like a supportive shadow, she's there as long as I need her, a few steps behind, a supportive presence.

Against all odds, my family, people I love and trust, friends and all convention, I fight to get my bag back, to regain my identity, to re-own things that matter to me, retrieve important possessions. My wallet, with money and credit cards, my way of transacting with the world and acquiring my needs, are in it, as is my phone, my mode of communication with others, as well as other things that are important to me.

The dream follows the journey of my descent in a way, from the beginning to the end. I started off by having to fight and stand up to people in my life who were more obviously destructive and poisonous, like Cara and Dell, people who spoke behind my back and meant me harm, bitter, unhappy people who thrive on spreading poison and harm.

I then had to face the truth about my parents and draw my boundaries with them, be myself in spite of them, stand up to them and their way of being, seeing, judging, labelling. I realised the truth of the steel gates around my heart and my grandmother's poison passed on from her to my dad and from him to me and carried by me as my own.

And last, and hardest, was facing things, people, ideas and ideals that were close to my heart, that meant a lot to me, that had defined me all my life. I had to claim myself from them as well to be able to find my real person. Even against people I love dearly like my aunt and old conventions and morals and ideas that I had taken for the truth, even these I had to let go of, even what I had always perceived as good, right and valuable.

In life I gradually, step by step, went through these different layers of retrieval, as I do in the dream.

At the stage my father is there, I end up on a rubbish heap, where we end up when we are completely broken. We find connection to our heart only when all else has left has, when we have lost everything and feel utterly broken and full of despair. My dad was not able to follow me there, he can't take the leap, he can't face his shadow and question everything he has spent all his life, his energy and resources on so far, so he lives shut down, unconcious.

Uri is a guy I knew in high school, someone I was never especially close to and have had practically no contact with since graduation. I wonder why he is the person who helps me. It occurs to me that he is a happy, successful man now. He is very happily married to an absolutely lovely wife and they have at least once child together. He seems emotionally centred, self-confident and comfortable in his own being. But he is short for a man. However he does not carry the usual little man complex that is so commonly carried by men of below average height. He is at peace with whom he is. Not only is he accepting, he is happy and strong.

In a way he is a person who has found happiness and success in spite of a limitation he was born with. And that is what I have found now. In spite of having been born to the parents I was born to, in spite of all the abuse I received growing up, I have found ease, comfort and acceptance within myself and most importantly inner strength and happiness.

I have claimed who I really am, underneath all the layers of abuse and protective walls. My limitation, believing with my whole being that I am worthless and bad, no longer limits me.

The layers around my heart have been peeled off, one by one. The steel gates have crumbled. Life flows to and from it freely. I am connected to it and I thrive with its energy.

Light

I feel overwhelming boundless joy rising up out of me. It wants to break out, to make me laugh and dance. I don't understand it. I grip it tightly. There is no reason for it. My entire life has come crushing down. Everything is destroyed and broken. All is in rubbles around me, over me, burying me. Yet this indescribable joy, full of life and energy is wanting to break out.

I'm afraid of it. I don't understand it, it seems wrong somehow. I hold on to it, pushing it down. How could I be happy with so much destruction in my life? It can't be true, it can't belong to me. Yet it does. It's there, alive and kicking.

I let go of my struggle. I let the energy take over. I laugh and start dancing. I feel happy, truly happy.

I start painting. I have decided to paint the image of my decent, the beginning of my journey, the journey down deep into the dark caves to save Persephone, to bring her out to light.

I paint fast, it's flowing from my heart. I'm not thinking, deciding, choosing colours. I just let the painting flow, it has a life of its own and it's directing my hand. When the painting's done I'm startled to see the result.

I had always imagined that dream in a very dark setting. Persephone's at the bottom of the caves, depressed, surrendered, ready and even wanting to die. She is buried in deep darkness, earth caving in all around her. She has no will to ascend, no will to live. She is my buried unconscious, my wounded side that had to be seen. I, on the other hand, entering the caves from above, from safety and sunlight, choose to go down. I am afraid, but won't leave her there to die, so the descent begins.

After all the bodywork, internal analysis and soul searching, the picture born from inside is a very different one. The caves are dark, but Persephone is light. She is emanating light somehow. She is serene and at peace. She is glowing, her head lifted up towards spirit, as if she is connected to a higher energy, to God, to the spiritual. Her peace is one not of surrender and defeat, but of understanding, fulfilment and happiness. She is glowing, touched by divine energy.

I, on the other hand, am scrambling down on all fours. I am part of the darkness, I blend into the shadows. I look only semi human and semi shadow, a mere partial being.

A dream is alive and transforms with the person. The image of my dream has also transformed over time. The image is what it is, just like a dream is what it is. I did not choose to paint the descent the way I did, it flowed out of me without any control or decision on my conscious part. It flowed from my heart and from my unconscious. I believe what I see. It is telling me something, it has a message. It is not by mistake or chance that she is glowing with light and I am a mere shadow. I take notice of what has come to light.

As I went further and further down, along my journey, I realised more and more that the hidden, buried part of me was my heart and pure soul. It wasn't shadow, it was pure light and beautiful, but it had been buried under so many layers of protection, dirt and trauma, I had no idea it existed. What I found in the depths of the caves was not a shadow to be feared, that had to be accepted and integrated to become whole, it was me, the me who is worthy of love, who has value, who is loveable and in fact is loved. I found the ability and heart to love, accept and value myself, as I am, for who I am.

I realised I had been hiding from life, protecting myself from being alive and happy, I had been living a half-life, partly covered by darkness and shadow, I was a mere shadow of who I truly could be. I had denied myself my value and worth and my full potential all my life.

It is the wound that brings us closer to the Divine. I had been drawn down by the desire and will to save Persephone, who I thought was lost and dying. I found light when I arrived and realised I had made the journey not to save her, but to save myself.

So much light! I'm surrounded by light. So much light born out of such deep darkness. Every moment of life is bringing me joy, warming my heart. I feel my heart energy guiding me. I feel it rise and spread throughout my body.

My descent felt like a curse at times, but has been a true blessing. I feel confident of myself and my life. I feel grateful and happy. I see and feel people's love for me and I am able to take it in, it brings me warmth and no longer fear. I have found I am surrounded by many mirrors, held up by many people and events, reflecting back to me a glowing, true Sophia. One that is worth loving and has so much to give. I like what I see. I no longer feel the dark hole, no more scraping, no more fear. I feel whole, complete, satisfied, content and happy. I am grateful for my descent.

A year on and life is very different for me now. There is an internal calmness, serenity and contentment I had not experienced in such a complete way, enduring for such a long time, before.

Outwardly, my life continues much as it was before. It throws difficulties and hardships my way. I encounter challenges all the time. I still work, pay bills, deal with rude customer service employees, travel on overcrowded buses and trains, contend with delays and cancellations, face friends or complete strangers' odd behaviours or judgements, get drenched in rain, have to deal with emergency plumbing, in short, everything that anyone living on this planet needs to deal with. Every annoyance and hardship that was in my life before is still there and always will be. But somehow it's all different now, because something inside of me is different, something core. My responses, reactions and feelings around these events are different. I no longer get angry, frustrated, resentful. I'm not rushing through life as much. Someone pushing me on the tube no longer upsets me. I am calmer and at peace with myself and the world.

People don't upset or anger me as they used to. The strength I feel inside keeps me centred and helps me face life with equanimity.

Others can't torment me, their actions and words flow pass me, leaving my inner peace intact.

I used to get severe period cramps. They were at times so severe, I would pass out. I no longer get any pain or discomfort during my periods at all. I believe this is because I have made peace with my femininity and my body.

I feel grateful for everything and everyone in my life. Not only the obvious, the 'good', the beauty of nature, the opportunities I have, my friends and teachers; but also for my difficulties and suffering. As painful as my journey was, even though at times I saw no light and had no hope, I thought I would never make it out, the darkness seemed so complete and endless, now that I have surfaced at the other end, I can look back and be grateful for all that I have learned and all of that pain that helped me grow and become more whole. Not because I have already forgotten the depths of the suffering and pain I felt, but because the light I stand in now has a different quality than the one I was in before. And this new light, the experience of it, its warmth is worth the trouble and effort of the journey through those caves.

This new light belongs to me, it comes from me and is reflected back to me by my surroundings. I feel strong, strong enough to be true to myself in any instance, strong enough to accept my vulnerability, knowing I will not break. I feel confident and am proud of my achievements. I value myself in a way I had not done before. I like the world I live in and I like myself as I am. I am accepting of life as it is, the good and the bad, joyful and difficult, but even more importantly I am accepting of who I am, with all that I am. I accept my mistakes and my weaknesses and no longer beat myself up about them. The self-inflicted torture is over.

I no longer feel needy for others' good opinions, their acknowledgement, even their love. I value the people I love, but no longer am driven by a desire to please, to be liked. I stand by who I am and can love and give truly, without compromising from myself. I can accept others' love and their presence brings me warmth and joy and not fear.

My relationship with my father is much better. We are closer and there is a deeper understanding between us. My relationship with my mother remains difficult and will take further work, but that is okay. She no longer has the power to cut me up inside.

I am enjoying life, every aspect of it. I am grateful for who I am, where I am and what I have.

I am happy.

CPSIA information can be obtained at www.ICGtesting.com
Printed in the USA
BVOW02s1426210415

397069BV00033B/427/P

9 781784 621780